Probability and Experimental Errors in Science

JOHN WILEY and SONS, INC.

 New York
and London

PROBABILITY AND EXPERIMENTAL ERRORS IN SCIENCE

An elementary survey

LYMAN G. PARRATT

Professor of Physics
Chairman of the Department of Physics
Cornell University
Ithaca, New York

DEDICATION

This book is dedicated
to those timeless intellectuals
who have so shaped our cultural pattern
that experimental science can live as a part of it,
a science that seriously tampers with
the plaguing and hallowed
uncertainty
in man's comprehension of his gods
and of the universe.

Preface

ALTHOUGH the concepts of probability and statistics underlie practically *everything* in science, the student is too often left to acquire these concepts in haphazard fashion. His first contact with quantitative probability may be in extracurricular gambling games, and his second in some requirement of a laboratory instructor who insists arbitrarily that a ± number should follow a reported measurement. In his undergraduate training, he may be introduced in a social science to sampling procedures for obtaining data, in a biological science to formulas for the transmission of genes in inheritance characteristics, and in a physical science to Heisenberg's uncertainty principle, which he intuitively concludes is essentially nonsense. Such experiences, good as far as they go (except, of course, any excess in gambling and the conclusion as to nonsense), are left woefully disconnected and do not prepare him adequately to understand the *intrinsic "open-ended" feature* of every measurement and concept in science.

Probability is the lens that brings science into philosophic focus. Without a fairly clear comprehension of this fact, the scientist cannot be really "at home" in his own field. And, at a time when as never before the results of science rush on to overwhelm society, the scientist, for lack of focus, is a poor ambassador. Not only is he spiritually uncomfortable in his own field, but science itself, as he portrays it, cannot fit comfortably in the society of other human activities and knowledge.

In a very humble way, we are attempting at Cornell University to introduce the undergraduate student to the unifying concepts of probability and statistics as they apply in science. This is a difficult task at this level of the student's development. The subject in its broad scope is no doubt the most mature and sophisticated one with which man has ever struggled. But it is believed that the best time to instill a general attitude in a student is when he is young—he will have less trouble later in maturing properly.

This is admittedly the objective of a teacher rather than of a book. But experience shows the impracticality of trying to teach undergraduate students without a book. The present volume has been assembled to fill this pedagogical need, at least to fill it in part. The book is patterned to be a base from which the teacher may go on to discuss further aspects, especially those aspects that deepen and broaden the understanding of science. A few suggestions are given of such excursions in the understanding of science, particularly in the first chapter.

The books begins with brief comments on the different meanings of probability, then goes into the classical games of chance as examples of the classical or a priori meaning. Although these games have almost nothing to do with science, they provide a convenient framework for the teaching of basic principles, for example, of combinatorial analysis which is fundamental in all probability reasoning, and of the sampling process inherent in scientific measurements. The games are also remarkably successful in arousing the undergraduate's interest in the subject, and in providing numerous problems to help him develop his feelings for probability into quantitative concepts. Once the basic principles are well established, we turn to their applications in problems more serious than gambling games.

In the bulk of the book, emphasis is placed on the experimental definition of probability rather than on the classical definition. After the ideal games, and after comments on the role in science played by both kinds of probability, namely, classical and experimental, the discussion shifts to measurements and to the general statistical concepts. These concepts include maximum likelihood, rules for the propagation of errors, curve fitting, several applications of the least-squares method, consistency tests, a little on the analysis of variance, a little on correlation, and so on. Then, the normal (Gauss) and the Poisson models of mathematical probability are explored both analytically and with typical problems. The normal and the Poisson models are given about equal weight, this weighting being roughly commensurate with their invocations in modern scientific measurements. Especially in the subject of statistics our discussion is very elementary—just the essentials for an undergraduate student in an experimental science. But in both statistics and probability, the point of view taken in this book is somewhat different from that of the professional statistician or mathematician.

Numerous problems are given in each of the five chapters. Many of these problems are intended to provoke discussion, and the instructor should look them over carefully before he assigns them to the student.

The most commonly used equations in statistics and probability are gathered together for convenience and placed at the end of the book, just before the index.

I am pleased to express my indebtedness and thanks to Professor K. I. Greisen of Cornell University for reading the manuscript, for checking the problems, and for making numerous helpful general suggestions.

And, needless to say, practically all that I know about the subject I have learned from others.

> When 'Omer smote his bloomin' lyre,
> 'E'd 'eard men sing by land and sea;
> An' what he thought 'e might require,
> 'E went an' took—the same as me!
>
> Kipling

In partial acknowledgment, the following books are listed and I recommend them for collateral reading.

1. T. C. Fry, *Probability and Its Engineering Uses* (D. Van Nostrand Co., New York, 1928).
2. P. G. Hoel, *Introduction to Mathematical Statistics* (John Wiley & Sons, New York, 1954), 2nd ed.
3. A. G. Worthing and J. Geffner, *Treatment of Experimental Data* (John Wiley & Sons, New York, 1943).
4. H. Cramér, *The Elements of Probability Theory and Some of Its Applications* (John Wiley & Sons, New York, 1955).
5. A. M. Mood, *Introduction to Theory of Statistics* (McGraw-Hill Book Co., New York, 1950).
6. B. W. Lindgren and G. W. McElrath, *Introduction to Probability and Statistics* (Macmillan Co., New York, 1959).
7. E. B. Wilson, Jr., *An Introduction to Scientific Research* (McGraw-Hill Book Co., New York, 1952).
8. R. B. Lindsay and H. Margenau, *Foundation of Physics* (John Wiley & Sons, New York, 1943).
9. William Feller, *An Introduction to Probability Theory and Its Applications* (John Wiley & Sons, New York, 1957), 2nd ed.
10. R. D. Evans, *The Atomic Nucleus* (McGraw-Hill Book Co., New York, 1955), Chapters 26, 27, and 28.
11. Emanuel Parzen, *Modern Probability and Its Applications* (John Wiley & Sons, New York, 1960),

Ithaca, New York　　　　　　　　　　　　　　　LYMAN G. PARRATT
May 1961

Contents

"For there was never yet philosopher
That could endure the toothache patiently,
However they have writ the style of gods
And make a pish at chance and sufferance."

WILLIAM SHAKESPEARE

"Life is a school of probability."

WALTER BAGEHOT

Early Developments: Ideal Games of Chance

A. INTRODUCTION

Every *fact* in science, every *law of nature* as devised from observations, is intrinsically "open-ended," i.e., contains some uncertainty and is subject to future improvement. This may sound harsh but it is simply the way of things, and this book is written to help the student of science to understand it.

The subject of probability has many facets and needs many different introductions. This book has three introductions: (1) the Preface, (2) Sections 1-1 and 1-2 of the present chapter, and (3) Section 2-1 of Chapter 2. The student is advised to read them all in the order named before he progresses into Section 1-3.

Although the primary objective of the book is to acquaint the student with the modern philosophic focus in science, viz., through the lens of probability, the elementary tools (methods and formulas) of statistics and of the popular mathematical models of probability are also discussed to about the extent commonly needed in the practice of an experimental science. Actually, most of the pages are devoted to these more or less conventional practical topics.

The treatment of the subject presumes that the reader has studied some experimental science for about one year. Elementary and intermediate algebra suffice as the mathematics background for the bulk of the book, but full comprehension of a few of the formulas requires just a little knowledge of calculus.

1

1-1. "Three" Meanings of Probability

The concept of probability is of great antiquity. Its first development was no doubt intuitional. Indeed, one of the "three" general meanings of probability in acceptable use today is a subjective or an intuitional one. This meaning refers to a qualitative state of mind or intensity of conviction, a meaning that is not intended to be, or else cannot be, quantitatively measured. Examples of this meaning are found in the statements "She probably would have won the beauty contest if she had entered," "Shakespeare's plays were probably written by Bacon," and "Life probably exists on Mars."

In many examples of intuitional probability, some cogent arguments, even some quantitative arguments, may be marshaled in support of the intensity of the conviction. When an appreciable amount of quantitative support is arrayed, this meaning of probability emerges as one of the two quantitative meanings discussed in this book.

Actually, of course, there exists a whole gamut of partially quantitative meanings. The spread is according to the degree of quantitativeness. Let us illustrate one end of this gamut. Suppose the doctor tells his patient that he has a mild attack of what appears to be appendicitis and that the probability is *good* that he will recover without immediate surgery. The doctor's appraisal of the situation is based on his experience, both direct and indirect, which involves a large number of more or less similar cases. If pressed, he may give a quantitative value of the recovery probability, such as 0.6, and have in mind an uncertainty of say ± 0.3 or so, but he would be very reluctant (and properly so) to state any such quantitative values. He knows that there is still a large amount of nonquantitative "art" in his meaning of probability. At the other end of the gamut, a mathematician, when he speaks of probability, refers (unless he says otherwise) to a quantity having an *exact* value, an axiomatic or "classical" value. In real-life situations, the exact numerical value may not be known, but it is presumed to exist, and, anyway, obtaining the numerical knowledge is not the mathematician's problem. On the other hand, a statistician works with a large amount of real-life data and deduces therefrom a rather precise quantitative value of probability. He presumes that all the data are equally good (or have known weightings) and, concerned with an "internally consistent" analysis, he injects none of the nonquantitative or subjective evaluation that is inherent, for example, in the practice of the physician. The statistician is generally rather close to the mathematician in the high degree of quantitative intent in his probability, but he knows that his value is not 100% precise (as is the mathematician's) because his data, numerous to be sure, are only a limited sample of all possible data.

Let us turn next to the scientist. He is in the business of both making measurements and interpreting them in terms of the laws of nature. In a sense, he is more concerned with a sort of "external consistency" than is the statistician. This is because the scientist's view of the laws of nature returns to plague him when more precise measurements are made. In reporting a measurement, he states the numerical value and then gives a numerical $\pm$ value to indicate (implicitly) its quantitative reliability or the probability that the measurement is "correct." The $\pm$ value is typically deduced from a combination of (a) a more or less careful statistical analysis of his trials and (b) a guess based on his experience in setting up and performing measurements of this sort, and perhaps from a few unrecorded test measurements made in the process of adjusting the apparatus. Also, he indulges in the guess because he suspects that his measurement contains some undetermined amount of systematic error. His statistical analysis is often a bit careless for another reason, viz., the interpretation he has in mind for the measurement may not require greater care. But note well that if, by the design of the experiment, he judges the systematic error to be relatively small and/or the interpretation to demand a high degree of reliability, he must then make a *very careful statistical analysis*. Hence, depending upon the particular measurement and its interpretation, the experimental scientist works in the range of quantitative probability somewhere between the physician and the statistician. But the scientist also, when he is conjecturing about nature in the *absence of pertinent measurements*, resorts perforce to the classical type of probability of the mathematician. This he does in *desperation*, as discussed later in this chapter. The tentative description of nature in terms of classical probability is *improved* as soon as actual pertinent measurements become available.

To make clearer the distinction between the probability of the mathematician (or of the desperate theoretical scientist) and that of the statistician (or of the scientist in his eventual description of nature), let us amplify briefly one of the points made above. This is beyond doubt the most subtle point in the concept of quantitative probability.

A quantitative measure of anything always implies an unambiguous operational definition of the thing being measured. But the definition (hence meaning) of probability in a real-life or scientific situation always contains a certain amount of *inherent arbitrariness*, an arbitrariness that exists in addition to the effect of the subjective guess in evaluating the systematic error just mentioned. This stems from the fact that, in a given situation, we can never imagine or evaluate *all* the things that *might* happen. As a matter of practical experience, we are usually content to bound the situation with a closed group of separately and individually evaluated possibilities. If the group is reasonably comprehensive, the amount of arbitrariness is small. It is primarily this feature of inherent arbitrariness, often small but *always partially unknown*, that infuses philosophical (and theological) fascination into the subject. In our elementary treatment, we shall for the most part side-step the conventional philosophical (and theological) implications.* But we point out now that it is really in an attempt to reduce the residual arbitrariness in the definition of probability in real-life situations that we progress from the first to the second of the two so-called quantitative meanings. We shall return to different aspects of this arbitrariness in Sections 1-5 and 1-10, and generally throughout the book.

The first of the two quantitative meanings is called the *classical* or *a priori* probability. The classical meaning, discussed with examples in Part B of this chapter, is based on the presumption that the probability (for the occurrence of a specified event) can be determined by an a priori analysis in which we can recognize *all* of the "equally possible" events. The usefulness of this meaning is limited to a rather specialized class of "mathematical" probability situations, such as those encountered in the *ideal* gambling games (e.g., dice, cards, coin tossing, etc.), and to real-life situations where we are desperate for lack of reliable objective knowledge (measurements).

The second of the two quantitative meanings is called the *experimental* or *a posteriori* probability. This probability concept, having by far the greater profundity in the description and understanding of nature, has to do with situations in which the number of "equally possible" events has admittedly not been or cannot be determined. This is the case in *all* real-life probability situations.

It is of little consequence in the limited discussion in this book whether our failure to make the a priori determination of probability in real-life situations is due to a limitation (temporary or inherent) of our knowledge or analytic ability, or is due to an inherent characteristic of the events under consideration.† In either case, the causal factors in the *individual* events in such probability situations are not understood in sufficient detail to allow us to make reliable individual-event predictions; each such event may be said to be at the whim or caprice of nature. But it is especially noteworthy that in these probability situations when a large number of events are considered by the methods of statistics an amazing degree of regularity

---

* An introduction to probability from the philosophical point of view is given, e.g., by E. Nagel, *Principles of the Theory of Probability* (International Encyclopedia of Unified Science, vol. 1, no. 6, Chicago, 1939).

† We may, if we like, include as part of the event characteristic the perturbation introduced by the observation itself (Heisenberg's uncertainty principle).

becomes apparent—the capriciousness of nature is limited. With an experimental or a posteriori definition of probability, predictions of specified future events can be made, and, more, a significant quantitative degree of reliability can be assigned to each prediction!

The term "random mass-phenomena" is often applied to a class of events that are amenable to analysis by statistics and experimental-probability theory, events that are unpredictable in detail but are predictable as a whole.* Practically every intellectual discipline whose content deals with quantitative relationships—economics, sociology, political science, war science, biology, chemistry, physics, engineering, commercial business, medicine, to mention a few—is replete with phenomena that are effectively treated as random. Statistics and probability theory are rapidly being extended to more and more facets of all of these subjects.

In particular, the substance of any experimental science is measurement, and practically all measurements are in the class of essentially random mass-phenomena. Measurements are so classed because of one or both of the following reasons: (a) each measurement is merely a sample of a large number (essentially infinite in some instances) of *possible* measurements that differ more or less slightly among themselves, i.e., the experimenter is unable to control completely all the experimental factors involved, and (b) the property being measured may contain a degree of randomness as an inherent characteristic. And, equally important, an increasing fraction of modern scientific theories (i.e., generalizations drawn from measurements) are based on a view of the statistical behavior of nature. Examples of these features of measurements and of theories are discussed later.

For the student of any quantitative science, early recognition and understanding of random mass-phenomena are imperative. Obviously, such recognition and understanding require an early grasp of the fundamentals of statistics and probability theory. This book attempts to impart these fundamentals.

With this objective, the book is largely concerned with the third of the "three"meanings of probability as set forth above. However, for historical and pedagogical reasons, and because of the use of axiomatic probability by desperate theoretical scientists (desperate in the sense mentioned above), the next few sections of this chapter are devoted to a review of selected concepts and arguments that were developed in connection with the classical or a priori probability. This a priori meaning is much the easier one to grasp and to use to the extent that it is applicable. It should be kept

---

* This is our first use of the term "random," a term or concept that is inextricably present in any discussion of statistics and probability. Further discussion of the concept of random is given in Section 2-3.

in mind that all of these concepts and arguments (excepting, of course, the definition of probability itself) are also applicable to random mass-phenomena in which the experimental meaning of probability is the appropriate one.

1-2. Historical Perspective

The subject of statistics and probability as we know it today is dually rooted in (a) ideal games of chance and (b) accumulated records such as those of human life and death. Both of these roots, in really recognizable form, date from about the middle of the seventeenth century. The concepts of classical (a priori) probability grew mainly from the first root (ideal games of chance), and the experimental (a posteriori) concepts, based on statistics, grew mainly from the second. In most of this chapter, the development from the first root is reviewed, but, as was just mentioned, most of these aspects have general applicability.

Before we launch into the classical part of our study, a few more comments are in order on historical perspective.

Around 1650, gambling was very popular in fashionable circles of French society. Games of dice, cards, coin tossing, roulette, etc., were being rather highly developed. As personal honor and increasing amounts of money were involved, the need was felt for some formulas with which gambling chances could be calculated. Some of the influential gamblers, like de Méré, sought the help of the leading mathematicians of the time, such as Pascal, Fermat, and, later, d'Alembert and de Moivre.* Fortunately, the mathematicians accepted the problems as their own, and soon the subject of classical probability took shape.

The a priori definition of probability was formulated in correspondence between Pascal and Fermat in 1654. Huygens published the first treatise on the subject in 1657. The famous Bernoulli theorem and the binomial distribution were introduced in 1713. The general theorem known as the probability multiplication rule was proposed by de Moivre in 1718, and de Moivre also published the first indication of the normal probability distribution (and the first special case of the powerful "central limit theorem") in 1733 to 1738. Further development of the normal distribution was later made by Gauss, whose name is often attached to it, and it was soon used by Gauss and by Laplace independently in the analysis of errors of measurements in physical and astronomical observations. The important principle of least squares was formulated by Legendre at about this time, and the "theory of errors" was well on its way.

---

* See, e.g., Todhunter's *History of the Mathematical Theory of Probability* from the time of Pascal to that of Laplace (Macmillan, Cambridge and London, 1865).

Laplace in his classical treatise of 1812,* a treatise in which the a priori type of probability holds supreme sway,† gives a rather complete summary of the mathematical theory of games of chance. Soon after 1812, contact with classical mathematicians was almost lost.

Continued development of the subject was made by statisticians in various fields such as in actuarial work, in certain branches of social, biological, and physical sciences in the treatment of errors in measurements, and in theoretical physics in what is called statistical mechanics. In its present form, the subject of statistics and the root of experimental probability apparently began in the life and death records published by Gaunt in England in 1662.‡ Such records and interpretations were significantly extended by Halley a few years later, and Halley is sometimes called the father of statistics. Statistics flourished for some 200 years without much further progress in probability theory, except for the new definition.

Vigorous contact with mathematicians was re-established in the 1920's, and basic development along the lines of mathematics is today continuing apace with the multitude of new applications. The work of the mathematicians is again closely akin to the classical (a priori) concepts in the sense that probability is taken as axiomatic. The new mathematical theorems are valid, of course, irrespective of the method whereby the numerical value of probability is obtained.

Philosophical aspects of probability continued to develop as scholars in

---

* Pierre S. de Laplace, *Théorie analytique des probabilités* (1812), and the companion treatise *Essai philosophique sur les probabilités* (1814). For selections from several contributors to probability theory, including Laplace, see *The World of Mathematics* (Simon and Schuster, New York, 1956), ed. James R. Newman.

† Why was Laplace—along with most of the leading mathematicians and scientists of his time—so uncritical of the a priori definition of probability? Such questions are interesting but of course difficult to answer. Perhaps it was because of the intellectual fashion in those days to believe that complete knowledge was available to man, that *all* of the "equally possible" outcomes in *any* situation were knowable. This was related to the philosophy of sufficient reason, and to what later became the principle of determinism. This philosophical fashion was dominant in intellectual circles throughout the nineteenth century, and did not yield until the advent of quantum physics early in the twentieth century. With Heisenberg's uncertainty principle, the whole of science was recognized as ultimately based philosophically on the concepts of experimental probability.

‡ There exist very early records of a type of insurance business in the protection of Greek merchants from the maritime hazards of ships at sea, but these records do not indicate a very good statistical basis on which the insurance "premiums" were determined. To marine insurance, the Romans added health and burial insurance, again with rather inadequate statistical records. In the year 1609, Count Anton Gunther in Germany refused the request of his people for financial protection against the hazard of fire; he refused for fear of "tempting the gods." As a matter of history, it appears that the English started the first fire insurance company in 1680.

general devoted themselves to the subject. Activity in philosophical probability has been particularly intense since the widespread dissemination of Heisenberg's uncertainty principle of 1927. This principle is based in quantum physics.*

The general subject of probability at the present time is a combination of (a) mathematics, (b) measurements or statistical data, (c) theory of nature, and (d) theory of knowledge itself. Typically, the student begins the study from some one rather specialized approach, but he is soon obliged to broaden his view to include *all* of them. This, perhaps more than any other, is a humbling subject, because it is so all-inclusive.

B. CLASSICAL (A PRIORI) PROBABILITY

I-3. Definition of Classical Probability

In a simple ideal game, the chance of winning is easily deduced. For example, if an ideal coin is honestly tossed into the air it will settle either heads or tails. There are two possible outcomes of the toss and the chance is the same for either outcome. The chance for either a head or a tail is one out of two, i.e., the probability is $\frac{1}{2}$. By similar argument, if an ordinary (six-sided) ideal die is honestly cast, there are six possible outcomes, and the chance for a particular face number (a specified event) is one out of six, i.e., the probability is $\frac{1}{6}$. Also, we may readily see that the probability of drawing the ace of spades from an ordinary deck of 52 cards is $\frac{1}{52}$; and the probability of drawing a spade is $\frac{13}{52} = \frac{1}{4}$.

The underlying conditions for such simple calculations of probability are that

(1) every single trial must lead to one of a definite known number of outcomes or events, and

(2) every possible outcome must have an equal chance.

Let w be defined as the number of events recognized as "win," and let n be the total number of equally possible events. Then, the probability of winning, p, is given simply by the ratio

$$p \equiv \frac{w}{n} \qquad (1\text{-}1)$$

and the probability of losing, q, is given by

$$q \equiv \frac{n - w}{n} \qquad (1\text{-}2)$$

* W. Heisenberg, *Z. Physik*, **43**, 172 (1927).

Equation 1-1 constitutes the definition of classical or a priori probability, a quantitative definition that was no doubt generally understood and used very early in our history. Nowadays, this is sometimes called the Laplace definition because it was so well formulated by him (in 1812). It is an a priori definition since it allows determination of p *before* the game has been played.

Application of the classical definition required increasingly critical thought as games of somewhat greater complexity were considered. The definition does not give a *criterion* for determining the values of w and of n, especially of n, and the proper values become rather obscure as the complexity of the game increases. As an example, consider a game in which a penny is tossed twice in succession and the game is won if a head appears at least once. Denote heads by H and tails by T. One argument says that there are four equally possible events, viz., HH, HT, TH, and TT, and the game is won in each of the first three events. Hence, $p = \frac{3}{4}$. But an alternative argument says that the events HH and HT are winners on the first toss and that the second toss in these two cases is not made. Accordingly, there are only three equally possible events, viz., H, TH, and TT, and the first two events are winners. The proponents of this argument concluded that $p = \frac{2}{3}$ instead of $\frac{3}{4}$. Which is correct?* The student should recognize that in the second argument the three outcomes are not *equally* probable.

It was paradoxes such as this (and this is a very simple example) that caused the gamblers to go to the famous mathematicians of the time. The mathematicians were soon able to resolve the ambiguities in the numbers w and n in Eq. 1-1 for the ideal games of chance by the methods known as probability combinations and combinatorial analysis, subjects that we shall take up briefly now.

1-4. Probability Combinations

For convenience in terminology, let A, B, C, $\cdots$ stand respectively for the various possible specified outcomes or events in a probability situation. A may be heads in a penny toss, or it may be red in the draw of a card from an ordinary deck; B may be tails in the penny toss, or it may be a face card in the card draw; C may not even exist, or it may be the deuce of spades; etc. Or one of the events may be more complex, e.g., it may be a 7 in the cast of two dice, or it may be either a 7 or an 11, etc. Compound events are very commonly specified, and the determination of their

---

* Curiously, the early mathematicians were divided on this question. The argument leading to $p = \frac{3}{4}$ is the correct one; the paradox is resolved if the event H in the second argument is given twice the weight of either TH or TT.

probabilities requires in general very careful analysis indeed. Two rather simple combinations involve either mutually exclusive or independent component events.

Mutually exclusive events. Two events A and B are mutually exclusive if only one of them can occur in a single trial. For example, a head and a tail are mutually exclusive in a penny toss. The probability of occurrence of an unspecified member of a set of mutually exclusive events is the sum of the component probabilities. This statement is conveniently written as

$$p(\text{either } A \text{ or } B) = p(A) + p(B) \qquad (1\text{-}3)$$

It follows that the sum of the probabilities of *all possible* mutually exclusive events is unity, i.e.,

$$p(A) + p(B) + p(C) + \cdots = 1 \qquad (1\text{-}4)$$

Independent Events. Events A and B are independent if the occurrence or nonoccurrence of A in no way affects the probability of occurrence of B. Examples of independent events are found in successive tosses of a penny, or in successive samplings of differently colored balls from a jar if each sample is replaced and the jar shaken before the next sample is taken. The probability of occurrence of two or more independent events is the product of the component probabilities,

$$p(A \text{ and } B \text{ and } C \cdots) = p(A) \cdot p(B) \cdot p(C) \cdots \qquad (1\text{-}5)$$

The probability of tossing a penny three heads in a row is $\frac{1}{2} \cdot \frac{1}{2} \cdot \frac{1}{2} = (\frac{1}{2})^3$, the three specified events being independent. The probability of tossing two heads in a row and then a tail is also $(\frac{1}{2})^3$. But the probability of tossing two heads and a tail in three tosses, if the particular sequence of events is not specified, is $(\frac{1}{2})^3 + (\frac{1}{2})^3 + (\frac{1}{2})^3 = 3(\frac{1}{2})^3$. In the latter case, we have a combination of mutually exclusive and independent events. Similarly, if two pennies are tossed together three times, the probability of seeing two matches and one mismatch in any (unspecified) sequence is $3(\frac{1}{2})^3$, since the outcome of the first penny is never specified but in each of the three tosses the outcome of the second penny is specified (with $p = \frac{1}{2}$), and there are three independent ways (different possible sequences) in which the winning outcomes may appear. The three independent ways refer, of course, to the fact that the mismatch may follow the two matches, come between them, or precede them.*

Another example of the combined probabilities of independent events is found in the following. Suppose an incident is witnessed by one person

---

* Another view of this problem is to consider that the outcome of each penny toss is specified. Then, the probability of each outcome is $(\frac{1}{2})^6$, and there are 24 different

who describes it to another person who in turn transmits it on. If 20 people are in the chain before the incident is related to you, and if the component probability for truth is 0.9 per person, what is the probability that you are told the truth? This combined probability is $(0.9)^{20} \approx 0.1$, and you should not put much credence in the story as you hear it. We might inquire as to the number N of such people in the chain before the combined probability has dropped to 0.5. The answer is given implicitly in the equation $(0.9)^N = 0.5$.†

In connection with the independence of events, a remark must be made in regard to the popular "law of averages." This so-called law is commonly quoted in support of a fallacious belief that a run of bad luck presages a run of good luck such that the two runs will average or cancel. This is, of course, merely wishful nonsense if the events are truly independent and if the component probabilities remain unchanged. The only acceptable or nonfacetious interpretation of this "law of averages" is the one implied in the experimental definition of probability as discussed later. By this definition, the probability is determined only after an extremely large number of identical trials (an infinite number in the limit), and a run of either kind of luck is eventually of negligible consequence as the number of trials continues to increase (assuming that the probability so defined is unique, an assumption also discussed later).

Compound events: general addition theorems. Now consider the probability of a general compound event when the component events are overlapping or have what are called overlapping probabilities. Overlapping component events are not entirely mutually exclusive. For example, if one card is drawn from each of two ordinary decks of 52 cards,

---

ways of having two matches and one mismatch. In this view, $p = 24(\frac{1}{2})^6 = 3(\frac{1}{2})^3$. The 24 ways are seen from the table :

HH	HH	HT	HH	HT	HH	HT	HH	HH
HH	HH	TH	HH	TH	HH	TH	HH	HH
TT	HH	HT	TT	HT	HH	HT	TT	HH
TT	HH	TH	TT	TH	HH	TH	TT	HH
HH	TT	HT	HH	HT	TT	HT	HH	TT
HH	TT	TH	HH	TH	TT	TH	HH	TT
TT	TT	HT	TT	HT	TT	HT	TT	TT
TT	TT	TH	TT	TH	TT	TH	TT	TT

† An interesting variation of this example has been told as follows. Suppose that each time the Bible goes through a new edition it loses a fraction f of its truth. This loss is due to the fallibility of humans, the changing meaning of words, etc. If f for each edition and the time between editions were known, then we could calculate the time at which Christians might expect (at least need) the second coming of Christ.

what is the probability that at least one of them (i.e., either one or both) is the ace of spades? This probability is not just the sum of the component event probabilities, viz., $\frac{1}{52} + \frac{1}{52}$, because this sum includes *twice* the probability that *both* cards are the ace of spades. The correct answer is the sum of the probabilities for (a) an ace on the first draw and anything on the second and (b) no ace on the first draw and an ace on the second, viz.,

$$\tfrac{1}{52} \cdot 1 + \tfrac{51}{52} \cdot \tfrac{1}{52} \qquad \text{or} \qquad \tfrac{1}{52} + \tfrac{1}{52} - (\tfrac{1}{52} \cdot \tfrac{1}{52})$$

where the term in parentheses corrects for the probability of simultaneous appearance (or overlap) of both component events. This and other examples of probabilities of compound events made up of overlapping independent component (nonmutually exclusive) events are illustrated by the following equations:

$$p(\text{neither } A \text{ nor } B) = [1 - p(A)] \cdot [1 - p(B)]$$
$$= 1 - p(A) - p(B) + p(A) \cdot p(B) \qquad (1\text{-}6)$$
$$p(\text{either } A \text{ or } B, \text{ not both}) = p(A) \cdot [1 - p(B)] + p(B) \cdot [1 - p(A)]$$
$$= p(A) + p(B) - 2p(A) \cdot p(B) \qquad (1\text{-}7)$$
$$p(\text{either } A \text{ or } B \text{ or both}) = p(A) \cdot p(B) + p(\text{either } A \text{ or } B, \text{ not both})$$
$$= 1 - p(\text{neither } A \text{ nor } B)$$
$$= p(A) + p(B) - p(A) \cdot p(B) \qquad (1\text{-}8)$$

Equations 1-6, 1-7, and 1-8 are commonly known as the general *addition theorems*. Equation 1-3 is the special case for mutually exclusive independent events.

The concept of "sample space" is a very convenient one. In a given probability situation *all* possible outcomes comprise sample space. For example, in the drawing of one card from a deck of 52 cards, there are 52 points in sample space. (Sample space may be visualized as points appropriately arranged on a sheet of paper.) The convenience of the concept is readily seen in the idea of overlapping component events. Consider the 52-point space just cited: of the four points representing aces, two also are found among the 26 points representing red cards. Other examples are given in the problems of Sections 1-6 and 1-9.

Conditional probability: multiplication theorem. The general *multiplication theorem*, of which Eq. 1-5 is the special case for independent events, involves the ideas of partially dependent events. This leads to a branch of the subject known as conditional probability. If event B cannot occur unless some condition is imposed, say unless event A has occurred, then the probability for B must include the probability that the condition is satisfied. In this simple example, the probability for the compound event (A and B) may be written

$$p(A \text{ and } B) = p(A)p_A(B) \tag{1-9}$$

where $p_A(B)$ is to be read as the probability, on the assumption that A has already occurred, that B will occur. Often, $p_A(B)$ is written as $p(B \mid A)$. Equation 1-9, in its general form in which B depends upon more than one condition, is known as Bayes' theorem. (Bayes' theorem is usually stated a little differently, viz., as the probability that B was preceded by the specified events A_1, A_2, $\cdots$; this is also known as inverse probability.)

Incidentally, the definition for the independence of events A and B is that

$$p(B \mid A) = p(B) \quad \text{and} \quad p(A \mid B) = p(A)$$

Consider the following example. Three white balls and one black ball are placed in a jar and one white ball and two blacks are placed in an identical jar. If one of the two jars is selected at random and one ball withdrawn from it, what is the probability that this ball will be white? We argue that on the condition that the first jar is chosen the white probability is $\frac{3}{4}$; and that on the condition that the second jar is chosen the white probability is $\frac{1}{3}$. Either jar is chosen with a probability of $\frac{1}{2}$. Hence, the probability that a white is drawn from the first jar is $\frac{1}{2} \cdot \frac{3}{4}$; and from the second jar, $\frac{1}{2} \cdot \frac{1}{3}$. The over-all probability for drawing the white ball is the sum

$$p_0(W_1) = \frac{1}{2} \cdot \frac{3}{4} + \frac{1}{2} \cdot \frac{1}{3} = \frac{13}{24}$$

The subscript 0 on p indicates that this is the probability based on our knowledge before any ball has been drawn; we make use of the subscript notation later.

Another example of conditional probability is the following. Suppose that in a jar are two balls of which either is black (B) or white (W), and suppose that we have no additional a priori information about the particular color complex of the balls in the jar. What is the probability that the first ball drawn will be white? In the absence of any additional a priori information, it is customary to presume that there is an equal probability p_0 that each of the possible hypotheses is the correct one. We might further presume that there are three hypotheses, viz., two whites in the jar, a white and a black, and two blacks. With these two presumptions, we would write

$$p_0(\text{Hyp } WW) = p_0(\text{Hyp } WB) = p_0(\text{Hyp } BB) = \frac{1}{3}$$

Accordingly, the over-all probability for a white on the first draw is given by the sum

$$p_0(W_1) = \frac{1}{3} \cdot \frac{2}{2} + \frac{1}{3} \cdot \frac{1}{2} + \frac{1}{3} \cdot \frac{0}{2} = \frac{1}{2}$$

since the three hypotheses are mutually exclusive. In this problem, the three hypotheses are similar in the argument to the two jars, one of which is chosen at random, in the preceding problem.

It is to be emphasized that the presumption of equal probabilities for the three different hypotheses is really made *in desperation* since we have no information on which to form a better judgment. All we know in fact are (1) that the probability for each possible hypothesis is somewhere in the range of 0 to 1 and (2) that the sum of the probabilities for all possible hypotheses is unity.

This example has a further complication. Depending upon our view of the conditions under which the balls were placed or somehow got into the jar, we might presume that there are *four*, instead of three, equally probable hypotheses. According to this view we would write

$$p_0(\text{Hyp } WW) = p_0(\text{Hyp } WB) = p_0(\text{Hyp } BW) = p_0(\text{Hyp } BB) = \tfrac{1}{4}$$

For our purpose now, no distinction need be made between Hyp WB and Hyp BW, but as a unit it would be assigned a probability of $\tfrac{1}{2}$ instead of $\tfrac{1}{3}$ of being the correct one. Accordingly, the over-all probability for a white on the first draw is given by the sum

$$p_0(W_1) = \tfrac{1}{4} \cdot \tfrac{2}{2} + \tfrac{1}{2} \cdot \tfrac{1}{2} + \tfrac{1}{4} \cdot \tfrac{0}{2} = \tfrac{1}{2}$$

a probability that is the same as that determined on the basis of three equally likely hypotheses. But if the color of the first ball drawn is noted, the ball replaced and the jar shaken, and then a second ball is to be drawn, it can be easily shown that the numerical value of the white probability $p_1(W_2)$ is dependent upon the number of equally likely hypotheses assumed at the time of the first draw. (As an exercise, the student should show this dependence.)

The ambiguity as to the "proper" number of a priori equally probable hypotheses is an inherent part of problems of this sort. This is one nontrivial aspect of the arbitrariness inherent in the concept of probability as mentioned in Section 1-1.

For practice, let us rephrase the problem and extend it, knowing however that the numerical values from here on depend upon the initial number of equally probable hypotheses assumed. Consider a thin metal disk which we propose to toss as a true coin. Suppose that there are only three hypotheses: (a) that the disk has a mark on both sides that we may call heads, Hyp HH; (b) that it has a different mark on both sides that we may call tails, Hyp TT; and (c) that it has heads on one side and tails on the other, Hyp HT.* With no a priori information as to which of these

---

* Again, if Hyp TH were recognized as different in any way from Hyp HT, e.g., owing to the process of manufacture of the disk, we would start with four equally likely hypotheses instead of three.

three hypotheses is the correct one, suppose that we assume *in desperation* an equal probability, viz.,

$$p_0(\text{Hyp } HH) = p_0(\text{Hyp } HT) = p_0(\text{Hyp } TT) = \tfrac{1}{3}$$

If we write $p_{HH}(H_1)$ as the probability that the first toss is heads on the condition that Hyp HH is correct, $p_{HT}(H_1)$ as the probability that the first toss is heads on the condition that Hyp HT is correct, and $p_{TT}(H_1)$ as the probability that the first toss is heads on the condition that Hyp TT is correct, then we may write the expression for the probability that the first toss is heads as

$$p_0(H_1) = p_0(\text{Hyp } HH) \cdot p_{HH}(H_1) + p_0(\text{Hyp } HT) \cdot p_{HT}(H_1)$$
$$+ p_0(\text{Hyp } TT) \cdot p_{TT}(H_1)$$

where the subscript 0 on p refers to the probability before the outcome of any toss is known. Substituting the known quantities as discussed above,

$$p_0(H_1) = \tfrac{1}{3} \cdot 1 + \tfrac{1}{3} \cdot \tfrac{1}{2} + \tfrac{1}{3} \cdot 0 = \tfrac{1}{2}$$

as expected.

Next, we toss the thin metal disk and observe that the outcome *is* heads. Now we have some information about the relative probabilities of the three hypotheses; viz., we know that

$$p_1(\text{Hyp } TT) = 0$$

and, furthermore, that*

$$p_1(\text{Hyp } HH) > p_1(\text{Hyp } HT) < \tfrac{1}{2}$$

The subscript 1 on p refers to the probability after the outcome of one toss is known. Again let us point out that all we really knew before noting the outcome of the first toss was that each hypothesis had a probability somewhere in the range 0 to 1, and it was only *in desperation* that we guessed the same probability, $\tfrac{1}{3}$, that each hypothesis was correct. The quantitative evaluation of each of the remaining two hypotheses is made by the same

---

* We might fail to recognize the second feature of the additional information, arguing that if the other side of the disk were in fact tails it would not be altered by the outcome of the first toss. This argument would be valid if we *knew* that the other side were *in fact* tails, but this we do not know; we are concerned merely with the probability that it is tails. Only the Omniscient knows for sure that it is tails, if it is.

Belief in equal probabilities for the two remaining hypotheses before and after the toss, i.e., that the relative probabilities are unaltered by the outcome of the first toss, implies belief in unaltered probabilities after *many* tosses regardless of their outcomes. That this belief is untenable, unless revealed by the Omniscient, is easily seen. Suppose that a long sequence of heads were to appear; even a novice gambler would suspect that the disk were *HH*. And an expert gambler or logician would be a *little bit* suspicious even after the first toss.

type of reasoning as before, using respective probabilities instead of events in Eq. 1-1. Thus,

$$p_1(\text{Hyp } HH) = \frac{p_0(\text{Hyp } HH) \cdot p_{HH}(1H)}{p_0(\text{Hyp } HH) \cdot p_{HH}(1H) + p_0(\text{Hyp } HT) \cdot p_{HT}(1H)}$$

and

$$p_1(\text{Hyp } HT) = \frac{p_0(\text{Hyp } HT) \cdot p_{HT}(1H)}{p_0(\text{Hyp } HH) \cdot p_{HH}(1H) + p_0(\text{Hyp } HT) \cdot p_{HT}(1H)}$$

where the event $1H$ is the heads observed in the first toss.* Hence,

$$p_1(\text{Hyp } HH) = \frac{\frac{1}{3} \cdot 1}{\frac{1}{3} \cdot 1 + \frac{1}{3} \cdot \frac{1}{2}} = \frac{2}{3} \quad \text{and} \quad p_1(\text{Hyp } HT) = \frac{\frac{1}{3} \cdot \frac{1}{2}}{\frac{1}{3} \cdot 1 + \frac{1}{3} \cdot \frac{1}{2}} = \frac{1}{3}$$

Now, the probability that the second toss will be heads, event H_2, is

$$p_1(H_2) = p_1(\text{Hyp } HH) \cdot p_{HH}(H_2) + p_1(\text{Hyp } HT) \cdot p_{HT}(H_2)$$
$$= \tfrac{2}{3} \cdot 1 + \tfrac{1}{3} \cdot \tfrac{1}{2} = \tfrac{5}{6}$$

We toss the disk a second time and observe that it again comes out heads. The HH hypothesis is further strengthened at the expense of the HT hypothesis. We have observed event $2H$, viz., two heads in a row, and we write

$$p_2(\text{Hyp } HH) = \frac{p_0(\text{Hyp } HH) \cdot p_{HH}(2H)}{p_0(\text{Hyp } HH) \cdot p_{HH}(2H) + p_0(\text{Hyp } HT) \cdot p_{HT}(2H)}$$

$$= \frac{\frac{1}{3} \cdot 1}{\frac{1}{3} \cdot 1 + \frac{1}{3} \cdot \frac{1}{4}} = \frac{4}{5}$$

$$p_2(\text{Hyp } HT) = \frac{p_0(\text{Hyp } HT) \cdot p_{HT}(2H)}{p_0(\text{Hyp } HH) \cdot p_{HH}(2H) + p_0(\text{Hyp } HT) \cdot p_{HT}(2H)}$$

$$= \frac{\frac{1}{3} \cdot \frac{1}{4}}{\frac{1}{3} \cdot 1 + \frac{1}{3} \cdot \frac{1}{4}} = \frac{1}{5}$$

---

* These expressions may be "derived" with the following type of argument. Let us make N tosses, using an HH disk $Np_0(\text{Hyp } HH)$ times and an HT disk $Np_0(\text{Hyp } HT)$ times. This arrangement ensures that the probability is $p_0(\text{Hyp } HH)$ that a disk chosen at random is an HH disk. In the N tosses, the number of heads that we obtain, on the average, is

$$Np_0(\text{Hyp } HH) \cdot p_{HH}(1H) + Np_0(\text{Hyp } HT) \cdot p_{HT}(1H)$$

Of these observed heads, $Np_0(\text{Hyp } HT) \cdot p_{HT}(1H)$ are with the HT disk. Then the probability that any one toss, chosen at random from among the N tosses, whose outcome is heads with an HT disk is

$$\frac{p_0(\text{Hyp } HT) \cdot p_{HT}(1H)}{p_0(\text{Hyp } HH) \cdot p_{HH}(1H) + p_0(\text{Hyp } HT) \cdot p_{HT}(1H)}$$

This can be stated alternatively as the probability that in any one toss giving a head, e.g., the first toss in a series of tosses, the disk will be an HT disk, i.e., $p_1(\text{Hyp } HT)$.

and the probability that the third toss will be heads is

$$p_2(H_3) = \tfrac{4}{5} \cdot 1 + \tfrac{1}{5} \cdot \tfrac{1}{2} = \tfrac{9}{10}$$

The outcomes of all tosses are, of course, assumed to be independent.

We may generalize and write the expression for the probability that the nth toss will be heads, if all $n - 1$ tosses were heads, as

$$p_{n-1}(H_n) = \frac{1}{1 + (\tfrac{1}{2})^{n-1}} \cdot 1 + \frac{(\tfrac{1}{2})^{n-1}}{1 + (\tfrac{1}{2})^{n-1}} \cdot \frac{1}{2} = \frac{2^n + 1}{2^n + 2} \qquad (1\text{-}10)$$

for any integer $n > 1$ (remember, for $n = 1$, we had three hypotheses instead of two).* After observing n heads in a row ($n > 0$), the probability for the *HH* hypothesis, viz.,

$$p_n(\text{Hyp } HH) = \frac{2^n}{2^n + 1} \qquad (1\text{-}11)$$

rapidly approaches unity as n increases, but the hypothesis never becomes completely certain—after n tosses, the $(n + 1)$th toss may be tails and the *HH* probability would drop abruptly to zero.

1-5. Inferred Knowledge

The above examples of conditional probability illustrate also the basic feature of inferred knowledge. This is the real substance of science.

In the last example, as only H's appeared in n trials, we became rather certain by inference that the disk consisted of two heads. But, even though the probability is small for tails on the $(n + 1)$th toss, it may indeed be tails, and, in this event, the reliability of the *HH* hypothesis would drop abruptly to zero. Such is the possible fate of any inferred knowledge, i.e., of any knowledge based on a limited number of observations. Any such knowledge is actually a hypothesis which, as our confidence in it increases with experience, may be dignified by being called a theory or a generalization.†

Any and all knowledge in an experimental science is inferred from a

---

* If the problem were initially stated in terms of a disk having unlike sides or like sides, i.e., a good coin or a bad coin, the expression for $p(\text{Hyp bad})$ would be the same as here given for $p(\text{Hyp } HH)$ and the restriction $n \neq 1$ would be removed. This is the case in the "sunrise" example discussed presently.

† C. S. Pierce, *The Collected Papers of Charles Sanders Pierce* (Cambridge, Mass., 1931–35), ed. Hartshorne and Weiss, said in effect, "All beliefs and all conclusions, however arrived at, are subject to error. The methods of science are more useful than old wives' gossip for achieving stable and reliable conclusions, but science offers no access to perfect certitude or exactitude. We can never be absolutely sure of anything." Then to the objection that the proposition "There is no absolute certainty" is itself inconsistent, Pierce answered "If I must make any exception, let it be that the assertion 'Every assertion but this is fallible' is the only one that is absolutely infallible."

limited number of observations. Usually, however, the evidence on which a scientific generalization rests is so complex that the outcome of more than one experiment is needed to topple it completely. Rather than toppled, a well-based theory, when confronted with an unexpected outcome, is usually altered (i.e., further developed) to include the new information as "expected." Such is the progress of inferred knowledge of any sort; and such is the central feature of experimental probability as discussed later.

It was said earlier that deciding upon the "proper" number of equally probable a priori hypotheses is an inherent part of each problem of inferred knowledge. Let us explore this a little further and ask the question, What is the probability that the sun will rise tomorrow? One assumption is that there are only two hypotheses to be considered—either the sun will rise or it will not rise—analogous to the two outcomes in the toss of a coin. These two hypotheses are presumed *in desperation* to be equally probable, each probability being $\frac{1}{2}$ at the start of things, i.e., before the first sunrise. Some people argue that the probability that the sun will rise again, after having risen n days in a row, is $(\frac{1}{2})^{n+1}$, but this is obviously erroneous (notice how small it is!) because it does not allow for an increase in the sunrise probability as experience accumulates. So, other people argue that, after the first and more sunrise observations, the the probability decreases that the hypothesis "the sun will not rise" is the correct one. This argument is identical to the one in the thin metal disk problem as discussed above, and the desired probability is $(2^n + 1)/(2^n + 2)$. As a third and last argument, we might consider that at the dawn of history or at whatever time $n = 1$, all hypotheses in the entire range of probabilities from 0 to 1 are equally probable. This assumption of equal probabilities for each of an infinite number of hypotheses is again a desperation-in-ignorance type of assumption. It is to the effect that our universe was chosen at random from a collection of universes in which all conceivable universes in regard to the sunrise probability were equally probable. On this argument we would conclude that the desired probability is $(n + 1)/(n + 2)$.* Laplace advanced this last argument in 1812,

---

* This result may be derived along lines of conditional probability without specifically evaluating hypotheses as such. Imagine $N + 1$ jars, each containing N black and white balls such that the ith jar contains i black and $N - i$ white balls, i taking on integer values from 0 to N. A jar is chosen at random and n balls drawn one by one with replacement after each draw. Suppose event (nB) has occurred, i.e., that all n balls are black. What is the probability that the next ball drawn from the jar will also be black? If we choose the ith jar, the probability for (nB) is $p_i(nB) = (i/N)^n$. Therefore,

$$p(nB) = \frac{1}{N + 1} \sum_{i=0}^{N} p_i(nB)$$

and the expression for the probability $(n + 1)/(n + 2)$ is called the Laplace law of succession. Laplace offered publicly to bet anyone 1,826,214 to 1 that the sun would rise tomorrow (he reckoned n as 5000 years†).

These three arguments conclude with quite different numerical values of the desired probability, aside from the question of the proper value of n, and serve to illustrate the inherent difficulty in the development and test of the reliability of knowledge. The problem is, of course, most acute when a bit of *new* knowledge is just being conceived. At this time, what are the equally likely hypotheses, or what are the particular hypotheses even worth considering? Think of the plight of the observer, who was born during the night 5000 years ago and who has never seen or heard of the sun or of a tomorrow, contemplating the prospect that the sun will rise tomorrow, or, if he has seen it just once, contemplating the probability that it has regular habits. Of course, now, with our accumulated experience, confidence in our knowledge that the sun will rise tomorrow is great, and the difficulties in the origin of this knowledge may be amusing. But the alert student will see immediately many modern examples of such inherent difficulties in *new* hypotheses or theories and of the inherent arbitrariness in the probability or reliability of a prediction in terms of a new theory—or, indeed of *any* theory, old or new.

Further comment is in order in regard to the desperation assumption. This assumption is that, with *no information* whatsoever, each of only two possible outcomes should be assigned a probability of $\frac{1}{2}$. On this assumption we would say that the probability of "life on Mars" is $\frac{1}{2}$. We would

---

since choices of jars are mutually exclusive events. Then,

$$p(nB) = \frac{1^n + 2^n + \cdots + N^n}{N^n(N + 1)}$$

and, likewise, the probability that $n + 1$ balls drawn in a row are all black is

$$p((n + 1)B) = \frac{1^{n+1} + 2^{n+1} + \cdots + N^{n+1}}{N^{n+1}(N + 1)}$$

The required probability, viz., that $(n + 1)B$ occurs *after* we know that nB has occurred, is

$$\lim_{N \to \infty} \frac{p((n + 1)B)}{p(nB)} = \frac{n + 1}{n + 2}$$

[Dividing by $p(nB)$ in the last step is equivalent to evaluating and using the appropriate hypotheses in the example with the thin metal disk, but this may not be obvious.]

† The modern scientist would find numerous inferred reasons for believing that the sun had been rising regularly for many years before 5000 years ago. For example, we may invoke generalizations about planetary motion, interpretations of archeological and geological records of sun-dependent life preceding the earliest records of man, of the time involved in the evolution of stars, etc.

also say that the probability of cats on Mars is $\frac{1}{2}$, of elephants is $\frac{1}{2}$, indeed, of every individual form of life is $\frac{1}{2}$. If there are N different forms of life, the probability of at least one form is $1 - (\frac{1}{2})^N$ which, if N is large, is very near certainty and much greater than the first answer of $\frac{1}{2}$. What is wrong? Nothing is wrong. As soon as we know or profess to know that there is a reasonable probability for more than one form of life on Mars, we are no longer in such complete desperation as to answer $\frac{1}{2}$ to the first question. Nor is our ignorance quite so profound as for us to answer $\frac{1}{2}$ for any of the additional questions, although we are admittedly rather disturbed when confronted with such questions. We must be very careful in making the complete desperation assumption. There are numerous classical "paradoxes" that have been expounded on this point. Additional knowledge always modifies a probability, except for the Omniscient for Whom the answer to *any* probability question is always either zero or unity.

1-6. Problems

Note: A numerical answer to a problem is *not* a complete answer; the student should justify the application of the equation(s) he uses by giving an analysis of the problem, pointing out how the problem meets satisfactorily the conditions on which each equation is based. To develop his "intuition," the student should contemplate the comparison of the correct answer with his a priori expectation. To this end, answers are given to most problems.

1. What is the probability of drawing at random each of the following from a jar containing 3 red and 5 black balls:

(a) 2 red balls simultaneously, (ans. $\frac{3}{28}$)

(b) 3 red balls in successive draws with replacement after each draw, and (ans. $\frac{27}{512}$)

(c) 2 reds and a black in a single draw of 3 balls? (ans. $\frac{15}{56}$)

2. Ten people are arranged at random (a) in a row, and (b) in a ring. What is the probability that 2 given people will be (i) next to each other, and (ii) separated by 1 person between them? [ans. (a) (i) $\frac{1}{5}$, (ii) 0.178; (b) (i) $\frac{2}{9}$, (ii) $\frac{2}{9}$]

3. Two cards are drawn simultaneously from a 52-card deck. What is the probability that

(a) at least one of them is a spade, (ans. $\frac{15}{34}$)

(b) they are both red, and (ans. $\frac{25}{102}$)

(c) one is an ace and the other a black ten? (ans. $\frac{4}{663}$)

4. With two dice cast together, what is the probability for

(a) an even number on each die, (ans. $\frac{1}{4}$)

(b) either a 7 or an 11, and (ans. $\frac{2}{9}$)

(c) neither a 12, nor an 11, nor a 7 in the first cast, and a 7 in the second cast? (ans. $\frac{1}{8}$)

5. What is the probability that, in tossing a penny,

(a) 5 heads appear in the first 5 tosses, (ans. $\frac{1}{32}$)

(b) the second head appears on the fifth toss, and (ans. $\frac{1}{8}$)

(c) in 5 tosses, a head appears exactly twice? (ans. $\frac{5}{16}$)

6. In how many throws of 1 die is there a probability of less than 0.2 of

(a) seeing a 5, (ans. 1, i.e., <2)

(b) seeing a 5 for the first time in the last throw, and

(c) not seeing a 5? (ans. 9)

7. Two dice are cast together. Let A be the event that the sum of the faces is odd, B the event of at least 1 ace. Are these 2 events independent? Mutually exclusive? What are the probabilities that

(a) both A and B occur, (ans. $\frac{1}{6}$)

(b) either A or B or both occur, (ans. $\frac{23}{36}$)

(c) A and not B occurs, and (ans. $\frac{1}{3}$)

(d) B and not A occurs? (ans. $\frac{5}{36}$)

Note that the sum of answers (a), (c), and (d) gives the answer to (b).

8. A coin is tossed until for the first time the same result appears twice in succession. What is the probability that

(a) the experiment ends before the sixth toss, and (ans. $\frac{15}{16}$)

(b) an even number of tosses is required? (ans. $\frac{2}{3}$)

9. A Cornell student parked illegally overnight on 100 randomly selected nights. He received a total of only 12 "tickets" and all these on either Monday or Friday nights. What is the probability of getting a ticket if he parks

(a) next Monday night, (ans. 0.42)

(b) on only Mondays and Fridays, and (ans. 3×10^{-7})

(c) on no more than two unspecified nights? (ans. 6.2×10^{-6})

For part (a) assume, in the absence of more knowledge, that 6 of the 12 tickets were on Monday nights, and for parts (b) and (c) assume that the police check on random nights.

10. On an empty chessboard of 64 squares, the white and black queens are placed at random except that they cannot occupy the same square. What is the probability that the 2 queens are in striking position, i.e., are on the same horizontal, vertical, or diagonal row? (ans. $\frac{13}{36}$)

11. A marksman hits a target on the average 4 times out of 5. Assume that the probability of a hit is constant. What is the probability that he hits the target

(a) exactly 4 times in 4 shots, (ans. 0.41)

(b) exactly 4 times in 5 shots, and (ans. 0.41)

(c) the first 4 times but misses on the fifth shot? (ans. 0.082)

In what sense is this an a priori probability problem? In what sense is it not?

12. What is the probability that the birthdays of 12 people randomly selected, assuming equal probabilities for all months, fall

(a) in the same calendar month, (ans. 1.34×10^{-12})

(b) in January, and (ans. 1.12×10^{-13})

(c) in 12 different calendar months? (ans. 5.37×10^{-5})

13. A man belongs to a club of 10 members. Every day he invites 5 members to dine with him, making a different party each day.

(a) For how many days can he do this?   (ans. 126)

(b) How many parties will each man attend?   (ans. 70, 126)

14. A closet contains 9 pairs of shoes with no 2 pairs alike. If 4 shoes are chosen at random, what is the probability that there will be no complete pair among them? Generalize the answer for the case of n pairs of shoes with $2r$ shoes chosen at random ($2r < n$).   (ans. $\frac{56}{85}$)

15. Suppose that 6 white and 9 black balls are in a jar.

(a) If the color of the first ball drawn at random is not known and this ball is not replaced, what is the probability that the next ball drawn will be white?   (ans. $\frac{2}{5}$)

(b) If the first ball is known to be white and is not replaced, what is the probability that the second draw will be white?   (ans. $\frac{5}{14}$)

(c) If the first ball is known to be white but the color of the second ball drawn is not known, and neither is replaced, what is the probability that the third ball drawn will be white?

(d) Why is the answer to part (a) the same as the probability for drawing the first ball white?

16. Suppose that the 15 balls of Problem 15 are divided between 2 jars with 4 white and 1 black in one and with 2 white and 8 black in the other.

(a) If a jar is selected at random and a single ball drawn, what is the probability that it will be white?   (ans. $\frac{1}{2}$)

(b) If this ball is not replaced and its color is not known, what is the probability that the next ball drawn (from a randomly selected jar) will be white? Should this answer be expected to be the same as the answer to part (a)?

(c) If the first ball is not replaced but is known to be white, what is the probability that the second ball drawn (from a randomly selected jar) will be white?   (ans. 0.47)

(d) What is the probability for the successive drawing of 2 white balls without replacement from randomly selected jars?   (ans. 0.235)

17. Suppose that someone has a penny that you suspect has one chance in a million of being bad, i.e., of having heads on both sides. The penny is then tossed n times and every time it comes up heads.

(a) How large would n have to be before your suspicion that the penny is bad increases to 1 chance in 2?   (ans. $n = 20$)

(b) How large must n be if you were initially certain that the penny was and remains good?   (ans. In this case experimental evidence is not relevant)

18. Referring to Problem 9, calculate the ticket probability for next Wednesday night. Assume that the 100 random parkings occur during a period of 9 months, and assume that only two hypotheses are reasonable, viz., the police check either (A) randomly among the 7 days of each week or (B) randomly on only Mondays and Fridays. (The *general* answer would include all possible hypotheses as to checking systems.) An answer in the form of an equation suffices.

I-7. Combinatorial Analysis

As stated in Sections 1-2 and 1-3, methods for determining the total number of equally possible events in somewhat complicated ideal games of chance were soon worked out by the mathematicians. These methods constitute the subject of combinatorial analysis; they give formulas for computing the number of permutations and the number of combinations. These formulas are discussed next.

Permutations. Consider a set of n objects having different colors or some characteristics that make each object different from any other. Arrange the n objects in some order, e.g., along a line. This arrangement is called a permutation of the n objects. If two objects are interchanged in their positions, a different permutation results. Now select k of the n objects and arrange them in order, e.g., along a line. How many permutations are possible as k objects are selected from the population of n objects?

Suppose for simplicity that the k objects are selected one by one. Any one of the n objects may be chosen to fill the first of the k positions; hence there are n possible choices in the selection of the first object. Then, $n - 1$ objects are left from which one is chosen for the second position. Since there are n possible choices in selecting the first object and $n - 1$ possible choices in selecting the second object, there are a total of $n(n - 1)$ possible choices in selecting both objects. Continuing, there are $n - 2$ objects left from which the third is selected. In selecting all three objects, there are $n(n - 1)(n - 2)$ possible choices. In general, the kth object is selected from $(n - k + 1)$ objects, and the total number of possible choices in selecting all k objects is $n(n - 1)(n - 2) \cdots (n - k + 1)$. Since each possible choice represents one permutation, the total number of permutations is given by

$$_nP_k = n(n - 1)(n - 2) \cdots (n - k + 1) = \frac{n!}{(n - k)!} \qquad (1\text{-}12)$$

The symbol $_nP_k$ is commonly read as the number of permutations of n things taken k at a time.* In case $k = n$, the number of permutations is

$$_nP_n = n! \qquad (1\text{-}13)$$

---

* The phrase "n things taken k at a time," commonly used in the discussion of permutations, requires amplification. In a given sample, it is the k things that are "taken" rather than the n things, but the total number of permutations is equal to the total number of different ordered samples of size k that can be taken from the population n. In this sense, the n things are *taken* as one "boundary condition" and the sample size k is *taken* as a second "boundary condition" in the sampling process.

This is consistent with the convention in factorial algebra of taking $0! = 1$.* Of course, k can be any number from 0 to n.

As implied above, a permutation is defined as one possible ordered sample of a set of nonidentical objects. The sample size may be equal to or less than the total population, i.e., the total number of objects in the set.

It is not necessary that the k objects be selected one by one; they may all be withdrawn simultaneously and subsequently placed in order. It is instructive to consider the problem from this view. Suppose that we have n bins, and that we wish to distribute k objects among these bins, no more than one object to a bin. In placing the first of the k objects, we have n possible choices; in placing the second object, we have $n - 1$ possible choices; etc. The total number of possible choices in distributing all k objects is the same as given by Eq. 1-12.

As a simple example, consider the number of permutations that may arise when four different letters are taken two at a time. In this case, $_4P_2 = 4!/(4 - 2)! = 4 \cdot 3 = 12$, and these permutations, if the letters are a, b, c, d, can be written as ab, ba, ac, ca, ad, da, bc, cb, bd, db, cd, and dc.

Stirling's formula. Numerical evaluation of a factorial number is often inconvenient. Help is frequently found in the use of Stirling's formula,

$$z! = \sqrt{2\pi z}\,(z/e)^z\left(1 + \frac{1}{12z} + \frac{1}{288z^2} - \frac{139}{51840z^3} + \cdots\right) \qquad (1\text{-}14)$$

where z is any integer. The first term of this expression is, as an approximation, good to 2% for $z = 5$, and to better than 1% for $z > 9$. For $z \lesssim 9$, the straight factorial evaluation is usually the more convenient, and the practical use of Eq. 1-14 is usually limited to the first term.

The essential part of Stirling's formula can be derived as follows. The natural logarithm of $z!$ is

$$\log(z!) = \log 2 + \log 3 + \log 4 + \cdots + \log z$$

Consider a graph of $y = \log z$, as in Fig. 1-1, and mark off ordinate values $\log 2$, $\log 3$, $\log 4$, etc., and abscissa values 1, 2, 3, etc. Then, $\log(z!)$ is clearly equal to the sum of the areas of the rectangles indicated in the figure, each rectangle having unit width and having a height equal to $\log 2$, or $\log 3$, $\cdots$, or $\log z$. This area is approximately equal to the area

---

* This is often stated as follows: By the definition of a factorial number, $(n - 1)! = n!/n$, and, if n is taken as unity in this expression, $n!/n = 1$. It follows that $(1 - 1)! = 0! = 1$.

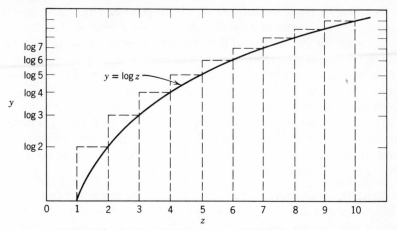

Fig. 1-1. Graphical interpretation of Stirling's formula.

under the smooth curve $y = \log z$ out to z, the approximation improving as z increases. Hence, for large z,

$$\log (z!) \approx \int_0^z \log z \, dz$$

and, integrating by parts,

$$\log (z!) \approx z \log z - z + 1 \approx z \log z - z$$

Putting this in exponential form, we have

$$z! \approx (z/e)^z$$

which, with the insertion of the factor $\sqrt{2\pi z}$, is the first term of Stirling's formula, Eq. 1-14. The additional terms enter in the complete derivation to take account of the excess area between the step curve and the smooth curve in Fig. 1-1.*

* Mathematicians commonly define $z!$ as

$$z! = \int_0^\infty x^z e^{-x} \, dx \tag{1-15}$$

which applies whether z is integral or not. Later, we shall use the factorial of a negative integer. It is in terms of Eq. 1-15 that such factorials can be shown to be infinite. Interpreted graphically, Eq. 1-15 refers to the area under the curve $y = x^z e^{-x}$. The integration indicated in Eq. 1-15 can be carried out by parts,

$$z! = -x^z e^{-x} \Big|_0^\infty + z \int_0^\infty x^{z-1} e^{-x} \, dx = z(z-1)! \tag{1-16}$$

Further discussion of this integration, as well as of the complete derivation of Stirling's formula, can be found in standard textbooks of mathematics. [Incidentally, $(z - 1)!$ is called the gamma function of z, written $\Gamma(z)$, and Stirling's formula is often discussed under this title.]

Sampling without replacement. Either procedure just described in arriving at the number of permutations of n things taken k at a time, or, in other words, the number of different ways k objects can be placed in n bins, is also called sampling *without* replacement. With this terminology, $_nP_k$ is read as the number of different samples of size k that can be taken from a population of n elements. In this case, the term "sample" refers to a particular permutation of the k objects.*

The a priori probability of drawing, or of otherwise realizing, a particular permutation or properly specified sample of size k from a population of n elements is $1/_nP_k$, assuming each possible permutation or sample to have an equal probability.

Sampling with replacement. If the first object selected from the n objects is noted and then replaced before the next selection is made, we have sampling with replacement. A given object may be selected more than once; repetitions are permitted. It follows that in selecting two objects, the total number of possible choices is $n \cdot n = n^2$; in selecting three objects, the total number is $n \cdot n \cdot n = n^3$; and in selecting k objects, the total number of possible choices is n^k. We say that n^k is the number of ordered arrangements of size k, repetitions permitted, that can be taken from a population of n different objects. Note that in this type of sampling no restriction is placed on the magnitude of k; the sample size k may be smaller or larger than the population n.

Tossing coins, casting dice, etc., are examples of sampling with replacement. In tossing a coin, the population n is 2, viz., heads and tails, and the sample size is the number of tosses.

When random sampling is done with replacement, the assumption is made in a priori probability that each of the possible samples is equally probable. Hence, for each specified ordered sample of size k, repetitions permitted, the probability is $1/n^k$. In the tossing of a coin, if the sequential order of heads and tails is specified as, say, five heads in a row, the probability for this sample (five independent events as discussed earlier) is $1/2^5$.

Some interesting probability problems involve, in a sense, both kinds of sampling. For example, what is the probability that five randomly selected digits are all different? In this problem, although a selected digit

---

* The term "sample" has various meanings: as a verb it refers to a process, as a noun it refers to something selected; here, it means a permutation; in the next paragraph, it means an ordered arrangement of k objects that are not necessarily all different; and in "combination" problems discussed presently, sample refers to different objects but without regard to their particular sequential order. The term "arrangement" is also a general one, like "sample," and is also often used in special senses without the proper qualifying phrases. Some authors use the term "combination" in a similar general way, but usually it has the restricted meaning assigned presently.

is not "replaced," there are assumed to be an infinite number of each type of digit in the imaginary jar from which selection is made; hence the problem is really one of sampling with replacement. It is immaterial whether sampling is one by one or is a single group of five together. We note that, in this example, $n = 10$ and $k = 5$, and that there are therefore 10^5 possible ordered arrangements, repetitions permitted, each assumed to be equally probable. There are $_{10}P_5$ permutations (i.e., ordered arrangements without repetitions). Hence, the answer to the question is

$$p = \frac{_{10}P_5}{10^5} \approx 0.3024$$

Consider another problem. An elevator has seven passengers and empties with stops at ten floors, and we ask, What is the probability that no two passengers leave at the same floor? Assuming equal probability for each of the 10^7 ordered arrangements with repetitions permitted, we find the answer to be

$$p = \frac{_{10}P_7}{10^7} \approx 0.06048$$

Combinations: binomial coefficients. Suppose now that the k objects, instead of being ordered by sequential drawings from n different objects or by individual positions in an n-place bin, are considered to be a single *unordered* group. Such an unordered group is a type of sample called a combination. Thus, in the case of the four letters a, b, c, and d, the two-letter sample ab is the same combination as ba, but is different from ac, etc. The total number of combinations possible in selecting k objects from n different objects may be denoted by $_nC_k$ or, in more modern notation, by $\binom{n}{k}$. Either of these two symbols is read as the total number of combinations of n things taken k at a time, or as the total number of combinations of size k from a population of n elements. Again, $0 \leqslant k \leqslant n$.

The expression for the total number of combinations, $\binom{n}{k}$, is obtained as follows. The k objects as an unordered group make one combination, whereas one particular order of the k objects makes one permutation. The total number of permutations in one combination of k objects is $k!$, and the total number of permutations in $\binom{n}{k}$ combinations is $\binom{n}{k}k!$. Thus,

$$_nP_k = \binom{n}{k}k!$$

from which, with Eq. 1-12,

$$\binom{n}{k} = \frac{_nP_k}{k!} = \frac{n!}{k!(n-k)!} \tag{1-17}$$

It is apparent from the denominator of the last part of this expression that $k!$ and $(n - k)!$ can be interchanged. It follows that

$$\binom{n}{k} = \binom{n}{n - k} \tag{1-18}$$

The symbol $\binom{n}{k}$ is called the binomial coefficient because it appears in Newton's binomial expansion

$$(a + b)^n = \binom{n}{0}a^n + \binom{n}{1}a^{n-1}b + \binom{n}{2}a^{n-2}b^2 + \cdots + \binom{n}{k}a^k b^{n-k}$$

$$+ \cdots + \binom{n}{n}b^n \tag{1-19}$$

The coefficient $\binom{n}{k}$ is arranged in an interesting way in Pascal's triangle:

$$
\begin{array}{rccccccccccccc}
n = 0 & & & & & & & 1 & & & & & & \\
= 1 & & & & & & 1 & & 1 & & & & & \\
= 2 & & & & & 1 & & 2 & & 1 & & & & \\
= 3 & & & & 1 & & 3 & & 3 & & 1 & & & \\
= 4 & & & 1 & & 4 & & 6 & & 4 & & 1 & & \\
= 5 & & 1 & & 5 & & 10 & & 10 & & 5 & & 1 & \\
= 6 & 1 & & 6 & & 15 & & 20 & & 15 & & 6 & & 1 \\
= 7 & 1 & 7 & 21 & 35 & 35 & 21 & 7 & 1 & & & & \\
\end{array}
$$

etc.

Entries in the nth row are the respective values of $\binom{n}{k}$ given by successive values of k. Note that the basic idea of the triangle is that each entry (except for the unused apex) is the sum of the two immediately and diagonally above it; i.e.,

$$\binom{n + 1}{k} = \binom{n}{k} + \binom{n}{k - 1}$$

(As an exercise, the student should prove this equality.)

Familiarity with combinations is best achieved from specific examples; let us consider a few examples.

The number of two-letter combinations (sample size $k = 2$) that can be selected from the four letters a, b, c, and d (population $n = 4$) is given by

$$\binom{n}{k} = \binom{4}{2} = \frac{4!}{2!(4 - 2)!} = 6$$

and these are ab, ac, ad, bc, bd, and cd.

Consider further the example about a random sample of five digits discussed in the previous section, where the problem specified five digits, all different, in an *ordered* group or permutation. Now let us ask, In how many ways can five different digits be selected if the sequential order is of no consequence? The answer to this question is $\binom{10}{5}$, i.e., reduced from $_{10}P_5$ by the factor 5!

Another example is found in the problem, How many different single bridge hands can be dealt from a 52-card deck? A hand contains 13 cards and the particular order of the cards in a hand is of no consequence. So the question can be rephrased, How many combinations of size 13 can be taken from a population of 52? The answer is $\binom{52}{13} \approx 635,013,559,600.$* And the number of permutations, i.e., with the sequential order in the deal specified, is even greater by the factor (13)!

Among all these $\binom{52}{13}$ possible bridge hands, how many have only red cards? Each hand is a sample of size 13 cards from the population of 26 red cards.† Hence, the number of possible all-red hands is $\binom{26}{13}$. The probability that a hand contains only red cards is then

$$p = \frac{\binom{26}{13}}{\binom{52}{13}}$$

It is perhaps instructive to solve this problem by the long-hand method of writing the product of the probabilities of successive independent single-card deals. Thus, the probability that the first card is red is $\frac{26}{52}$; that the second is red is $\frac{25}{51}$; etc., and the probability of the event that all 13 cards are red is given by the product of the component events, viz.,

$$\frac{26}{52} \cdot \frac{25}{51} \cdot \frac{24}{50} \cdots \frac{14}{40} = \frac{\frac{26!}{13!}}{\frac{52!}{39!}} = \frac{\frac{26!}{(26-13)!}}{\frac{52!}{(52-13)!}} = \frac{\frac{26!}{13!(26-13)!}}{\frac{52!}{13!(52-13)!}} = \frac{\binom{26}{13}}{\binom{52}{13}}$$

In general, it is simpler to use the shorthand method of the binomial coefficients, i.e., to think in terms of a sample size k from a population of

* A bridge player immediately after looking at his hand rose up and shot the dealer. At the trial he pleaded that the dealer had obviously stacked the deck, and he was acquitted when he proved that if the deck had not been stacked the probability of his getting that particular hand of cards would have been only 1 in 635,013,559,600. What should have been the counterargument of the prosecuting attorney?

† It is not valid to argue that the sample in this problem is 13 cards from a population of two colors, giving 2^{13} red hands, because this improperly presumes sampling *with* replacement.

size n, although in this particular example the most apparent simplification is in the notation.

Another example: What is the probability that a poker hand of five cards contains five different face values? The number of different hands (combinations) is $\binom{52}{5} = 2{,}598{,}960$. The number of different ways (combinations) the five cards having different face values can be selected from a single suit of 13 cards is $\binom{13}{5}$. If a suit were specified in the problem, the answer would be $\binom{13}{5} \Big/ \binom{52}{5}$, but no suit is specified. The number of different ways (arrangements with repetitions permitted) in which the specified five cards can be arranged among the four suits is 4^5. Hence, the answer to the problem, assuming all possible hands to be equally probable, is

$$p = \frac{4^5 \binom{13}{5}}{\binom{52}{5}} \approx 0.5071$$

Note that in each of the last two examples, component parts of each problem are analyzed in terms of different population numbers, and, in the last example, one component sampling is done with replacement. Different types of populations in a given problem are common.

Binomial distribution formula. In probability situations in which there are only two possible outcomes (outcome population $= 2$), each observation or sampling with replacement is called a *Bernoulli trial*. Obvious examples of Bernoulli trials are the successive tossings of a coin, the casting of a die for a six vs. a nonsix, etc. The essential features of Bernoulli trials are:

(1) successive trials must be independent,

(2) the outcome of each trial must be determined entirely by chance, and

(3) the probability for any specified outcome (called "success") must be constant for all trials.

Let p be the probability for "success," and let q be the probability for "failure." What is the probability for exactly k successes in n trials? The problem posed by this question is known as the *Bernoulli problem*. If the sequential order of successes and failures were important, the probability of exactly k successes and of exactly $n - k$ failures would be $p^k q^{n-k}$ since successes and failures, being mutually exclusive, are necessarily independent events. But since the sequential order is of no consequence, we must multiply $p^k q^{n-k}$ by the number of combinations of the trial population n taken k (or $n - k$) at a time. This multiplication is equivalent to adding up all the mutually exclusive combinations. Hence, the answer to Bernoulli's problem is given by

$$B(k;\ n,\ p) = \binom{n}{k} p^k q^{n-k} \tag{1-20}$$

and may be read as the Bernoulli (or the binomial, see below) probability for exactly k successes out of n trials with a success probability p. Since $p + q = 1$, it follows by the use of Eq. 1-19 that

$$1 = (p + q)^n = p^n + \binom{n}{1} p^{n-1}q + \binom{n}{2} p^{n-2}q^2$$

$$+ \cdots + \binom{n}{k} p^k q^{n-k} + \cdots + q^n \tag{1-21}$$

or

$$1 = \sum_{k=0}^{n} \binom{n}{k} p^k q^{n-k} = \sum_{k=0}^{n} B(k;\ n,\ p) \tag{1-22}$$

The first term in the sum of Eq. 1-21 gives the probability for exactly n successes in n trials; the second term gives the probability for exactly $n - 1$ successes; the third term the probability for exactly $n - 2$ successes; etc.; the last term, q^n, gives the probability for zero successes. The series up to and including the p^k term represents the probability that the event called success happens *at least* k times in n trials. The probability for at least one success is $1 - q^n$.

Because of its general form, Eq. 1-21 or 1-22 is called the binomial formula, and a graph of $B(k;\ n,\ p)$ vs. k is called the *binomial distribution* of probabilities. Such distribution graphs are shown in Fig. 1-2 for two particular pairs of values of n and p. The distribution is asymmetric except for the cases in which $p = \frac{1}{2}$ (symmetry in these special cases will be proved in the next chapter).

Examples of binomial probability are found in the tossing of a coin n times, seeking k heads (and $n - k$ tails), for which the head probability p per trial is known, e.g., is $\frac{1}{2}$; the casting of a die for which p for a particular face value is $\frac{1}{6}$, or for an even number is $\frac{1}{2}$; the casting of two dice for which p for a double ace is $\frac{1}{36}$; the hitting of a target k out of n times if the hit probability is known; etc.

It follows from the definition of the success probability p, Eq. 1-1, that, in n Bernoulli trials, the a priori expected number of successes k is given by the product np. This product np is called the *expectation value*. The expectation value is equal to the arithmetic mean value of k when all possible values of k are weighted by their respective probabilities as given by Eq. 1-20 or 1-21.

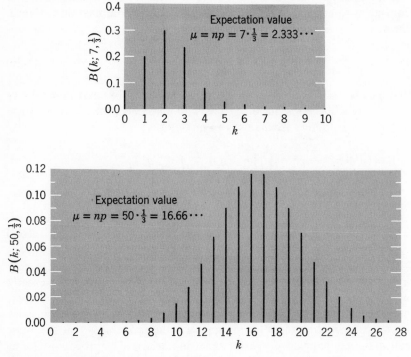

Fig. 1-2. Two binomial probability distributions. The asymmetry decreases as the expectation value, np, increases.

The most probable value of k, viz., k_0, is that value for which the binomial probability is a maximum. In some cases k_0 is double-valued, the two values differing by unity [see Problem 14(a) of Section 1-9]. k_0 never differs from np by more than unity.*

* This can be shown as follows. By the definition of k_0, in general

$$B((k_0 + 1);\ n, p) < B(k_0;\ n, p)$$

and also

$$B((k_0 - 1);\ n, p) < B(k_0;\ n, p).$$

By expressing each B as the appropriate term in Eq. 1-22, these inequalities can also be written as

$$\frac{p}{k_0 + 1} < \frac{1 - p}{n - k_0} \quad \text{and also} \quad \frac{1 - p}{n - k_0 + 1} < \frac{p}{k_0}$$

and, in consequence,

$$(pn - 1) < (pn + p - 1) < k_0 < (pn + p) < (pn + 1) \tag{1-23}$$

which proves that

$$|k_0 - np| < 1 \tag{1-24}$$

Before proceeding, let us recapitulate a little. In writing the expression for the binomial distribution formula we use n to represent the number of Bernoulli trials, whereas, in the discussion that led to the binomial coefficients, n refers to the number of unlike objects from which random selections of size k are made. It is important to realize that, although the terminology is different and the "unlikeness" of the "objects" is rather specialized, the two n's refer to the same thing. Each binomial coefficient is the number of combinations or ways in which an unordered sample of size k can be taken from the n unlike objects. The binomial probability for k successes is proportional to this coefficient, i.e, to the number of ways n trials can be taken k successes at a time. The k successes are of course in an unordered sequence with $n - k$ failures mixed in. The specialized unlikeness of the objects in this instance is that the population of n trials is made up of only *two* different kinds of things, viz., successes and failures, and we do not know which is success and which is failure until after the trial. But this does not impair the argument.

The binomial is a very important distribution since so many problems can be analyzed in terms of basic Bernoulli trials. Indeed, the normal (Gauss) and the Poisson mathematical models of probability, the two most important models in treating errors of measurement in any experimental science, may (but not necessarily) be considered to be special cases of the binomial model. The normal case is that for which n becomes very large (infinite in the limit) and p is sufficiently large that $np \gg 1$ (infinite in the limit). In practice the normal approximation is fairly good as long as $np > 5$ when $p \leqslant \frac{1}{2}$, and $nq > 5$ when $p > \frac{1}{2}$. The formula for what is called the probability density in this distribution is

$$G(z;\ h) = \frac{h}{\sqrt{\pi}} e^{-h^2 z^2} \qquad (1\text{-}25)$$

where $h = 1/\sqrt{2npq}$ and $z = np - k$. Equation 1-25 is derived in Chapter 4. The Poisson special case obtains when n becomes very large (infinite in the limit) and p becomes very small (zero in the limit) but in such fashion that the product np remains moderate in magnitude, viz., that $np \ll \sqrt{n}$. The Poisson formula (derived in Chapter 5) is

$$P(k;\ \mu) = \frac{\mu^k e^{-\mu}}{k!} \qquad (1\text{-}26)$$

where $\mu = np$.

The special conveniences of Eqs. 1-25 and 1-26 and their application to measurements are discussed in detail in Chapters 4 and 5, but one immediately apparent convenience, when compared with the binomial formula, is that evaluation of large factorials is avoided.

When n is small, Eq. 1-20 is used directly and the computation is not excessive. When n is large and p is not small, the normal approximation Eq. 1-25 is used. And when n is large and p is small, the Poisson approximation is used. Thus, all possibilities have been considered.

Because of the importance of the binomial distribution it is instructive for the student to perform a little experiment to check it. Toss five "honest" pennies. Pick up those that are not heads and toss them a second time. Finally, toss any that are not heads this time a third time. Now, after the

Table I-I. Values of $B(k; 32, p_i)$

For $p_1 = (\frac{1}{2})^5 = \frac{1}{32}$; $p_2 = (1 - \frac{1}{4})^5 = \dfrac{243}{1024} \approx 0.237$; and

$$p_3 = (1 - \frac{1}{8})^5 = \frac{16807}{32678} \approx 0.513$$

k	First Toss	Second Toss	Third Toss	k	Third Toss (cont.)
0	0.362	0.0002	—		
1	0.374	0.0017	—		
2	0.187	0.0083	—		
3	0.060	0.026	—	18	0.120
4	0.014	0.058	—	19	0.093
5	0.003	0.101	—	20	0.064
6	—	0.141	0.0001	21	0.038
7	—	0.164	0.0005	22	0.020
8	—	0.159	0.0016	23	0.0092
9	—	0.131	0.0045	24	0.0037
10	—	0.094	0.0110	25	0.0012
11	—	0.058	0.0230	26	0.0003
12	—	0.032	0.0425	27	0.0001
13	—	0.015	0.069	28	—
14	—	0.0064	0.098	29	—
15	—	0.0024	0.124	30	—
16	—	0.0008	0.138	31	—
17	—	0.0002	0.137	32	—

third toss, if any of the five pennies is a tail the experiment has failed. Success is counted if and when all five pennies are heads. Repeat the experiment 32 times and record the number of successes after each of one, two, and three tosses. With Eq. 1-21, the expected number of successes can be calculated. The calculated probabilities of k successes in 32 trials are listed in Table 1-1, and each of these probabilities must be multiplied by 32 to give the expected number of successes. First, be sure o understanding of the values of p_i listed at the head of the table,* and then check a few of the binomial probabilities as listed in the table. Use Stirling's formula where it is accurate enough and convenient. The numbers n and np, at least in the third-toss case, are sufficiently large that fair accuracy can be achieved with the simpler normal approximation, Eq. 1-25; also, $B(k; 32, p_i)$ may possibly be satisfactorily represented by the Poisson approximation, Eq. 1-26. Try these approximations in a few instances in each of the one-, two-, and three-toss cases to test their accuracy and their relative convenience. Then compare the observed numbers of successes with the calculated frequencies and discuss the discrepancies. Later, in Chapter 4, we discuss the so-called χ^2 test for determining whether or not the observed discrepancies are reasonably compatible with the assumption that the five pennies *are* "honest" (i.e., that each has a head probability of $\frac{1}{2}$).

Multinomial coefficients. We have discussed permutations and combinations of n different objects taken k at a time. In many problems the n objects are not *all* different from one another. Thus, in an ordinary 52-card deck, 4 cards are aces, 13 are spades, 26 are red. Suppose that there are r different kinds of objects; then $n = k_1 + k_2 + k_3 + \cdots + k_r$, $r \leqslant n$. The expression for the number of permutations $_nP_{k_1,k_2,\cdots,k_r}$ can be arrived at by the same type of reasoning as was used in obtaining $\binom{n}{k}$ from $_nP_k$. The k_1 similar objects in a single combination represent $k_1!$ permutations of the $n!$ total number of permutations that would exist if all n objects were different. Likewise, the k_2 similar objects in a single combination represent $k_2!$ permutations if all n objects were different. By continuation of this argument, the number of permutations $_nP_{k_1,k_2,\cdots,k_r}$ when multiplied by $k_1!k_2! \cdots k_r!$ gives the total number of permutations

---

* Calculation of p_1 is easy. To calculate p_2, note that the chance of a penny failing to show heads twice in succession is $\frac{1}{4}$; hence the probability for heads on either the first or the second try is $(1 - \frac{1}{4})$. The probability that all five pennies will do this is $p_2 = (1 - \frac{1}{4})^5$. By the same type of argument, the probability of success in three tries is $p_3 = (1 - \frac{1}{8})^5$.

p_2 may also be calculated as follows. The probability for n heads and $5 - n$ tails on the first try is

$$\frac{1}{2^5} \cdot \frac{5!}{n!\,(5 - n)!}$$

Thereafter, $5 - n$ pennies are tossed again. The chance that they are all heads is $1/2^{5-n}$. If these two factors are multiplied and summed over n from $n = 0$ to $n = 5$, we obtain p_2. This sort of argument also gives

$$p_3 = \sum_{n=0}^{5} \sum_{m=0}^{5} \frac{1}{2^5} \cdot \frac{5!}{n!\,(5 - n)!} \cdot \frac{1}{2^{5-n}} \cdot \frac{(5 - n)!}{(5 - n - m)!} \cdot \frac{1}{2^{5-n-m}}$$

that would be present if all n objects were different. Hence, we may write

$$_nP_{k_1,k_2,\cdots,k_r} = \frac{n!}{k_1!k_2!\cdots k_r!} = \frac{n!}{\prod\limits_{i=1}^{r} k_i!} \tag{1-27}$$

where the symbol Π means the product. This is to be read as the total number of ways in which n objects can be divided into r groups of which the first contains k_1 objects, the second contains k_2 objects, etc., when the order of the r groups is preserved. Only the order within each k group is relaxed, making it a combination.

It is instructive to derive Eq. 1-27 by a different route, this time following the line of reasoning that led to the expression for $_nP_k$ directly rather than to the expression for $\binom{n}{k}$ as above. As a first step, consider n to be divided into just two groups of like objects in each group. Then, $n = k_1 + k_2$. In this case, after the k_1 like objects have been selected from the n objects, we have $n - k_1$ objects left. We can write $_nP_{k_1,k_2}$ as the product of the number of ways k_1 objects can be selected from n objects and the number of ways k_2 objects can be selected from $n - k_1$ objects. Thus,

$$_nP_{k_1,k_2} = \binom{n}{k_1}\binom{n-k_1}{k_2} = \binom{n}{k_1} = \frac{n!}{k_1!k_2!} = \frac{n!}{\prod\limits_{i=1}^{2} k_i!} \tag{1-28}$$

since $k_2 = n - k_1$ and $\binom{n-k_1}{n-k_1} = 1$. Now consider the next step in which there are three groups of like objects, $n = k_1 + k_2 + k_3$. By the same argument as in the first step,

$$\begin{aligned}
_nP_{k_1,k_2,k_3} &= \binom{n}{k_1}\binom{n-k_1}{k_2}\binom{n-k_1-k_2}{k_3} \\
&= \frac{n!}{k_1!(n-k_1)!}\frac{(n-k_1)!}{k_2!(n-k_1-k_2)!}\frac{(n-k_1-k_2)!}{k_3!(n-k_1-k_2-k_3)!} \\
&= \frac{n!}{k_1!k_2!k_3!} = \frac{n!}{\prod\limits_{i=1}^{3} k_i!}
\end{aligned}$$

since $(n - k_1 - k_2 - k_3)! = 0! = 1$. By generalizing, we see that

$$_nP_{k_1,k_2,\cdots,k_r} = \frac{n!}{k_1!k_2!\cdots k_r!} = \frac{n!}{\prod\limits_{i=1}^{r} k_i!} \tag{1-29}$$

It is perhaps clearer in this derivation than in the former that the order is preserved among all the r groups, each group being a single combination.

The symbol $_nP_{k_1,k_2,\cdots,k_r}$ appears as the coefficient of each term in the algebraic expansion of $(a_1 + a_2 + \cdots + a_r)^n$, and it is for this reason that it is called a multinomial (or polynomial) coefficient.

Consider a few illustrative examples. First, how many different ways can five letters be arranged if three of the letters are x and two are j? The answer is $_5P_{3,2} = 5!/3!2! = 10$, and these ten arrangements are *xxxjj*, *xxjxj*, *xjxxj*, *jxxxj*, *xxjjx*, *xjxjx*, *jxxjx*, *xjjxx*, *jxjxx*, and *jjxxx*. Note again that the group sequential order is important; e.g., *xxxjj* is different from *jjxxx*, although the order is not preserved in the x's or in the j's.

In an earlier example, we inquired as to how many different single bridge hands could be dealt from a 52-card deck. Now let us ask how many permutations are possible when the four hands are dealt in the normal way. We are concerned with permutations because, in the game of bridge, the sequential order of North, East, South, and West is important. There are four combinations, each of size 13 cards, to be selected from a population of 52 cards. Hence,

$$_nP_{k_1,k_2,k_3,k_4} = \frac{52!}{13!13!13!13!}$$

which is a very large number, viz., $(5.3645 \cdots)10^{28}$.

Multinomial distribution formula. The binomial distribution formula can easily be generalized to the case of more than two possible outcomes, i.e., to the case in which the object population or outcome population is subdivided into more than two groups of like elements. For example, a die has six different sides, a jar may contain balls of more different colors than two, a deck of cards has four different suits, molecules in a gas have *many* different values of velocity, etc.

Consider a probability situation in which there are r mutually exclusive possible outcomes, viz., A_1, A_2, A_3, $\cdots$, A_r. Let p_i be the probability that outcome A_i occurs at a trial and let n independent trials be made. The probability that outcome A_1 occurs exactly k_1 times, that outcome A_2 occurs exactly k_2 times, etc., is calculated in a manner identical to that used in deducing the binomial formula. The probability p of obtaining a particular sequence of outcomes is $p_1^{k_1}p_2^{k_2}p_3^{k_3} \cdots p_r^{k_r}$, and if we are not interested in the sequential order in which the A_i outcome occurs in the k_i times it is observed, and if we do wish to preserve the sequential order in which the various groups of like outcomes occur, we must multiply by the multinomial coefficient $_nP_{k_1,k_2,\cdots,k_r}$ from Eq. 1-29. Thus,

$$p(\text{particular sequence}) = \frac{n!}{k_1!k_2! \cdots k_r!} p_1^{k_1}p_2^{k_2} \cdots p_r^{k_r}$$

$$= M[(k_1; n, p_1)(k_2; n, p_2) \cdots (k_r; n, p_r)] \qquad (1\text{-}30)$$

which may be read as the probability that in n independent trials A_1 occurs exactly k_1 times, A_2 occurs exactly k_2 times, etc., when the respective outcome probabilities are p_1, p_2, etc. Here, k_i is any integer from 0 to n with the condition, of course, that $\sum_{i=1}^{r} k_i = n$. Also, of course, $\sum_{i=1}^{r} p_i = 1$. The symbol M in Eq. 1-30 stands for multinomial. It can be shown easily that the sum over all values of k in Eq. 1-30 gives the expression for the multinomial

$$(p_1 + p_2 + \cdots + p_r)^n = 1 \tag{1-31}$$

and Eq. 1-30 is known as the multinomial formula. Equation 1-30 may be put in graphical form if the graph has $r + 1$ dimensions; such a graph for all values of k represents the multinomial distribution of probabilities.

An understanding of the multinomial coefficients and distributions is imperative if the student seeks an understanding of the kinetic theory of gases or, indeed, of any physical theory involving statistical mechanics. Note well that such theories are of increasing importance in all the physical sciences.

We may point out in the interests of general perspective that later, in the analysis of errors of experimental measurements, we shall conceive of some probability distribution as being the subdivided population of "objects" from which a sample, i.e., a single measurement or a limited number of trial measurements, is taken. Each measurement or trial set is a sample, with replacement, from a rather specially subdivided population of the same sort as that described in our considerations of the multinomial coefficients, and the probability per outcome, e.g., the probability of a particular measurement, is given by the population distribution probability. This distribution, for which n is very large, infinite in some instances, may remain unknown or it may be assumed to be known. It is also called the "parent" distribution. Commonly *assumed* parent distributions in an experimental science are the normal (Gauss) distribution and the Poisson distribution, both of which may be considered as special cases of the binomial distribution as stated earlier in this section. The statistical problem in experimental measurements is generally to infer from a limited number of trial measurements (a) what is the most appropriate parent probability distribution, e.g., normal or Poisson, and (b) what are the quantitative values of its descriptive parameters. Help in the answer to (a) is usually afforded from a priori experience and the particular type of measurement or from statistical analysis from a rather large number of trials; obtaining the answer to (b) is often solely an a posteriori problem. The features of the measurement problem should become clear as the reader progresses in this book.

Sampling from subdivided populations without replacement: lottery problem and bridge hands. A basic condition in the binomial distribution and in the multinomial distribution is that the component probability p be constant for all trials. This condition restricts applications to sampling with replacement. But, the use of the binomial coefficient as giving the number of combinations can be further illustrated by, or extended to, a common type of problem in which sampling is done without replacement from a subdivided population. This type of problem is one in which we ask for the probability that a random sample of size j contains exactly i elements of a specified type k from a population of n elements subdivided into $n = k_1 + k_2 + \cdots + k_r$, with $r \leqslant n$, when the sampling is done without regard to sequential order among the i elements.

Suppose, first, that there are only two different subdivisions in n, viz., $n = k_1 + k_2$. To make the problem concrete, let k_1 be the number of winning tickets in a lottery in which n tickets have been sold, j be the number of tickets we have bought, and i be the number of winning tickets that we hold. Then, the desired probability is given by*

$$p(\text{exactly } i) = \frac{\binom{k_1}{i}\binom{k_2}{j-i}}{\binom{n}{j}} \qquad (1\text{-}32)$$

Here, $\binom{k_1}{i}$ is the number of ways in which our winning tickets can be distributed among all the outstanding winning tickets, and $\binom{k_2}{j-i}$ is the number of ways our losing tickets can be distributed among all the outstanding losing tickets. Since any single combination of winning tickets can occur with any single combination of losing tickets, the product of the two numbers gives the total number of ways that our tickets, both winning and losing, can be arrived at from the total number of outstanding tickets. The denominator of Eq. 1-32 is simply the number of combinations of n tickets taken j at a time.

To make this example numerical, suppose that there are 400 tickets sold, that we bought ten of them, and that there are four prizes. Then, the probability that we will win exactly one prize is

$$p(\text{exactly } 1) = \frac{\binom{4}{1}\binom{396}{9}}{\binom{400}{10}} \approx 0.0934$$

* Equation 1-32 is also known as the hypergeometric probability formula; a graph of $p(i)$ vs. i is called the hypergeometric distribution of probabilities.

Incidentally, it should be obvious that the probability that we will win one or more prizes is given by

$$p(1 \text{ or more}) = \frac{\sum_{i=i}^{4} \binom{4}{i}\binom{396}{10-i}}{\binom{400}{10}} \approx 0.0967$$

since the events of winning exactly one prize, exactly two prizes, etc., are mutually exclusive. Of course, had we bought all 400 tickets, the probability of winning all four prizes would be given by

$$p(\text{all } 4) = \frac{\binom{4}{4}\binom{396}{400-4}}{\binom{400}{400}} = 1$$

As another easy example with $n = k_1 + k_2$, consider the combination problem given earlier about the number of all-red hands possible in a single hand of bridge. This problem can be discussed in terms of $n = 52$ cards divided into $k_1 = 26$ red and $k_2 = 26$ black cards. An all-red hand corresponds to $i = 13$ and $j = 13$. The answer to the problem can be written as

$$p(13 \text{ red, } 0 \text{ black}) = \frac{\binom{26}{13}\binom{26}{0}}{\binom{52}{13}} = \frac{\binom{26}{13}}{\binom{52}{13}}$$

Or, the probability that a single bridge hand will contain one ace is seen to be

$$p(1 \text{ ace, } 12 \text{ nonace}) = \frac{\binom{4}{1}\binom{48}{12}}{\binom{52}{13}}$$

Next, consider an example in which n is subdivided into four groups of like elements. Let us ask, What is the probability that a bridge hand of 13 cards consists of s spades, h hearts, d diamonds, and c clubs? The number of ways h hearts can be found in 13 heart cards, $h \leqslant 13$, is $\binom{13}{h}$; and similarly for the other suits. The total number of combinations possible in the hand is $\binom{52}{13}$. So the desired probability is

$$p(\text{specified number in each specified suit}) = \frac{\binom{13}{s}\binom{13}{h}\binom{13}{d}\binom{13}{c}}{\binom{52}{13}}$$

Numerically, if $s = 5, h = 4, d = 3$, and $c = 1$, the answer is $0.00538 \cdots$. If the problem did not specify the particular suit distribution, the probability that a hand consists of, say, five of one suit, four of another, three of a third, and one of the fourth suit is $4! \, (= 24)$ times greater, viz., $0.1293 \cdots$.

As a final example, consider a case in which n is subdivided into four groups and in which the particular sequential order of the four groups is important. We may ask, What is the probability that each of the four bridge hands contains one ace? First, how many ways can four aces be arranged into four ordered groups each of size 1? The answer to this ace question is

$$_{48}P_{1,1,1,1} = \frac{4!}{1!1!1!1!} = 4!$$

Second, how many ways can the remaining 48 cards be distributed among the four ordered hands? The answer to this question is

$$_{48}P_{12,12,12,12} = \frac{48!}{12!12!12!12!}$$

Then, since each permutation of the aces and each permutation of the nonaces are mutually exclusive, we must add up all the separate ways in which they can occur together, i.e., we must multiply the two respective numbers of permutations to obtain the required probability. Hence, this probability is

$$p = \frac{4!48!/(12!)^4}{52!/(13!)^4} = \frac{24 \cdot 48! \cdot (13!)^4}{52!} \approx 0.105$$

This, except for problems in Section 1-9, is as far in this book as we shall pursue the arguments in ideal games of chance. These games have served well in helping us to get acquainted not only with classical or a priori probability but with the basic principles of probability combinations and of combinatorial analysis. The principles are, of course, just as applicable when the experimental or a posteriori definition of probability is used.

1-8. Classical Probability and Progress in Experimental Science

As implied above, the progress of any experimental science is based upon the constant repetition of three steps: (1) the invention of a model or a conception of the behavior of nature as best we understand it, (2) a calculation of the a priori probabilities on the basis of such a conception, and, then, (3) a comparison of the a priori probabilities with actual measurements, i.e, with the experimental or a posteriori probabilities.

Confidence in the a priori conception increases to the degree that the comparison is favorable; and the conception is modified to the degree that the comparison is unfavorable. Then, more a priori calculations are made with the new model, more measurements taken, etc. Measurements are always the final arbiters, and in this sense the experimental or a posteriori meaning of probability is the more significant one. But note well that both types of probability are essential in scientific progress.

In fact, we have already seen in our discussions of conditional probability and of inferred knowledge some easily recognized examples of the modification of conceptions of nature (hypotheses or theories), and of the modification of our degree of confidence in them as new experience of actual observations becomes available. These are good, albeit simple, examples of the elements of progress in science.

Applications in statistical mechanics. To illustrate further the probability arguments in science, let us amplify very briefly the earlier reference to statistical mechanics. The following illustrations of binomial and multinomial probability are extremely cryptic; if the reader has had no previous introduction to the subject of statistical mechanics he may be well advised to skip directly from here to Section 1-9.

In the subject of statistical mechanics we are generally interested in specifying the simultaneous values of six properties of each of a large number of interacting particles, viz., the three mutually perpendicular components of position and of momentum. These properties are commonly expressed in a six-dimensional "phase space." To express the frequency distribution of these six properties at any given instant of time for N particles, we need a seven-dimensional graph, the seventh dimension being the number of particles (and if time is also a variable we need eight dimensions). (As a special case, in considering only the velocity distribution of molecules of a monatomic gas we are interested in only the three components of velocity, and then we deal with the conventional three-dimensional space and a four-dimensional graph.) We imagine that phase space is subdivided into numerous regions called cells, each cell having the same shape and small numerical size. The problem is to specify the frequency distribution of the N particles among all the cells, k_i particles being assigned to the ith cell. If there are r cells, the number of ways this distribution may be made is given by

$$W = {}_N P_{k_1, k_2, \cdots, k_r} = \frac{N!}{\prod_{i=1}^{r} k_i!} \tag{1-33}$$

where some cells may have no particles and some more than one. W is known as the "thermodynamic probability" of the system if the system can be defined in this manner, and the most probable distribution of particles is that for which W is a maximum. (W is not a true probability because it is greater than unity, but it is proportional to probability; and, incidentally, the logarithm of W is proportional to the entropy.)

Classical statistics. The so-called Maxwell-Boltzmann statistics is based on the hypothesis that both the position and momentum of a particle can be simultaneously *exactly* specified. This is a reasonable initial hypothesis in view of our experience in macroscopic mechanics. Each point in a cell in phase space corresponds to a possible specification of position and momentum of any one particle. A second initial hypothesis is that every cell is equally probable for every particle, subject to the boundary conditions imposed by the conservation of energy and of the total number of particles. In this case, placing $dW/(dt) = 0$, where t refers to time, and imposing the boundary conditions, we find (although we shall not prove it now) the Maxwell-Boltzmann distribution $k_i = (N/Z)e^{-\beta w_i}$, where Z and β are constants of the system and w_i is the energy of a particle in the ith cell.

Quantum statistics: bosons and fermions. Then, as experience accumulates, the Heisenberg uncertainty principle tells us that the position and momentum of a given particle cannot be exactly specified at any given time, and, as a consequence, the volume of a cell in phase space *cannot be arbitrarily small.* The smallest volume must now be taken as h^3, where h is Planck's constant. The cell of interest is much larger than h^3, so we are obliged to make a finer subdivision of each cell; now we reckon n compartments, each of volume h^3, in each cell. This greatly increases the magnitude of W but does not alter the relative probabilities.

Another new feature of quantum statistics is that of the *indistinguishability of identical particles.* In classical statistics, if two identical particles exchange cells, we count the new arrangement as a different permutation; but in quantum statistics, if two identical particles exchange compartments or cells, we count the new arrangement as the same permutation. This both reduces the magnitude of W and alters the relative probabilities.

A third new development in quantum statistics, a result of the further accumulation of experience and the modification of former hypotheses, is the new property of each type of particle called its *spin.* Spins are quantized angular momenta and the quantum numbers are of only two kinds: integer values (0, 1, 2, $\cdots$) and half-integer values ($\frac{1}{2}$, $\frac{3}{2}$, $\cdots$). Particles having integer spin are called *bosons* (photons, neutral atoms, α-particles, π-mesons, etc.); particles having half-integer spin are called *fermions* (electrons, protons, neutrons, neutrinos, μ-mesons, etc.) There is no limit to the number of bosons that can occupy a given compartment in phase space; but the number of fermions per compartment is severely limited by the Pauli exclusion principle, this limit being $2J + 1$, where J is the magnitude of the spin quantum number. The spin of an electron is $\frac{1}{2}$, so the occupancy by electrons is limited to 2. (Incidentally, the Pauli exclusion principle also governs the arrangements of electrons in atoms where the other quantum numbers enter into the picture; the coordinates of the h^3 volume in phase space correspond to the other quantum numbers.)

In the case of bosons, since there are n compartments in the ith cell, there are $n(n + N_i - 1)!$ ways of distributing the N_i particles. But of these ways, many represent indistinguishable ways in which particles are merely interchanged between different compartments and between different cells. The net number of distinguishable distributions is

$$W_i = \frac{n(n + N_i - 1)!}{n! N_i!} = \binom{n + N_i - 1}{N_i} \tag{1-34}$$

and of the system as a whole, all cells considered,

$$W = \prod_{i=1}^{r} W_i = \prod_{i=1}^{r} \binom{n + N_i - 1}{N_i} \tag{1-35}$$

This is the basic formula for the Bose-Einstein statistics.

In the case of fermions of spin $\frac{1}{2}$, the maximum number of available sites in each cell in phase space is $2n = 2v/h^3$, where v is the volume of the cell. In the ith cell, which contains $2n$ sites, k_i of the sites are occupied and $2n - k_i$ are empty. The thermodynamic probability for the ith cell is given by the number of distinguishable ways $2n$ sites can be divided into two groups, viz., occupied and empty, and this is $W_i = \binom{2n}{k_1}$, much simpler than in the boson case. The general expression for the system is

$$W = \prod_{i=1}^{r} \binom{2n}{k_i} \tag{1-36}$$

This is the basic formula for the Fermi-Dirac statistics.

In each of these kinds of statistics, the frequency or probability distribution is obtained by maximizing W consistent with the boundary conditions as stated above. The respective distributions, although not derived here, are

$$k_i = \frac{2n}{Be^{\beta W_i} + 1} \quad \text{for fermions} \tag{1-37}$$

and

$$k_i = \frac{n}{Be^{\beta W_i} - 1} \quad \text{for bosons} \tag{1-38}$$

where B and β are constants of the system. These expressions are to be compared with that given earlier for the Maxwell-Boltzmann statistics; the classical Maxwell-Boltzmann expression is the special case of the boson expression for which $(k_i/n) \ll 1$.

Statistical mechanics provides an excellent example of the progression of hypotheses or theories from the desperation-in-ignorance type of guess to rather complex conceptions that are more consistent with nature's behavior as our experimental knowledge of that behavior accumulates. No one can claim with impunity that our knowledge is at all yet complete. Inferred knowledge of phase space and of the occupancy probabilities is still growing, each theory giving way to new information and to a better theory as the science develops.

Further pursuit of this subject, and indeed a proper understanding of the features lightly touched upon here, are beyond the scope of this book.*

1-9. Problems

Note the "instructions" preceding the problems in Section 1-6.

1. Solve Problems 1(a) and (c), 3(a) and (b), 5(b) and (c), 6(a), (b), and (c), 11(b) and (c), 12(a), (b), and (c), 13(a) and (b), and 14 of Section 1-6 by using equations of combinatorial analysis.

2. What is the probability that among 9 random digits the digit 7 appears
(a) exactly 3 times,
(b) 3 times or less, and
(c) more than once?

3. A horseshoe contains 8 nails.
(a) In how many different orders may they be driven?
(b) If 1 shoe were to be attached in a different way to each horse, and if each horse were shoed in its own 6-ft stall, how many miles of stalls would be required?

4. How long must a series of random digits be so that there is a probability of 0.9 that the digit 7 appears
(a) at least once, and
(b) at least twice?

5. How many dice must be cast together in order for the probability to be
(a) $<\frac{1}{3}$ for no ace, and (ans. 7)
(b) >0.5 for at least 1 pair of aces? (ans. 9)

6. Make the histogram, and indicate the position of the expectation value, for the binomial distributions
(a) $B(k; 6, \frac{1}{2})$, and
(b) $B(k; 7, \frac{1}{10})$.

* For an elementary treatment of these features of statistical mechanics, see, e.g., F. W. Sears, *Thermodynamics, The Kinetic Theory of Gases, and Statistical Mechanics* (Addison-Wesley Publishing Co., New York, 1955), 2nd ed.

7. What is the probability that in 7 tosses of a coin the odd tosses will show heads and the even tosses tails?

8. If birthdays are random among n people at a certain party, how large is n in order that the probability be $\geqslant 0.5$ that 2 and only 2 of the people have the same birthday? An answer in the form of an equation suffices.

9. The letters of the word "tailor" are written on cards. The cards are then thoroughly shuffled, and 4 drawn in order. What is the probability that the result is "oral"?

10. The letters of the word "pepper" are written on cards. The cards are then thoroughly shuffled, and 4 drawn in order. What is the probability that the result is "peep"?

11. A set of dominoes runs from double blank to double N.

(a) If 1 domino is drawn, what is the probability that at least 1 of the 2 numbers on it is N?

(b) If 2 dominoes are drawn, what is the probability that neither of the numbers on either of them is N?

12. According to a table of mortality, of 100,000 persons living at the age of 10 years, 91,900 on the average are living at the age of 21 years. Each of 5 children is now 10 years old. What is the probability that

(a) exactly 3 of them will live to be 21,

(b) at least 3 of them will live to be 21, and

(c) none of them will live to be 21?

Why is this an a posteriori rather than an a priori probability problem?

13. How would you plot the frequency distribution of a trinomial distribution? Discuss the distribution of 800 random digits (this is a decanomial distribution).

14. (a) Show that, in a binomial distribution, the most probable value k_0 is double-valued if $(n + 1)p$ is equal to an integer.

(b) Show that if the binomial probability $f(k) = B(k; 12, \tfrac{1}{3})$, then

$$f(k + 1) = \left(\frac{12 - k}{k + 1}\right) \frac{1}{2} f(k).$$

(c) What is the general expression for the binomial probability $f(k + 1)$ for any n and for any p?

15. What are the probabilities

(a) that (i) 1 ace and (ii) at least 1 ace will appear in a cast of 4 dice, and

(b) that (i) 1 double ace and (ii) at least 1 double ace will appear in 24 casts of 2 dice?

[That the (a) probability in each case is greater than the (b) is known as de Méré's paradox. De Méré argued that, since 4 is to 6 (the total number of possible events in a cast of 1 die) as 24 is to 36 (the total number of possible events in a cast with 2 dice), the respective probabilities should be equal.]

16. What is the probability that in a sample of 10 random digits no 2 are equal? Compare the answer with that obtained by using Sirling's formula.

29. Consider the "pros" and "cons" of the following system of betting: Suppose in successive games, in each of which the odds are 50–50, you bet $1. At any time that you win, you pocket the winnings and start betting again at $1. At any time that you lose, you bet double the amount on the next game. No matter how long the series of consecutive losses, when you win you are $1 ahead as though the losses had not occurred.

(a) If you were the owner of a gambling house, under what conditions would you allow a client to use this system?

(b) How would you alter the system if the odds were known to be 75–25?

(In considering both parts of this problem, ignore the usual bias imposed by the house in its own interest.)

C. EXPERIMENTAL (A POSTERIORI) PROBABILITY

I-I0. Definition of Experimental Probability

Suppose that for some reason we wish to check the classical (a priori) idea that the probability for observing a head with a tossed coin is $\frac{1}{2}$. The obvious thing to do is to toss the coin a large number of times and to keep a record of the results. We observe heads w_{obs} times after some moderately large number n_{obs} of independent trials. We say that the ratio w_{obs}/n_{obs} is, for this value of n_{obs}, the best experimental value of the probability for heads in any single toss, e.g., the next toss. Our confidence in this value increases as n_{obs} is increased. Indeed, if the value of this experimental probability is plotted as a function of n_{obs}, it is seen to fluctuate rather erratically when n_{obs} is small, but, as n_{obs} increases, the probability steadies down to an apparently constant equilibrium value. A typical graph of this sort is shown in Fig. 1-3. By definition, the experimental probability (sometimes called the frequency probability) is simply this ratio as n_{obs} becomes indefinitely large, viz.,

$$p_{obs} \equiv \lim_{n_{obs} \to \infty} \frac{w_{obs}}{n_{obs}} \tag{1-39}$$

if the outcome of each trial (toss) is (a) independent of all preceding trials, and (b) determined entirely by chance.

There are four difficulties with this definition. First, how can we be sure that all the trials are independent? The practical problem here is that the coin may wear out asymmetrically or that the person (or device) tossing the coin gradually but inadvertently acquires a "system" which favors a particular outcome. It should be noted here that we do not require the absence of a "system," but merely that if it is present it must

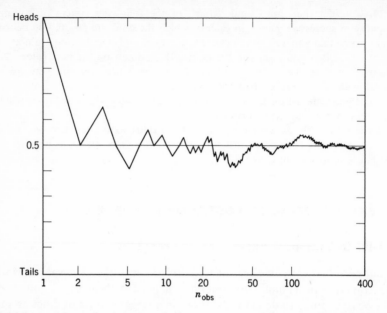

Fig. I-3. Experimental probability (frequency ratio for "heads") steadies down to an apparently equilibrium constant value as n_{obs} increases. (Note the logarithmic abscissa scale.)

remain constant. Second, how can we be sure that the outcome of each trial is determined entirely by chance? The practical problem here is related to the one for the independence of successive trials. Third, the limit $n_{obs} \to \infty$ is obviously impractical. In this regard, we substitute a conceptual extension of the experiment after n_{obs} has become "satisfactorily" large. However, the value of p_{obs} for any large but finite n_{obs} contains some small uncertainty in it as a consequence of the fact that n_{obs} *is* finite. Fourth, the ratio does not strictly converge mathematically no matter how large n_{obs} becomes. This is because, after any specified n_{obs}, there is a finite chance that a long run of heads (or of tails) will occur. The experimentalist points out that as n_{obs} increases, such a run must be of increasing length to have a given effect in the value of p_{obs}, and that after n_{obs} is very large the probability for having a significant effect of this sort is so small as to be negligible. This has been proved mathematically in terms of the so-called strong law of large numbers. It is important, nevertheless, that n_{obs} be very large indeed if p_{obs} is to be expressed with very high precision. Later we shall show that the standard deviation, a measure of the statistical uncertainty, in the measure of p_{obs} is inversely proportional to the square root of n_{obs}.

Even with these difficulties, the experimental definition is the one that must be invoked to "prove" that the coin is "satisfactorily honest," i.e., that the a priori probability is reasonably valid, or sometimes even to prove that a very complex combinatorial analysis is indeed correct.

Number of "equally probable outcomes" meaningless. Outside the realm of ideal games numerous probability situations exist in which the question of the number of equally probable outcomes is entirely meaningless. For these situations the classical probability, Eq. 1-1, cannot be evaluated. Examples are legion: A marksman shoots at a target; what is the probability of a hit? What is the probability that a particular person of given age will die within one year? What is the probability that a given house will be ravaged by fire within a specified time? If a baby is to be born, what is the probability that it will be a boy? What is the probability that John Doe, a candidate for public office, will be elected? What is the probability that the next measurement of cosmic-ray intensity will differ by a given per cent from the immediately preceding measurement? What is the probability that two different measurements of the velocity of light agree within the experimental errors? In such probability situations we are at a complete loss in trying to apply the classical definition for the probability. Rather than rely on "armchair" reasoning, or make a basic desperation-in-ignorance guess, we may experiment, make actual measurements, and use the experimental definition of probability.

1-11. Example: Quality Control

Determining the experimental probability of a specified outcome generally involves rather intricate statistical reasoning in order to achieve a satisfactory numerical value with a minimum of effort. The example of the heads probability in tossing a coin is very simple. To illustrate the typical complexity, let us consider the lottery type of problem discussed in the last part of Section 1-7. In this problem, a random sample of limited size j was selected from a large population n subdivided into $n = k_1 + k_2$ with all numerical values known. We inquired then as to how many elements of the kind k_1 may we expect to have in the sample j. Suppose now that we alter this problem as follows. The numerical value of n is known but the division of n between k_1 and k_2 is not known, and we wish, from an observation of the number i of k_1 elements in j, to determine the ratio k_1/n. This is a typical problem in what is called "quality control." It is instructive to consider this type of problem a little further because it illustrates one essential feature of the measurement problem in an experimental science.

A factory turns out a very large number n of supposedly identical items, but some unknown fraction are defective, and we wish, by sampling, to infer whether or not this fraction exceeds a specified value. The problem can be discussed in terms of the equation for the probability for having i defectives in sample j, viz.,

$$p(\text{exactly } i) = \frac{\binom{k_1}{i}\binom{n-k_1}{j-i}}{\binom{n}{j}}$$

As a first approximation, this expression for $p(\text{exactly } i)$ may be placed "equal" to the observed ratio i/j, and a value of the defective fraction k_1/n deduced therefrom. The difficulty is that a different value of k_1/n is obtained from each different sample ratio i/j. Of course, the reliability of the deduced value of k_1/n increases as the sample size increases or as the number of independent samplings increases to provide a more reliable mean value of i/j. The problem really is to determine, for preassigned reliability in k_1/n, the optimum sample size and number of samples commensurate with a minimum of effort in examining the samples.

There are various statistical arguments in treating quality control problems of this sort, and discussion of them is beyond the scope of this book. But one approach to this problem, in case n is very much larger than j, is mentioned now because it ties together some of the concepts discussed earlier in this chapter. In this case, the problem can be approximated by one of sampling with replacement. Then, the binomial equation can be used, Eq. 1-20, viz.,

$$p(\text{exactly } i) = \binom{j}{i} p^i q^{j-i}$$

and the problem becomes one of determining the parameter $p \ (= k_1/n)$ from the observed ratio i/j. Suppose that a guess as to the true value of p puts it in the range 2 to 4%, and that it suffices to know p to one significant figure. One procedure then is to make five mutually exclusive hypotheses, viz., $p = 1, 2, 3, 4,$ or 5% and to guess initially (in desperation) that they are all equally likely, i.e., probability $\frac{1}{5}$. The binomial probability distributions $B(i; j, p)$ may be calculated for each value of p, and comparison with the outcomes of successive independent samples serves to increase the probability that one of the hypotheses is to be favored over the others.

1-12. Example: Direct Measurements in Science

Now let us extend the quality control problem so as to make it similar to a typical measurement problem. This illustrates a most significant application of the multinomial probability distribution in the science of measurements. As a first step in this extension, suppose that the definition of "defective" involves an upper and a lower limit of tolerance in the pertinent aspect of quality, e.g., in a linear dimension such as the diameter of ball bearings. With this extension, n is subdivided into three categories, $n = k_1 + k_2 + k_3$, i.e., $r = 3$, with category k_2 being "nondefective." The problem, if n is very large compared to j, becomes one of multinomial probabilities with the respective probabilities p_1, p_2, p_3 unknown. In this case, the determination of the optimum sample size and number of samples, with consideration for the compromise between reliability and effort, is even more complicated than in the case in which n was divided into only two categories, and we shall not attempt it further here.

Next, suppose that the n elements are subdivided into a much larger number of different categories. Suppose that these categories are ordered in terms of some numerical characteristic of the elements, perhaps the diameter of the ball bearings. Our objective is to infer the average or arithmetic mean value of the entire population of n possible values from a sample of size j. In the determination of a length (e.g., the diameter of the balls as measured with a pair of calipers or with some other fine instrument), we take a number j of independent trial measurements, i.e., a sample of size j, from an essentially infinite population of possible trials. From the variety of values observed in this sample, viz., i_1 of k_1, i_2 of k_2, i_3 of k_3, $\cdots$, i_r of k_r, where

$$i_1 + i_2 + i_3 + \cdots + i_r = j \quad \text{and} \quad k_1 + k_2 + k_3 + \cdots k_r \leqslant n$$

we calculate the arithmetic mean. We infer that the length being measured has a value reasonably close to the measured mean value, a valid inference if j is reasonably large. The number of subdivisions r in n is in this case so large that adjacent numerical k values are as closely spaced as we can read the vernier caliper scale or the scale of some other instrument; indeed, if no upper or lower limit is imposed on the size of the ball bearings, r may be infinite even though the effective least count in the measurement scale is finite.

The quality control problem in simple form is also seen to be identical to the problem of determining the experimental probability of heads in a coin toss from a sample size n_{obs} $(= j)$ taken from an infinite population n. In this case, the number of subdivisions r of n is only two, viz., heads and tails. The problem in slightly extended form is also similar to the one of determining the experimental probability for a deuce in the cast of a six-sided die, $n = \infty$ and $r = 6$. However, as implied above, in a typical scientific measurement problem, n is infinite but the number of subdivisions, although infinite in principle, may be limited in practice by the effective least count of the measurement scale and by the real-life aspect of the largest and smallest possible measurements.

As mentioned earlier in this chapter and again in Chapters 4 and 5, it turns out in an experimental science that, in many of the problems of direct measurements, the very large population n (infinite) can be taken as subdivided according to either the normal (Gauss) distribution or the Poisson distribution. This knowledge makes for great simplification in determining the experimental probability with reasonable precision by invoking one of the mathematical models that is based on axiomatic or classical probability concepts.

But before we discuss these features let us introduce in the next chapter some basic notions about measurements in general and about elementary statistics.

2

"We are in the ordinary position of scientists of having to be content with piecemeal improvements: we can make several things clearer, but we cannot make anything clear."

FRANK PLUMPTON RAMSEY

"Probability is a measure of the importance of our ignorance."

THORTON C. FRY

Direct Measurements: Simple Statistics

A. MEASUREMENTS IN SCIENCE: ORIENTATION

2-1. The Nature of a Scientific Fact

Most people are strongly inclined to the idea that a so-called "fact" is immutable, an absolute truth, and that science especially yields such truths. But as we study science and its philosophical implications, we find that *absolute truth is entirely foreign to science.* It becomes necessary to distinguish two kinds of facts: (1) those known by the Omniscient, and (2) those devised by man. Only the former are absolute.*

Complete certainty is never the mark of a scientific fact, although it is the business of scientific endeavor to reduce the uncertainty as much as possible. In many instances, the residual uncertainty is very small indeed, and some people may be inclined to say that it is negligible. Such neglect is not valid in principle. Scientific knowledge is always inferred knowledge, i.e., knowledge based on a *limited* number of observations. But it is to be emphasized that, as our experience accumulates and our interpretations

---

* The late Justice Oliver Wendell Holmes wrote: "When I say a thing is true, I mean that I cannot help believing it. I am stating an experience as to which there is no choice. But . . . I do not venture to assume that my inabilities in the way of thought are inabilities of the universe. I therefore define the truth as the system of my limitations, and leave absolute truth for those who are better equipped." [From "Ideals and Doubts," *Illinois Law Rev.*, **10** (1915).]

become more critical and objective, scientific knowledge becomes steadily more and more reliable.*

Some people have argued that science, more than any other subject, is responsible for the progressive emancipation of men's minds away from the philosophy of absolute truths. Whether science directs away from absolutes, toward absolutes, or neither, is a matter of one's religious faith or ethics, for it is only in such faith or cultural patterns that absolutes have meaning. Science, per se, is necessarily silent on this question.† The concepts of science, like the concept of probability and for essentially the same reason, are "open-ended" concepts. Whether or not these concepts may be the basis of a new type of religion or ethics is also a matter of opinion which we shall not discuss in this book.

The feature that distinguishes scientific knowledge is not only that there is a clear recognition of uncertainty but that the degree of uncertainty can usually be rather well determined. This determination is carried out by the methods of statistics and probability theory. As we accumulate scientific facts, including knowledge of their intrinsic uncertainty, our philosophical intuition grows, and we are no longer dismayed that scientific facts are "merely" probable; indeed, we realize that probable knowledge, if the probable error is known, is *the most reliable of all knowledge* (*devised by man*) *because it includes a realistic self-appraisal.*

The fundamental truth or fact in an experimental science, e.g., in physics, chemistry, biology, engineering, etc., is always an observation, a measurement. Prediction, or a generalized description of the behavior of nature, is an important goal of the science, but the degree of reliability of the prediction or of the distilled principle is no better than the measurements upon which it is based. Careful analysis of the reliability of measurements therefore is necessarily an early step in achieving scientific maturity.

2-2. Trial Measurements and Statistics

As an example of a measurement, consider the direct determination of the length of a piece of wire. Suppose that we have made 12 independent measurements with a ruler having a least count (smallest scale division)

---

* During the last half of the nineteenth century, Newtonian mechanics and classical electromagnetic theory were able to "explain" just about all the observations that had been made in mechanics and electricity. Then, some measurements were made with greater precision, and some experiments were carried out in a new domain, viz., atomic physics. It was immediately necessary to modify the then-current theories to encompass the new observations. Examples of the need for, and the process of, increasing scientific reliability still continue in every active facet of science, and this situation will persist indefinitely so long as that facet of science remains active.

† This fact is in no sense a belittlement of the social and intellectual problems attending absolute truths; see the "Dedication" of this book.

Table 2-1. Typical Set of Measurements

Trial	Measured Value (mm units)
1	32.0
2	31.8
3	31.7
4	32.0
5	32.1
6	31.9
7	31.8
8	31.9
9	31.9
10	31.8
11	31.9
12	32.3

of 0.5 mm and that we have interpolated to 0.1 mm. Typical values are listed in Table 2-1 and are shown graphically as a histogram in Fig. 2-1. The measurements in this example might just as well have been the trial values of the atomic weight of iodine, of the velocity of light, of the intensity of cosmic rays, of the wavelength of the cadmium red spectral line, or (with the decimal removed) the number of defective screws found in successive sample boxes having 10,000 screws in each, etc. The number of trials ($n = 12$) in this example is not a large number; if this number were vastly increased the graph of Fig. 2-1 would presumably fluctuate around, and eventually assume, a constant shape. The eventual shape of the histogram would not be the same for all types of measurements: two common

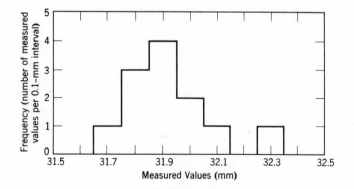

Fig. 2-1. Histogram: graph of observed variations (classification interval = 0.1 mm).

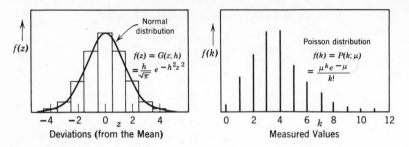

Fig. 2-2. Two often-encountered histograms, or frequency distributions, for a very large number of trials. The continuous curve in the normal case is called a frequency curve, obtained as the classification interval approaches zero and the number of trials approaches infinity. The Poisson distribution is discrete since k can take on only integer values.

histograms for very large n are illustrated in Fig. 2-2. (The continuous curve is purely hypothetical; such a curve is discussed in detail in Chapter 4.)

The three essential points of interest now are: (1) successive independent measurements, i.e., measurements that are meticulously carried out under conditions as nearly identical as possible, do not generally agree in value, (2) they tend to cluster about some more or less central value,* and (3) the clustering shows a type of statistical regularity that appears in the shape of the histogram or what is generally called the frequency distribution.

As stated in Chapter 1, the basic problem in this example, as in all examples in statistics, is to deduce from a *limited* number of trial measurements as much information as we can about the parameters (in particular the central value and the dispersion or spread) of that histogram which would obtain if *all possible* trial measurements were to be made. The "all possible" histogram is called the "parent" or "universe" distribution from which the actual trial set of measurements is a sample. This basic problem will be stated in different terms over and over again in this book, but now our task is to become acquainted with more of the fundamental terminology.

The meaning of the term "trial" is clearly implied in the above example, but it deserves further discussion. A set of observations or measurements is said to be an "ideal trial set" if they are all completely independent of each other and are carried out under strictly identical conditions. In practice, such measurements are never quite achieved, but, with meticulous care, actual measurements often come satisfactorily close to the ideal.

---

* Only very special types of measurements show more than one maximum in the histogram, e.g., the measurements of instantaneous position of an object in simple harmonic motion with the origin at the equilibrium position.

The branch of applied mathematics that treats and interprets trial data, or as nearly ideal trial data as possible, is called *statistics*.

A fundamental postulate in statistics is that the variations in a set of ideal (or near-ideal) trial data are strictly random, i.e., are due entirely to chance. (The concept of random is discussed in the next section.) It is assumed, of course, that the property being measured does not change during the measurements. The bulk of the problems in statistics deal with data for which the actual degree of approximation to random ideal trial data requires careful thought and test (e.g., ages of people at the time of death, sex distribution in a population, accidents on the highway, number of houses ravaged by fire, votes in an election, nutritive value of milk from cows on unintentionally different diets, etc.). But in a set of painstaking measurements in an experimental science, especially in laboratory physical science in which the subjects are inanimate, the random ideal trial nature of the measurements can often be safely assumed. Often, however, it is desirable to carry out a test to check specifically for the presence or constancy of systematic (nonrandom) errors in the measurements.

It is well known that, in comparison with the physical scientist who works under the "controlled" conditions of a laboratory, either the biologist or the nonlaboratory physical scientist* must typically put up with certain extraneous factors that make his experiments less well controlled. With diligent design and performance of his experiments to minimize the relative importance of these factors, he also often succeeds in approximating satisfactorily the conditions of random trial measurements. The social scientist, on the other hand, is frequently confronted with such extraneous factors that the majority of his measurements are perhaps better described as investigations than as scientific experiments. Certain methods in statistics have been developed to give special attention to the extraneous factors, and with these complications the subject of statistics is necessarily intricate. In this book for the student of experimental science, we shall for the most part pass over the statistical treatments of extraneous factors; if and when the student needs them, he can find these treatments in the literature.

2-3. Random Variation

The mathematician defines random (or stochastic) as the adjective modifying a variable whose value depends on the outcome of a random experiment. A random experiment is one whose possible outcomes are all equally probable, or, better, for which each possible outcome (each point

---

* Examples of nonlaboratory physical sciences are astronomy, meteorology, cosmic rays, geomagnetism, cosmology, etc.

in sample space) has a fixed probability. *Idealized* penny tossing, drawing a number from a hat, etc., are often cited as such "experiments." Also, to the mathematician, random numbers are digits arranged in a random manner. The phrase "random numbers" is short for "randomly generated numbers."* The experiment or the process of generation of random numbers in real life is left to the scientist to devise; and, confronted with this nontrivial task, even the scientist would prefer to be a mathematician (or an armchair philosopher).†

It is impossible to give a rigorous *operational* definition of random. The subjective meaning, however, is not difficult to grasp. The following statements may be helpful.

A set of generally nonidentical numbers has one essential feature of randomness if, as the numbers are successively revealed, the next number in the series has an a priori *equal* chance of being larger or smaller than the median value‡ of the already revealed numbers. Another necessary condition of randomness is that, in the absence of inconstant systematic errors, the first moment of the set is zero when taken about the arithmetic mean value, i.e., the *random deviations must add up to zero*. (The concept of moments is discussed presently.) Identification of randomness in terms of the mean value is not really practical because inconstant systematic errors are never completely absent; the attempt has significance, however, because it emphasizes consideration of the sizes of the deviations represented by the individual numbers as well as the respective algebraic signs. A single event in a set of generally different events, whether each event is a numerical measurement or some other type of observation, is random if it has an a priori *constant* chance of occurring regardless of the position of this event in the ordered set (although the magnitude of the chance may depend on the position in the set). The adjective "a priori" is used in two of these statements, and, strictly speaking, the a priori chance cannot be determined—it can merely be inferred.

The concept of random is an especially interesting one. In science, it is intrinsically an "open-ended" concept: It is properly defined in terms of the chance happening of a *future* event, always about the unknown. Hence, it does not properly apply in the description of a number or of a set of numbers (or of an event or of a set of events) that has already been

* A book of "random" numbers has been published, *A Million Random Digits*, by The Free Press, Glencoe, Ill.

† And the mathematician said "Let there be random numbers," and lo and behold it came to pass: there *were* random numbers. Only a mathematician can get away with this.

‡ The median, discussed later in this chapter, is defined as the middle value, or as the interpolated middle value, of a set of ordered numbers. If the histogram of the numbers is symmetrical, the median and the arithmetic mean have the same value.

revealed. Nor can any a posteriori test of the randomness of a number or of a set of numbers (or events) be completely satisfactory. The best we can do is to infer from the already revealed numbers whether or not the next-to-be-revealed number may be expected to be a random member of the set.*

This past-vs.-future aspect of random has philosophical fascination, and some people say (erroneously) that the inherent arbitrariness of any operational definition of random prevents the subject of probability from being properly a part of a science. Actually, every operational definition in science has a residual (albeit small in most cases) arbitrariness or uncertainty in it inasmuch as no scientific knowledge is complete, no measurement exact.

It should be mentioned that, as regards the experimental concept of random, the terms "equal chance" and "constant chance" in the respective statements above have significant meaning only in terms of a very large set of observations. The set must be sufficiently large that the statistical pattern of the variation, including the median or the arithmetic mean value of the already revealed numbers, has taken on an essentially equilibrium value (see the definition of experimental probability, Eq. 1-39).

It is apparent that the terms "trial" and "random" are somewhat related. An interesting distinction between them is the following: trial refers to an experimental process (although an impractical one since an actual process never has quite the perfection required in the strict definition of trial), whereas random is a mathematical condition. In a sense, trial implies a striving for a real-life perfection, whereas random refers to a kind of perfection by acclamation; this is a characteristic difference between a science and mathematics.

As was stated before, simple statistical methods treat sets of trial data in which the variations are assumed to be satisfactorily random. And, fortunately, in an experimental science, the assumption of random variations in successive trial measurements is often satisfactory per se.

2-4. Probability Theory in Statistics

In treating random trial data, it is often possible to invoke a *mathematical model* of the variations among the trials. If this model is not too complex, it enables the statistician or the experimenter to make quickly, i.e., with a limited number of trials, very significant computations about such properties of the set as (a) the best value and its reliability, (b) the frequency with which a particular result or measurement may be expected to occur

---

* Comment on the following story: The doctor shook his head as he finished examining the patient. "You have a very serious disease," he said. "Nine out of ten people having this disease die of it. But you are lucky because you came to me. I have already had nine patients all of whom died of it."

when a certain number of trials are made, (c) the number of trials that need be made for a specified precision in the best value, etc.

The branch of statistics that applies and/or develops mathematical models for random trial data is called *probability theory*.

The simplest mathematical model is the *binomial distribution*. This model, whose formula was derived and discussed in Chapter 1, was initially devised for the simple ideal games of chance (e.g., tossing coins, casting dice, dealing cards, etc.). The two mathematical models of outstanding importance in an experimental science are the *normal* (*or Gauss*) *distribution* and the *Poisson distribution*, both of which, mentioned briefly in Chapter 1, may be considered as limiting cases of the binomial distribution.

It turns out that one or the other of these two models very often satisfactorily "fits" a set of actual direct measurements,* and only a rudimentary knowledge of the subject is necessary to enable the experimenter to decide which of these two models is the one of interest. Procedures for testing the degree of fit are discussed later. These models do not involve advanced mathematics (beyond elementary calculus), and their applications are of immense help in designing the experiment in the first place and then in analyzing and interpreting the results.

2-5. Computed Measurements

The type of measurements discussed in the last section are *direct* measurements. Usually, at least in the physical sciences, computed or derived quantities, also called "measurements," are more frequently the focus of attention. An example of a computed measurement is that of velocity which is obtained from the directly measured quantities of distance and time. Other examples are legion. After the direct measurements have been recorded and the best value and its reliability determined, we apply the appropriate statistical formula for the *propagation of errors* and determine the reliability of the computed result. The probability model, if it exists, for computed results is generally different from that applicable to the direct measurements, and usually no simple model applies.† Hence, with little or no prospect of finding a satisfactory model for computed measurements, we must be content with the more limited

---

* "Fits" needs further comment. No mathematical model distribution conforms strictly to any set of experimental measurements. Whether or not the actual degree of "misfit" and the consequences thereof are serious depends upon the care and pains that the measurements justify or that the experimenter is willing to take.

† Note that if the direct measurements are made on a scale that is nonlinear with respect to the errors themselves, then generally no simple model applies; it is possible in such a case that a better fitting model may be found for the computed measurements than for the direct measurements.

potentialities of the statistical precision indices as discussed in Part C of this chapter.

2-6. Conclusions

With the special characteristics of most of the direct measurements in an experimental science, we usually assume satisfactory compliance with the two assumptions:

(1) random trial measurements, i.e., independent measurements carried out under identical conditions, and for which there is a constant characteristic chance that any particular possible measurement will occur as the next measurement, and

(2) a simple mathematical model of the variations.

Then, the pertinent principles and details of the generally complicated and specialized subject of statistics and probability theory are not very formidable even to the beginner. The reliability of computed measurements, and of any direct measurements that are not satisfactorily fitted by a simple mathematical model, may be obtained by the statistical precision indices without resort to any model.

The general objectives in the statistical treatment of measurements are (1) the determination of the best (or sometimes the median or the most probable) value from a limited number of trials, (2) the specification of the reliability of the best value, (3) a statement of the probability that the next trial measurement would have a particular value, and (4) assistance in the design and performance of the experiment so as to obtain a desired degree of reliability (expressed as an error) with a minimum of effort.

B. BASIC DEFINITIONS: ERRORS, SIGNIFICANT FIGURES, ETC.

There are many different specific aspects of the error concept. We shall discuss these aspects first as they apply to individual measurements and second, in Part C of this chapter, as they apply to sets of trial measurements. Errors in the latter case are especially interesting when the variation observed among the trials is fitted by a simple mathematical model, but in the remaining two parts of the present chapter individual measurements and sets of trial measurements are discussed without regard to any mathematical model. Discussion of the models and of the probability predictions will be delayed until later chapters.

Some basic concepts and definitions have already been given or implied in Part A of this chapter, viz., the nature of a scientific fact, trial measurements, random variations in measurements, histogram, frequency distribution, frequency curve, statistics as a general subject, probability theory, direct and computed measurements, etc. We now explore some additional terms, principally those dealing with errors, with elementary statistics, and with precision of direct measurements.

2-7. Types of Errors

It is convenient to subdivide the general concept of error into three broad types, viz., random errors, systematic errors, and blunders. In our present discussion, blunders should be immediately dismissed with the appropriate embarrassment, but a few examples are mentioned briefly below. In general, the term *experimental error* is some additive function of *all three*.

Random (or accidental) error. Random errors are of the greatest concern in the statistical analysis of measurements. Four separate meanings of random error are in common use as follows:

(1) A *deviation* or *statistical fluctuation* (Eq. 2-5) is the difference between a single measured value and the "best" value of a set of measurements whose variation is apparently random. The "best" value is defined for this purpose as the arithmetic mean of all the actual trial measurements. [For the deviations to be random it is necessary that the systematic errors (mentioned presently) be either absent or not change as the trial set is obtained.] For a symmetrical frequency distribution that is unimodal (has only one maximum in it), the arithmetic mean is obviously the "best" value and also the most probable value; for an asymmetrical distribution, the mean as the "best" value is somewhat arbitrary but is supported by the principle of least squares as shown later. For an asymmetrical distribution, "best" really depends upon the intended use, and sometimes the median or the most probable value is preferable; but for the determination of a deviation the mean is conventionally used.

(2) Random error sometimes refers to the *difference* between the arithmetic mean as determined from a certain number of random trials and the mean that is determined from a larger number of trials. Often the latter mean is the hypothetical or theoretical "true" value that we believe would be obtained from an infinite number of trials; it is often called the "parent" or "universe" mean. This error with respect to the hypothetical "true" value does *not* have experimental significance but is of great interest in more advanced statistics and in any discussion with a mathematical model.

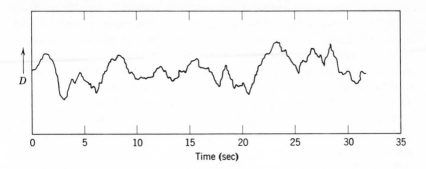

Fig. 2-3. Record of "zero-reading" deflections of a very sensitive torsion balance. These irregular fluctuations are due to elementary errors, perhaps dominated by Brownian motion in this case.

(3) A more difficult concept of random error has it as some one of numerous so-called *elementary errors* that are merely imagined to exist. According to the theory, these elementary errors conspire to be observed as a deviation or statistical fluctuation in certain types of measurements. See Fig. 2-3. Examples of the imagined random elementary errors, and their role in the measurement process, are discussed in Chapter 4 in connection with the normal (Gauss) mathematical model of probability. In this theoretical interpretation of deviations in real-life measurements, an elementary error may indeed be either a random error or an inconstant systematic error. The term "inconstant" refers either to the magnitude of the elementary error or to its algebraic sign as it adds into the sum to give the deviation; or it may refer to a time dependence in those measurements that are made in a time sequence, as most measurements are made.

(4) Finally, random error may refer to a quantitative statement of the reliability of a single measurement or of a parameter, such as the arithmetic mean value, determined from a number of random trial measurements. This is often called the statistical error and is one of the so-called *precision indices*. The most commonly used indices, usually in reference to the reliability of the mean, are the standard deviation, the standard error (also called the standard deviation in the mean), and the probable error. Precision indices are defined and discussed later.

The student may well have difficulty in immediately perceiving some of the fine points in the above distinctions, but they should become clearer later.

It is important to note that the algebraic sign of a random error is either positive or negative with an equal probability when the error is measured with respect to the *median* value. In the fourth meaning listed, the precision index is always measured with respect to the "best" value of the parameter under consideration, and the best value, as stated above, is the arithmetic mean rather than the median or the most probable value (the mode). Also note that when the distribution of measurements is asymmetrical (as, e.g., in the cases of the binomial and Poisson model distributions), the median, the mean, and the most probable values are all different. In this case, the precision index of reliability is properly (although in practice only occasionally) expressed, not as plus or minus some *symmetrical* error magnitude, but rather as plus one error magnitude and minus another error magnitude.

Sometimes we distinguish between (a) the random errors that are introduced specifically as a part of the measurement process and (b) the random phenomena that are inherent in the statistical nature of the property being measured. This distinction is perhaps not a fundamental one but is significant in certain types of measurements themselves. Let us elaborate on this a little. The former case typically refers to the role of the elementary errors as they conspire to produce an observed deviation in a measurement in a very fine-grained (perhaps continuous) sample space, whereas the latter very often (but not necessarily) refers to a measurement in which the sample space is obviously discrete. Examples of the former are found in measurements of a length or of a time; examples of the latter are found in so-called counting measurements (e.g., in counting nuclear disintegrations, in measuring with a counter the intensity of cosmic rays, or in the quality control problem of the last chapter in which "defective" is unambiguous). A count is an integer with no uncertainty in it, but whether or not a count occurs in a specified sample (in a selected batch or in a selected time interval, etc.) is due to chance which is itself due to an unfathomed array of elementary errors. In a counting experiment, we measure the probability that a count will occur in the selected sample with all the elementary errors lumped into a discrete "yes" or "no" type of answer, and the probability sought is some characteristic of nature just as is the length of a piece of wire.

The central feature of all statistical measurements, of whatever type, is that we seek to determine a measure, from a limited sample (number of trials), of a property of a large (often infinite) population. In whatever type, the reliability of the mean of the measurements increases in statistical fashion as the size of the sample increases. Only in the event that the "sample" is the entire population (often an infinite number of trials) are the random sampling errors reduced to zero. Distinction between the properties of a sample and of the entire ("parent" or "universe") population is basic in the second of the four meanings of random error as set forth above, and is the subject of several later discussions.

Systematic error. An error that always has or tends to have the same algebraic sign, either an additive or subtractive quantity introduced in the measurement process, is called a systematic error. If the magnitude of this error does not change with time, it appears as a constant error in all of the measurements and also in the median and arithmetic mean values. If it changes in magnitude, it introduces some skew (asymmetry) in the observed histogram. If the changes in magnitude occur in some irregular fashion, it is especially a most unpleasant and insidious error contribution. In any case, since systematic errors are not generally amenable to statistical treatment, they impair the reliability of the mean to a degree which can only be estimated and often not very well.*

The observed errors in *every* instance probably include *both* random and systematic errors.†

Examples of systematic errors are those caused by:

(1) Incorrect (or an unjustifiably assumed) calibration of an instrument, friction or wear in moving parts of an instrument (as in a "sticky" meter), electrostatic charge on the glass front of a meter, failure to correct for the "zero" reading, etc.

(2) Constructional faults in the apparatus, e.g., misaligned parts, thermal electromotive forces from poorly chosen materials, screw errors, etc.

(3) Inadequate regard to constancy of experimental conditions and imperfect measurement techniques, e.g., changes in dimensions owing to thermal expansion, one-sided illumination of a scale, nonvertical position of a liquid manometer, alteration of the property being measured as in chemical contamination or spilling part of a liquid sample, etc.

(4) Failure to make necessary corrections, e.g., for the effect of atmospheric pressure or of the variation of gravity with elevation or latitude in determinations of mass by weighing, meniscus corrections in a liquid

---

* Examples of classical situations involving large systematic errors are: (1) Prior to 1920, atomic weight determinations were, as was later shown, afflicted with unsuspected systematic errors that averaged fully *ten* times the stated experimental errors, and (2) in 1929 the accepted value of the electronic charge was 4.7700×10^{-10} esu (note the number of significant figures), and later it was changed to 4.80294×10^{-10} esu. (Significant figures are discussed in Section 2-8.) Examples of large unsuspected systematic errors are numerous in the scientific literature, far more numerous than is generally suspected. This is the "problem" in the apparent inconsistencies in the fundamental constants (e.g., see Cohen, DuMond, Layton, and Rollett, *Rev. Mod. Phys.*, **27**, 363 (1955), and Bearden and Thomsen, *Nuovo Cimento, Suppl.* (Ser. 10), **5**, no. 2, 267 (1957).

† And the pseudo scientist said, "Let there be no systematic errors," and lo and behold it came to pass: there *were* no systematic errors. Only the pseudo scientist can be so sure.

barometer, "stem" correction in a common mercury-glass thermometer, etc.

(5) Bias by the observer, e.g., more or less constant parallax, supposed improvement in technique in the midst of a set of measurements, desire for the "right" result, etc.

This list is not intended to be exhaustive, merely illustrative.

To justify the application of a mathematical model of variability, as we often attempt to do, we assume randomness in the observed variability, an assumption whose validity may be jeopardized by the presence of systematic errors. It is generally imperative that every effort be made to detect and to eliminate systematic errors. If a systematic error is not time-dependent, recognition of it may come from greater care or by comparison with the results from other apparatus or from some more ingenious method of measurement. If the error changes with time, a study of the time dependence of the mean value may reveal the error's presence. Tests of correlation and of consistency of means, discussed in Sections 3-3 and 3-7, are helpful.

Elimination of systematic errors often strains the ingenuity, judgment, and patience of the best of experimenters. After exhausting all methods, even though he does not believe them to be entirely absent, he resigns himself to their presence but assumes the variability to be random for the purpose of statistical treatment of the deviations.

However, note in this regard that a distinction is made between precision and accuracy.

Precision and accuracy. Precision in a mean value is proportional to the reciprocal of the statistical error and is "high" if the statistical error is small; accuracy is "high" if the net systematic error is small.* Usually, but not necessarily, high accuracy implies a small statistical error as well.

---

* As stated above, objective numerical determination of the residual systematic errors is not practical. The error for accuracy is usually appreciably greater than the one for precision, but its numerical value is perforce left to the observer's best judgment.

An arbitrary procedure, often used, is to estimate the *equivalent* statistical error caused by estimated component systematic errors. This estimate is usually deliberately very conservative—say about a 1 % or a 5 % chance that the "true" value lies outside of the limits given by the equivalent error. Some experimenters go further: With an assumed mathematical model of the "histogram" of the component systematic errors, e.g., the normal (or Gauss) distribution, such an estimated error is converted by the formulas of the model to the same "confidence limit" used in the statistical error; often this is the probable error. The assumption of a mathematical model for these component errors is admittedly highly *ad hoc* and is not to be much trusted; but there is apparently no better general procedure. (See next chapter.)

Precision and accuracy are *not* interchangeable terms.* Statistical methods give specifically a quantitative measure of precision, not of accuracy (however, see discussion of the consistency of means, next chapter).

Discrepancy. The difference between two measured values, e.g., values reported by two different observers, or the difference between a value by an observer and an "accepted" value as listed in a handbook, is called a discrepancy. *This difference is not an error*, although it implies the need of a statement of error, both statistical and systematic, in each value to provide a basis for interpreting the discrepancy.

Blunders. These are outright mistakes. A measurement known to contain one or more blunders should be corrected or discarded. Blunder errors include the following effects:

(1) Misunderstanding what one is doing, incorrect logic.
(2) Misreading of an instrument.
(3) Errors in transcription of data.
(4) Confusion of units.
(5) Arithmetical mistake, "slide-rule error."
(6) Misplaced decimal point.
(7) Listing of an improper number of significant figures, etc.

2-8. Significant Figures and Rounding of Numbers

Significant figures are the digit figures necessary to express a measurement so as to give immediately some idea of the accuracy of the measurement. There is no uniformly accepted rule for deciding the exact number of digits to use. One popular practice† is to drop all digits uncertain by more than 15 units. Accordingly, a measurement of, say, 63.7 cm indicates a "high" probability for a value between 63.55 and 63.85 cm but a "possible" range 62.2 to 65.2. Another popular practice is to retain the last digit that is uncertain by 10 units or less. In case either procedure is followed, it is recommended to include one more figure but to set it down slightly below the line of the significant figures. If this additional subfigure, with

* According to legend, it was desired to determine as precisely as possible the height of the emperor of China. It was unthinkable to bother the emperor with a direct measurement. So, the investigator, knowing about statistics and being of diligent mind, conducted an extensive poll. He selected at random a thousand, nay, a million Chinamen from all parts of the nation. Each was asked to give his opinion as to the height of the emperor, and was then sworn to secrecy. The average of all the numbers provided a very *precise* determination. But *none* of the Chinamen concerned had ever even seen the emperor!

† Recommended by The American Society for Testing Materials, *Manual on Presentation of Data* (ASTM, Philadelphia, 1937), 2nd printing, p. 44.

its uncertainty of more than 10 (or 15) units, were to be included as a significant figure, it would erroneously imply in some cases that the preceding figure was uncertain by *less* than 10 (or 15) units. "Uncertain" in a single measurement refers to the observer's best guess as to the "sum" of the random and systematic errors. Sometimes this guess is taken simply as the effective measuremental least count, i.e., either as the smallest division on the scale of measurement or as the observer's estimate of a meaningful interpolation. In the mean measurement, the precision part of the uncertainty is set by, say, the standard deviation or by the standard error (i.e., the standard deviation in the mean). Significant figures in the mean and in some precision indices are illustrated in Table 2-2 which is introduced and discussed in Section 2-11, and also in some of the problems and answers in Section 2-12.*

As a guide in determining the proper number of significant figures with which to express the precision of a mean determined from seven or more equally weighted measurements, the mean should have one more significant figure than has each measurement. In general, justification of this rule, and indeed the proper number of figures for the mean in any case, is indicated by the magnitude of, say, the standard deviation or, better, of the standard deviation in the mean.

As stated, the proper use of significant figures provides a rough method of expressing accuracy.† However, because it is only rough and involves an arbitrary criterion of uncertainty, it is by no means a good substitute for the assignment of the appropriate statistical error (e.g., standard deviation, standard error, or probable error), and also of a separate estimate of the net systematic error.

Rounding of numbers is the process of dropping one or more significant

* A man named Babbage read Tennyson's *The Vision of Sin*, and wrote the following letter to the poet: "In your otherwise beautiful poem there is a verse which reads:

'Every moment dies a man,
Every moment one is born.'

It must be manifest that, were this true, the population of the world would be at a standstill. In truth, the rate of birth is slightly in excess of that of death. I would suggest that in the next edition of your poem you have it read:

'Every moment dies a man,
Every moment $1\frac{1}{16}$ is born.'

Strictly speaking this is not correct. The actual figure is a decimal so long that I cannot get it in the line, but I believe $1\frac{1}{16}$ will be sufficiently accurate for poetry. I am, etc."

† Comment on the following story: A physics student in a mathematics class received a grade of zero on an examination in which ten equally weighted questions had been asked. He inquired of the instructor whether the examination was graded on a basis of 10 as perfect or on a basis of 100. The instructor insisted that the question was pointless, saying that zero was zero regardless of the basis of scoring.

figures when the measurement is used in computations for a computed result. The rules for the rounding of numbers are rather well developed and are stated below. When these rules are followed consistently, the errors due to rounding largely cancel one another.

To round off to n figures, discard (i.e., replace with zeros or with powers of ten) all digits to the right of the nth place. If the discarded number is less than half a unit in the nth place, leave the nth digit unchanged; if it is greater than half a unit in the nth place, add 1 to the nth digit. If the discarded number is exactly half a unit in the nth place, then leave the nth digit unaltered if it is an even number but increase it by 1 if it is an odd number.

In multiplication and division (indeed, in all computations except addition and subtraction) with numbers of unequal accuracy and of equal weights in the final result, a generally safe rule is: Retain from the beginning one more significant figure in the more accurate numbers than is contained in the least accurate number, then round off the final result to the same number of significant figures as are in the least accurate number. If unequal weights are involved, adjust the respective number of significant figures accordingly (weights are discussed later).

In the case of addition or subtraction, retain in the more accurate numbers one more decimal digit than is contained in the least accurate number. A decimal digit is a figure on the right of the decimal point regardless of the number of figures on the left.

The above rules presume that all the measurements are independent. If the measurements are at all correlated (see Section 3-7), the rules are not applicable and we must proceed with caution.

C. FREQUENCY DISTRIBUTIONS AND PRECISION INDICES

The variations in successive trial measurements are completely represented by a detailed graph of the frequency distribution of the measurements. The idea of a frequency distribution was introduced and discussed very briefly in Chapter 1 and also in connection with Figs. 2-1 and 2-2. It was mentioned that some distributions are symmetrical in shape and that others are asymmetrical.

In the remainder of this chapter, we shall comment on a few of the qualitative features of some typical empirical frequency distributions, and then we shall discuss some easily obtained numerical measures of the shapes of or the types of variations in distributions. We shall treat *general* distributions, symmetrical or otherwise, and regardless of any possible fit of a mathematical model. These numerical measures, except for the location values (e.g., the arithmetic mean), are called precision indices of dispersion.

2-9. Typical Distributions

Most actual sets of observations or measurements have frequency distributions somewhat like the *bell shape*, or like a more or less drastically *skewed bell shape* (Figs. 2-1 and 2-2). But it is possible that a distribution may have almost any conceivable shape. A variety of distributions are shown in Fig. 2-4(*a*) through (*g*). Each of the first three distributions shown in this figure has a rather large *classification interval*. If the classification interval in (*c*) were much smaller than it is, the distribution would undoubtedly drop to a low frequency value at very small ages and contain a narrow or strongly peaked maximum. As another example (not shown) a frequency distribution of the wealth of the average person in New York State according to age would probably be similar to (*b*) or (*c*) but with reversed skewness.

Comment is in order on a few additional features. In (*a*), the abscissa zero is displaced to the left, off the page. In the (*a*), (*b*), (*c*), and (*g*) examples, measurements are presumed to be possible that would have a nonuniform distribution within each indicated classification interval. The indicated interval size is imposed in (*a*) by perhaps the resolving power of the particular apparatus used, in (*b*) and (*c*) by perhaps some decision of convenience for the problem at hand. The problem in (*c*) evidently did not include finding the most probable age or the shape of the distribution for very small ages, or perhaps the investigator judged that a smaller classification interval would not be meaningful. Note in (*g*) the unequal classification intervals; the interval size is varied so as to avoid the vanishingly small frequencies per interval that would obtain in the higher intervals if a constant class size and a linear abscissa scale were used.

Terminology: types of distributions. Referring to Fig. 2-4, we have in (*d*) an example of a *discrete distribution*, "discrete" because only integer numbers of colonies of bacteria are possible by the nature of the observations. In (*e*), (*f*), and the fitted curve in (*g*), the distributions are *continuous* since they are calculated from the respective functional theoretical relations which are continuous.

The binomial mathematical models of Fig. 1-2, and the distribution curves, Fig. 2-2, may well be included among those of Fig. 2-4. The binomial and Poisson distributions are discrete; the normal distribution is continuous. The shape and "smoothness" of a model distribution are always as though the number of observations was infinite.

Another general feature of interest is the range or bounds. For example, the normal distribution curve extends from $-\infty$ to $+\infty$, the distribution of (e) is bounded by 0 and by $+\infty$, and the distribution of (f) is bounded at $\pm A$, etc.

The term *histogram* is often reserved for the block-area type of distribution such as in the (a), (b), or (c) type; *frequency diagram* for the (d) type; and *frequency curve* for the (e) or (f) type. In this terminology, the basic graph in (g) is a histogram; the fitted curve is a frequency curve. A histogram approaches a frequency curve as the classification interval goes to zero and the number of trials goes to infinity. In this book we use the term frequency distribution to refer to all of these types, either for actual measurements or for the mathematical models of probability distribution.

Another distinction in terminology is often made. A probability distribution has a unit sum if it is a discrete distribution and a unit area if it is a continuous distribution, by definition of probability; hence no ordinate value is greater than unity.* An observed frequency distribution has ordinate values greater than unity unless the observed values are "normalized," i.e., divided by the total number of observations. The normalized distribution is sometimes called the relative distribution. If it is a mathematical model it is called the frequency function.

Finally, we often have occasion to refer to the sum or to the area under the distribution between specified abscissa limits. The sum of the frequencies, either observed or relative, from an abscissa value of 0 (or of $-\infty$) to some specified value is called the cumulative distribution, or the distribution function, or the error function if the distribution is continuous and expressed analytically.

After a set of measurements has been classified, i.e., grouped into the appropriate class intervals, and plotted as a frequency distribution, the next task in statistics is to devise some simple numerical descriptions of the particular distribution. The features of primary interest are (1) a location index of the "center" of the distribution, and (2) a measure of the spread or dispersion. The simplest descriptions (simple in terms of the amount of arithmetic involved) give the least information. Of course, the distribution would be completely described if we had its analytical mathematical formulation and the necessary parameters. But in a typical experimental distribution, such a formulation is impractical.

We proceed to discuss some descriptions of the distributions, location indices as well as measures of dispersion, that are applicable to *any* set of experimental data (or to any mathematical model). The measures of dispersion are called the precision indices.

---

* The ordinate probability in a continuous distribution is proportional to the abscissa interval (e.g., see Eq. 4-10 and discussion); if the probability is expressed in terms of an altered *extended* interval, the numerical value may exceed unity.

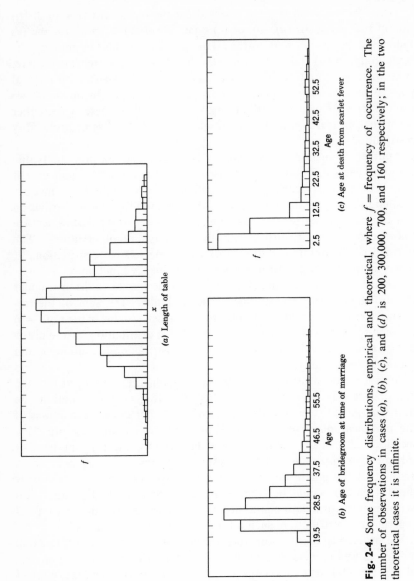

Fig. 2-4. Some frequency distributions, empirical and theoretical, where f = frequency of occurrence. The number of observations in cases (a), (b), (c), and (d) is 200, 300,000, 700, and 160, respectively; in the two theoretical cases it is infinite.

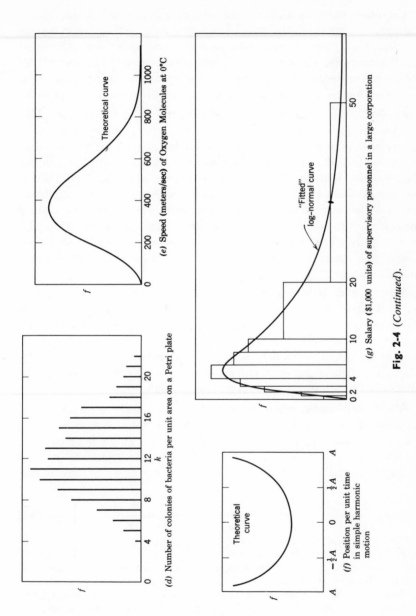

(d) Number of colonies of bacteria per unit area on a Petri plate

(e) Speed (meters/sec) of Oxygen Molecules at 0°C

(f) Position per unit time in simple harmonic motion

(g) Salary ($1,000 units) of supervisory personnel in a large corporation

Fig. 2-4 (*Continued*).

2-10. Location Indices

The three commonly used location indices are the median, the mode, and the mean. When the distribution has a single maximum in it and is symmetrical, these three location indices are all identical in value. Almost all practical cases are unimodal (have a single maximum) if the number of trial measurements is large enough for the meaningful application of statistical methods. But the condition of symmetry is less often realized in practice.

Median. The easiest location index to compute is the median. This is defined as the middle measurement of an odd number of measurements (all ordered as to magnitude), otherwise as the interpolated middle value. For some statistical problems the median is the most significant of the three location indices. This is apt to be the case when the distribution is strongly skewed. For example, we may be more interested in the median wage than in the mean wage of workers in a certain large industry for which the top executives' wages may give an undesirable distortion. However, even in a strongly skewed distribution of measurements in an experimental science, the mean is almost universely accepted as statistically the best location index.*

Mode (most probable value). Of especial interest in some asymmetrical distributions is the abscissa value at the peak position. This is the measurement, or the interpolated value, having the maximum frequency of occurrence. It is of much less interest in actual measurements than in mathematical model distributions because of the great difficulty of its accurate determination with real-life data; this difficulty is especially great when the classification interval is very small.

Mean (arithmetic average) m and μ. By far the most important location index is the mean. The experimental mean is denoted by m; the hypothetical ("parent" or "universe") mean for an infinite number of measurements, or the mathematical model mean, is denoted by μ. m is defined for n trial measurements, $x_1, x_2, x_3, \cdots, x_i, \cdots, x_n$, by the relation†

$$m \equiv \frac{x_1 + x_2 + x_3 + \cdots + x_n}{n} = \frac{\sum\limits_{i=1}^{n} x_i}{n} \tag{2-1}$$

* By the conventional criterion for statistical efficiency, the median as a location index is considerably less "efficient" than is the mean. In the *normal* distribution, for example, the median is only 64% as efficient as the mean (although both indices in this case have the same numerical "parent" values). The criterion for statistical efficiency is described in the discussion of the mean deviation in the next section and is also mentioned in Section 3-1. A few additional "inefficient statistics" are mentioned in Section 3-8.

† In this chapter, all measurements x_i are assumed to be individually equally weighted. The mean is defined in Section 3-3 in terms of unequally weighted measurements.

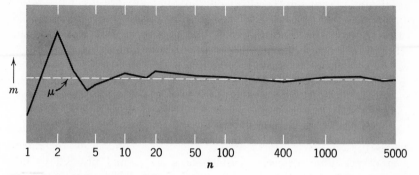

Fig. 2-5. Typical variation of the experimental mean as the number of trials increases. (Note the logarithmic abscissa scale.)

If one or more values of x are observed more than once, say x_i is observed f_i times, there will be n' ($n' < n$) *different* x values in the n trials. In this case, we may weight each x_i by its frequency of occurrence f_i, and write

$$m \equiv \frac{f_1 x_1 + f_2 x_2 + \cdots + f_i x_i + \cdots + f_{n'} x_{n'}}{n} = \frac{\sum\limits_{i=1}^{n'} f_i x_i}{n} \qquad (2\text{-}2)$$

$$m \equiv x_1 \frac{f_1}{n} + x_2 \frac{f_2}{n} + \cdots + x_i \frac{f_i}{n} + \cdots + x_{n'} \frac{f_{n'}}{n} = \sum_{i=1}^{n'} x_i p_i \qquad (2\text{-}3)$$

where, of course, $n = \sum_{i=1}^{n'} f_i$, and $p_i = f_i/n$ is the experimental probability for observing x_i.* The sum in Eqs. 2-2 and 2-3 could just as well be taken to infinity if it is understood that for some i's f_i may be zero.

Often we are interested in a comparison of two means determined on different days, or with measurements taken with different apparatus, or by different observers. The statistics of such a comparison is discussed in Section 3-3.

The hypothetical or mathematical mean μ is defined by a relation similar to Eq. 2-3 that would obtain if $n = \infty$. Of course, if x_i is a point in continuous sample space, the summation in Eq. 2-3 must be replaced by an integral. μ is also called the *universe* or *parent* mean, and m the *sample* mean. (In slightly more advanced statistics, m is called an "estimator" of the parent parameter μ.) Of course, μ cannot be experimentally determined, but its value can be approached as n is made larger and larger. As illustrated in Fig. 2-5, m may fluctuate rather violently for n small, but it gradually settles down to a steady value as n becomes large. The

---

* Just for practice, check that for the numbers 2, 3, 5, 6, 7, 8, 8, 9, 9, 9, 11, 11, 12 the mode is 9, the median is 8, and the mean is 7.6_9.

usual objective in the statistical interpretation of measurements with a limited number of trials is the best determination of μ, not of m, and this calls for some very interesting statistical arguments. Of course, in many sets of measurements the difference between m and μ may be believed to be very small. It turns out that for any given number of trials n the corresponding m from Eq. 2-1 is generally the *best available value* of μ. We shall presently define a precision index that gives the reliability of m for any given n.

In speaking of the mean of any mathematical model distribution, we necessarily refer to μ. If we are convinced that a model fits the experimental measurements, we approximate μ by m and proceed to take advantage of calculations and predictions by the model.

By the term "mean" without further qualification we always refer to the arithmetic mean. (Other possible means are the geometric, root-mean-square, etc.) The mean is the abscissa value of the center of area of the frequency distribution.

The phrase *expectation value* is often used to refer to the mean value m, or to μ in a model distribution.

Calculation of the mean m is usually rather laborious when it is carried out directly, but it can generally be simplified by the device known as the *working mean*. To effect this simplification, write for each measurement

$$x_i = w + x_i{}'$$

where w, the working mean, is an arbitrary constant value of x. w is chosen to be somewhere near m in magnitude, chosen to include all the invariant significant figures in all the actual measurements, and, for convenience, chosen such that $x_i{}' = 0$ for some one value of i. A convenient value for w is readily selected after a visual inspection of the measurements at hand. Then,

$$\sum_{i=1}^{n} x_i = \sum_{i=1}^{n} (w + x_i{}') = nw + \sum_{i=1}^{n} x_i{}'$$

and let

$$\Delta = \frac{\sum_{i=1}^{n} x_i{}'}{n} = \frac{\sum_{i=1}^{n} (x_i - w)}{n}$$

from which

$$m = w + \Delta \tag{2-4}$$

The convenience of the working mean is realized if w is so chosen as to make calculation of Δ, which is small in magnitude, appreciably easier than calculation of m. A simple example of a calculation with the working mean is given in Table 2-2, which is introduced later in Section 2-11.

2-11. Dispersion Indices

There are several indices of the spread (dispersion) of the measurements about the central value. The dispersion, as stated above, is a measure of precision. As with the location indices, the amount of information contained in each dispersion index increases roughly with the arithmetical labor involved.

Range. The simplest index of dispersion is the range. It is equal to the difference between the largest and the smallest measurements. For obvious reasons, the magnitude of the range generally increases with the number of trial measurements. Hence, whenever the range is specified, it should be accompanied by a statement of the number of trials.

Quantile. Suppose that all the n measurements are ordered as to magnitude and then divided into equal intervals, each interval having an equal number of measurements. If there are M intervals, each interval is called a quantile or an M-tile, or sometimes a fractile. The quartiles refer to the quarter divisions of the total number of measurements, there being two quartiles on each side of the median. Deciles refer to the division by tenths, etc. The dispersion information given by the quantiles increases as M increases, but it disregards the distribution of values within each quantile.

Deviation (statistical fluctuation). For the ith measurement in a set of n trials, the deviation is denoted as z_i or δx_i and is defined as

$$z_i \equiv x_i - m \equiv \delta x_i \tag{2-5}$$

From the definition of z_i it readily follows that

$$\sum_{i=1}^{n} z_i = 0 \tag{2-6}$$

The mean m is used as the reference value in this definition in order that the *sum of the squares of all deviations shall be a minimum*, as shown in the next paragraph. All the precision indices that have to do with the shape or dispersion of the frequency distribution are defined in terms of deviations.

Let S be the sum of the squares of the deviations when each deviation z_i' is defined in terms of some unspecified reference value m'. Then,

$$S = \sum_{i=1}^{n} z_i'^2 = \sum_{i=1}^{n} (x_i - m')^2 = \sum_{i=1}^{n} x_i^2 - 2m' \sum_{i=1}^{n} x_i + nm'^2$$

To find the particular value of m', call it m_m', that makes S a minimum, we differentiate S with respect to m', place the derivative equal to zero, and solve for m_m'. Since all the x_i values are constants their derivatives are zero. Then,

$$\frac{dS}{dm'} = -2 \sum_{i=1}^{n} x_i + 2nm_m' = 0 \quad \text{or} \quad m_m' = \frac{\sum_{i=1}^{n} x_i}{n}$$

which is the mean, m, as defined in Eq. 2-1 and as used in Eq. 2-5. Therefore, m is the reference value for which the sum of the squares of the experimental deviations is a minimum.*

A point which we encounter over and over again in dispersion indices dealing with experimental deviations is that any other reference value, such as μ, does *not* make S a minimum. Only when we refer to *all* possible deviations, i.e., to the "universe" (infinity) of deviations, does the reference value μ make S a minimum. But note that the objective of the measurements is μ, not m, and we really wish the precision dispersion index to refer to μ, not to m. The best we can do with a limited number of observations, however, is m and a dispersion index with respect to m. It is possible and practical in many situations to introduce additional information into the problem, as, for example, from more than one sample of n measurements each, or from samples of different sizes, or from a reasonably fitting mathematical model. Use of such additional information, introduces factors such as $\sqrt{n/(n-1)}$, $\sqrt{n(n-1)}$, etc., in the quantitative dispersion indices; these factors are discussed later.

When we deal with a mathematical model distribution, the reference value for S to be a minimum is μ.

Mean (average) deviation. This index is defined without regard to the algebraic signs of the individual deviations. The mean deviation $\bar{z}$ is defined as

$$\bar{z} \equiv \frac{\sum_{i=1}^{n} |z_i|}{n} \tag{2-7}$$

A small numerical value of $\bar{z}$ means that the individual measurements are closely grouped, and that the distribution is rather sharply peaked. The value of $\bar{z}$ also provides a sort of numerical guess as to the amount by which the next measurement is likely to differ from the mean value m.

The use of this measure of dispersion, $\bar{z}$, is rather widespread in scientific work, but it is not much used by statisticians. It is what the statisticians call an "inefficient" measure of dispersion, and this for the following reason. Suppose that a large number of trial measurements are made from which

---

* This is one application of the famous *principle of least squares;* it is really by this application that the mean of any distribution is said to be the "best" location value. The basis for this principle is discussed in Chapter 3.

the mean deviation is computed. Then suppose these measurements to be arbitrarily divided into many small subsets and the mean deviation $\bar{z}_j$ of each subset computed. (Each z_j in $\bar{z}_j$ is computed with respect to m_j, the mean of the jth subset.) The subset values $\bar{z}_j$ will show a rather large scatter about the value $\bar{z}$ for the grand total of the measurements. An efficient measure of dispersion is one that shows small scatter, i.e., is one that allows a statistically reliable estimate of the precision based on just *one* subset. Efficiency refers specifically to the reciprocal of the square of the standard deviation of the $\bar{z}_j$ distribution about the central value $\bar{z}$. (Standard deviation is defined in the next section.) In a practical sense, efficiency refers to the inverse of the number of measurements required for a given statistical precision: the smaller the number the greater the efficiency. Gauss showed that to have a given degree of precision in a set of measurements from a parent population having a normal distribution 14% more measurements are required if $\bar{z}$, rather than the standard deviation, is used as the precision index. Any set of measurements in real life is just one subset of a much larger number of possible measurements. Judged by this statistical efficiency criterion, the mean deviation does not justify the widespread use to which it has been put by scientists.

However, it is nonetheless a very useful index of dispersion if the larger deviations in the measurements are believed not to justify a higher weighting than the first power. (The standard deviation weights according to the second power.) Such measurement problems do arise in scientific work.

Another characteristic of the mean deviation is the following. Suppose that a large set of measurements is divided into subsets of two measurements in each subset, and suppose that the value $\bar{z}_j$ is computed for each subset. The average of these two values of $\bar{z}_j$ is generally less than, statistically only 0.707 of, the mean deviation of the parent set. It is true that the larger the number of measurements in each subset the closer the average of the subset values becomes to the value of the parent set. For subsets of three measurements each, the statistical average of the mean deviations $\bar{z}_j$ is 0.816 of the parent $\bar{z}$; for subsets of five measurements each, it is 0.894; for subsets of ten each, it is 0.943. Most actual sets of measurements in real life are not very large, and the mean deviation gives an unduly optimistic measure of the precision. This bias is also found in the experimental standard deviation, and in each case can be corrected by multiplying by the factor $\sqrt{n/(n-1)}$ as discussed later.

The fractional mean deviation is defined as

$$\text{fractional } \bar{z} \equiv \frac{\bar{z}}{m} \tag{2-8}$$

and is usually expressed in per cent.

Although the value of the fractional $\bar{z}$ is dimensionless, its numerical value depends upon the choice of zero of the x scale. For example, fractional $\bar{z}$ in a set of measurements of temperature is different if x is expressed in degrees centigrade or in degrees Kelvin. Hence, the fractional value is usually used only in those measurements for which the zero of the x scale is the physically significant zero. This restriction also applies to any fractional dispersion index, e.g., the fractional standard deviation as mentioned presently.

In Eqs. 2-7 and 2-8 the value of $\bar{z}$ is that obtained with the mean m, not μ, as the reference value.* Hence, $\bar{z}$ and fractional $\bar{z}$ are experimental quantities. The corresponding indices for a model distribution are not used because of their inefficiency and bias as stated above.

Experimental standard deviation s. Another measure of the dispersion of the frequency distribution is the standard deviation. With a limited number n of trial measurements, the *experimental* or *sample* standard deviation s is defined as†

$$s \equiv \left(\frac{\sum_{i=1}^{n} (x_i - m)^2}{n} \right)^{\frac{1}{2}} = \left(\frac{\sum_{i=1}^{n} z_i^2}{n} \right)^{\frac{1}{2}} \tag{2-9}$$

This expression can also be written, in case x_i is observed f_i times, as

$$s \equiv \left(\frac{\sum_{i=1}^{n'} (x_i - m)^2 f_i}{n} \right)^{\frac{1}{2}} = \left(\sum_{i=1}^{n'} (x_i - m)^2 p_i \right)^{\frac{1}{2}} \tag{2-10}$$

where $n' \leqslant n$ and p_i is the probability of occurrence of x_i. The quantity s is also called the *root-mean-square (or rms)* deviation. Taking the square root of the sum makes the dimensions and units of s the same as of x. (Again, the sums in Eq. 2-10 could just as well be taken to infinity.)

Note that the deviations in Eq. 2-9 are individually squared before the summation is made; this assigns more weight to the large deviations. Hence, as a measure of the dispersion, s is more sensitive to large deviations than is the mean deviation $\bar{z}$. It follows that, of two frequency distributions having the same mean deviation, the distribution with the relatively higher tails has the greater standard deviation. In a series of measurements, a large deviation is always cause for concern; its appearance increases our

---

* Sometimes in statistics a "mean deviation" is reckoned with the median as the reference value. This, however, is very uncommon in scientific work.

† This definition presumes all individual measurements x_i to be equally weighted, a typical presumption for a set of random measurements. The standard deviation is defined in Section 3-3 in terms of unequally weighted measurements.

a priori belief that another large deviation will soon appear. The standard deviation is a more efficient measure of the precision, as the statistician reckons efficiency, than is the mean deviation.

Of all the precision dispersion indices, the standard deviation is the one in widest use in statistics. And it is also widely used in experimental science, but nowadays the probable error, which is based on the standard deviation, seems to be about equally popular. The probable error is discussed in Chapters 3, 4, and 5.

Because of the squaring operations in Eq. 2-9, s does not allow distinction between the algebraic signs of the individual deviations and gives no indication of the degree of asymmetry of the distribution. For a symmetrical distribution, s can be indicated with meaning as $\pm s$ values on the graph of the distribution; for an asymmetrical distribution, it cannot be so indicated and it remains of mathematical significance only.

The standard deviation provides, as does any dispersion index, a numerical guess as to the likely range of values into which the next measurement may fall. With this interpretation, s is sometimes called the standard deviation *of a single measurement* rather than of the distribution itself. As we shall see in Chapter 4, if the normal model fits the experimental parent distribution of mean μ and standard deviation σ, the probability is 0.675 that the next measurement will fall within $\mu \pm \sigma^*$ which is very nearly the same as $m \pm s$.

Often we are interested in a statistical comparison of the precision of the means determined on different days, or with different apparatus, etc. This comparison is discussed in Chapter 3.

The fractional standard deviation is defined as

$$\text{fractional } s \equiv \frac{s}{m} \tag{2-11}$$

This index is extensively used in problems dealing with the propagation of error, discussed in Chapter 3. However, as with the fractional mean deviation, the fractional standard deviation is not especially useful in cases when the zero of the x scale is not physically significant.

Computation of s by Eq. 2-9 or 2-10 is often tedious and, unless very carefully done, is apt to be somewhat inaccurate. One reason for the inaccuracy is a consequence of the fact that more significant figures must be used in the value of m than in each value x_i. To reduce this difficulty

---

* It can be shown that, in any distribution, the probability p of observing a deviation $z \geqslant ks$ is $p \leqslant 1/k^2$, where k is any positive number. (This is known as Tchebycheff's theorem or inequality.)

in the calculations, a convenient expression for s is obtained by expanding $(x_i - m)^2$ in Eq. 2-9 and by using Eq. 2-1; thus,

$$s = \left(\frac{\sum\limits_{i=1}^{n} (x_i - m)^2}{n} \right)^{1/2} = \left(\frac{\sum\limits_{i=1}^{n} x_i^2 - 2m \sum\limits_{i=1}^{n} x_i + nm^2}{n} \right)^{1/2}$$

$$= \left(\frac{\sum\limits_{i=1}^{n} x_i^2 - nm^2}{n} \right)^{1/2} \qquad (2\text{-}12)$$

A further simplification is achieved by using the working mean introduced in Eq. 2-4, viz., $w = m - \Delta$. From a visual inspection of the set of measurements at hand, or better, of the frequency distribution graph, a working mean w is chosen which may be a convenient round number, if the classification interval is bounded by round numbers, and which contains all the invariant significant figures in all the x_i's. For convenience, w is chosen to be close in value to m. Then, in terms of $(x_i - w)$, which may be called an adjusted deviation,

$$s^2 = \frac{\sum\limits_{i=1}^{n} (x_i - w - \Delta)^2}{n} = \frac{\sum\limits_{i=1}^{n} (x_i - w)^2 - n\Delta^2}{n} \qquad (2\text{-}13)$$

where, as for Eq. 2-4,

$$\Delta = \frac{\sum\limits_{i=1}^{n} (x_i - w)}{n} \qquad (2\text{-}14)$$

A check of the calculation for s^2 can be made relatively quickly by choosing a different value of the working mean and by performing an independent calculation.

An example of the shortened computational method for s [and, incidentally, for the mean m and for the coefficient of skewness (discussed later)], is given in Table 2-2. In this table, f_i, the frequency of occurrence of the observed value x_i, is used to shorten the tabulation. Note that in the table the computed value of m is expressed with one more significant figure than is each value x_i. This is justified because the mean is obtained from such a large number of x_i's, and this justification is confirmed by the numerical value of the standard deviation in the mean, s_m, a precision index introduced presently.

Moments. The square of the standard deviation is also known as the second moment about the mean. Since moments higher than the second are also mentioned presently, it is worthwhile now to become acquainted with moments in general.

Table 2-2. Sample Calculations for Mean and Standard Deviation
(Using the "Working Mean")

Measured Value x_i (cm)	Frequency of Observation f_i	Adjusted Deviations and Moments with Working Mean $w = 128$ cm			
		$(x_i - w)$ (cm)	$f_i(x_i - w)$ (cm)	$f_i(x_i - w)^2$ (cm^2)	$f_i(x_i - w)^3$ (cm^3)
125	2	−3	−6	18	−54
126	3	−2	−6	12	−24
127	9	−1	−9	9	−9
128	16	0	0	0	0
129	11	1	11	11	11
130	7	2	14	28	56
131	2	3	6	18	54
132	1	4	4	16	64
	$\Sigma = 51$		$\Sigma = 14$ cm	$\Sigma = 112$ cm^2	$\Sigma = 98$ cm^3

$$\Delta = \tfrac{14}{51} = 0.27_4 \text{ cm}$$

$$\text{mean} = m = 128 + 0.27 = 128.2_7 \text{ cm} \qquad \text{(Eq. 2-4)}$$

$$\text{experimental "variance"} = s^2 = \frac{112 - 51(0.274)^2}{51} = 2.12_2 \text{ m}^2$$

$$\text{standard deviation} = s = 1.4_7 \text{ cm} \qquad \text{(Eq. 2-13)}$$

$$\text{fractional } s = \frac{1.47}{128.27} = 1.1_5\% \qquad \text{(Eq. 2-11)}$$

$$\text{stand. dev. in the mean} = s_m = \frac{1.47}{\sqrt{51}} = 0.20_6 \text{ cm} \qquad \text{(Eq. 2-31)}$$

$$\text{coefficient of skewness} = +0.05_1 \qquad \text{(Eq. 2-37)}$$

The kth moment about the *origin*, $\theta_k{}^0$, of a frequency distribution of n measurements in which x_i occurs f_i times, is

$$\theta_k{}^0 \equiv \frac{\sum_{i=1}^{n'} x_i^k f_i}{n} = \sum_{i=1}^{n'} x_i^k p_i \qquad (2\text{-}15)$$

where $n' \leqslant n$ and p_i is the probability of occurrence of x_i. It is apparent from Eq. 2-3 that the mean is simply the first moment about the origin,

$$\theta_1{}^0 = m \qquad (2\text{-}16)$$

The kth moment about the *mean m*, $\theta_k{}^m$, is

$$\theta_k{}^m \equiv \frac{\sum\limits_{i=1}^{n'} (x_i - m)^k f_i}{n} = \sum\limits_{i=1}^{n'} (x_i - m)^k p_i \tag{2-17}$$

from which, with Eq. 2-10,

$$\theta_2{}^m = s^2 \tag{2-18}$$

as stated above.

If the mean deviation were defined differently than it is in Eq. 2-7, i.e., specifically, if the absolute brackets on z_i were removed and regard were maintained for the algebraic signs of the individual deviations, then this $\bar{z}$ would be the first moment about the mean. But the first moment about the mean, viz., $\theta_1{}^m$, is equal to zero by the definition of the mean, and this is the reason that $\bar{z}$ is defined without regard to algebraic signs.

A useful relation exists between the second moments about the origin and about the mean respectively. This is shown by essentially the same expansion made in Eq. 2-12, viz.,

$$\theta_2{}^m = \sum\limits_{i=1}^{n'} (x_i - m)^2 p_i = \sum\limits_{i=1}^{n'} x_i{}^2 p_i - 2m \sum\limits_{i=1}^{n'} x_i p_i + m^2 \sum\limits_{i=1}^{n'} p_i$$

$$= \theta_2{}^0 - 2m\theta_1{}^0 + m^2$$

and by substituting Eq. 2-16 for $\theta_1{}^0$, we have the desired relation

$$\theta_2{}^m = \theta_2{}^0 - m^2 \tag{2-19}$$

This expression is identical to the well-known formula relating the moments of inertia of a body of unit mass about two different parallel axes a distance m apart, with one axis through the center of mass.

Variance σ^2: "universe" or "parent" standard deviation σ. If all the infinite population of possible measurements in the "universe" were known (a purely hypothetical situation), μ would be known and we could use μ instead of m as the reference value in computing each deviation. The standard deviation of a set of n deviations, as $n \to \infty$, with μ as the reference value is denoted by σ, and its square

$$\sigma^2 = \frac{\sum\limits_{i=1}^{n} (x_i - \mu)^2}{n} = \frac{\sum\limits_{i=1}^{n'} (x_i - \mu)^2 f_i}{n} = \sum\limits_{i=1}^{n'} (x_i - \mu)^2 p_i \tag{2-20}$$

is known as the variance. σ is also called the "universe" or "parent" standard deviation. The variance is a parameter of the universe or parent distribution whether it is of the "imagined real-life" type or is a mathematical model. In case the parent distribution is continuous, the summation in Eq. 2-20 may be replaced by an integration.* Thus, using f as the continuous frequency function from 0 to ∞,

$$\sigma^2 = \frac{\displaystyle\int_0^\infty (x - \mu)^2 f \, dx}{\displaystyle\int_0^\infty f \, dx} \tag{2-21}$$

The integral in the denominator is included in this expression to be sure that the frequency function is normalized; when a model probability function is used, the integral in the denominator is unity by definition.

The variance σ^2, i.e., the second moment about μ, is statistically the most important parameter in describing the dispersion of any universe or parent distribution, including any mathematical model distribution. With either the "real-life" imagined universe distribution or the model distribution, we must assume that μ is known in order to calculate σ^2. The value of μ, hence of σ^2, can *never* be exactly known from any real-life set of measurements. We use the "best" estimate that can be obtained.

---

* In going from a discrete to a continuous frequency distribution, we use the basic argument of calculus. For some students, it may be helpful to review this argument.

Consider the 12 measurements listed in Table 2-1 and graphed in the discrete distribution of Fig. 2-1. Or consider any list of a large number n of measurements. The range of the abscissa or x axis of interest can be arbitrarily divided into a large number N of equal increments Δx_i. The number of measurements that fall into the ith interval is n_i, and the normalized frequency (or the experimental probability) with which a measurement is observed within this interval is

$$p_i = \frac{n_i}{\displaystyle\sum_{i=1}^{N} n_i} = \frac{n_i}{n}$$

The normalized frequency distribution is the graph of p_i vs. $\bar{x}_i$, where $\bar{x}_i$ is the coordinate of the interval Δx_i and is taken as the average of the measurements within this interval. This distribution is, of course, discrete so long as Δx_i is finite in size.

We wish now to approximate the discrete frequency distribution $p_i(\bar{x}_i)$ by a continuous function $f(x)$, i.e., one for which $\Delta x_i \to 0$ in the limit as $n \to \infty$. This function can be defined by means of the relation

$$p_i(\bar{x}_i) = f(\bar{x}_i) \, \Delta x_i$$

which says that the value of $f(x)$ at $x = \bar{x}_i$ is to be made such that the product of this value and the width of the interval Δx_i is equal to the normalized frequency of the observed measurements within this interval.

Actual real-life measurements are far too few in number in any given situation to determine $f(x)$ in fine detail (i.e., Δx_i small, zero in the limit) by direct use of this definition. We are usually content to guess the "way $f(x)$ should go" reasonably consistent with the actual measurements at hand. This gives a continuous function that approximates not only the actual discrete frequency distribution but also the presumed-to-be-continuous parent distribution.

For a set of n measurements, as stated above, the best value of μ is generally taken as the experimental value m; and the best approximation to σ^2 that can be deduced from a set of n measurements is generally taken as†

$$\sigma^2 \approx \frac{n}{n-1} s^2 \qquad (2\text{-}22)$$

[The sample standard deviation s is one estimator of σ, but $\sqrt{n/(n-1)}\,s$ is generally considered to be a better estimator of σ because the radical factor corrects for a bias inherently present in s. This bias was mentioned earlier, in connection with the mean deviation, and is discussed again below.]

Combining Eqs. 2-9 and 2-22, we note that

$$\sigma \approx \left(\frac{\sum\limits_{i=1}^{n} (x_i - m)^2}{n-1} \right)^{\!\!1/2} \qquad (2\text{-}23)$$

In practice, this is commonly put in the form of a guess that a particular known continuous function satisfactorily "fits" the finite set of actual measurements; in other words, the guess is made that more measurements, were they to be taken, would merely increase our satisfaction that the analytic function fits and describes the parent distribution. Then, the common problem becomes one of determining the best guesses as to the important parameters of the continuous function. For example, for the means of the sample and of the parent distribution respectively, we write

$$m = \frac{\sum\limits_{i=1}^{N} \bar{x}_i}{n} = \sum\limits_{i=1}^{N} p_i(\bar{x}_i), \qquad \mu \approx m, \qquad \text{and} \qquad \mu = \int_0^\infty f(x)\, dx$$

and for the sample and the continuous-parent k moments about the mean (see Eq. 2-17),

$$\theta_k{}^m \underset{\text{(experimental)}}{=} \sum\limits_{i=1}^{N} (\bar{x}_i - m)^k p_i(\bar{x}_i) \qquad \text{and} \qquad \theta_k{}^\mu \underset{\text{(parent)}}{=} \frac{\displaystyle\int_0^\infty x^k f(x)\, dx}{\displaystyle\int_0^\infty f(x)\, dx}$$

† That these are the "best" values is discussed with more or less general statistical arguments in the appendix of the paper by R. H. Bacon, *Am. J. Phys.*, **21**, 428 (1953). Later, in Chapter 3, we show that taking these as the best estimators of μ and σ^2 in the normal distribution is consistent with the method of maximum likelihood; see Eqs. 3-12, 3-14, and 3-97 and the discussions attending these equations.

In general, of course, other estimators exist for the parent parameters μ and σ but they are of no great interest to us at our present level of discussion. But it is worth mentioning that there is no rigorous proof that m and $\sqrt{n/(n-1)}\,s$ are *in fact* the *best* estimators. Such a proof requires the introduction of some condition or criterion in addition to the conventional theory of probability. Maximum likelihood is such a condition, and it leads to useful estimators that are generally taken as best for all practical purposes in experimental science.

and this is the best practical formula (or estimator) for the universe or parent standard deviation. Note that in this expression for σ in terms of m, the denominator is $n - 1$ instead of n. Often, no distinction need be made between the numerical values of s and σ since neither is numerically very significant unless n is reasonably large, and then the differences between m and μ, and between n and $n - 1$, are relatively small. For small n, say <10 or 15, the factor $\sqrt{n/(n - 1)}$ which corrects for the bias must be applied to s whenever the standard deviation of the *parent* distribution is desired. And, regardless of the size of n, the difference *in principle* between s and σ (and between m and μ) is *fundamental* in statistical theory and, indeed, in the philosophy of science.

It is of importance that Eq. 2-22 or 2-23 not be interpreted in any sense as a definition of σ; σ refers to the parent population and the equations here merely provide a means of *estimating* the value of σ.

The "approximately equals" sign in Eqs. 2-22 and 2-23 approaches "equals" as $n \to \infty$. On the average, even for n rather small (but of course greater than unity), the expression is very nearly exact. It is interesting to note that, for $n = 1$, Eq. 2-23 gives $0/0$ and σ is indeterminate, as is proper in this case; and, for $n = 1$, Eq. 2-9 gives $s = 0$, as is mathematically proper in this case although, here also, "indeterminate" expresses a more appropriate meaning.

Degrees of freedom. The factor $n/(n - 1)$ enters in Eq. 2-22 by an argument in statistical theory, and we shall encounter it again in Chapter 3 in connection with various tests and in Chapter 4 in connection with the χ^2 test of the fit of a model distribution to an experimental distribution. So let us take a moment to see at least its plausibility. This has to do with the concept of the "degrees of freedom," which has the same meaning here that it has in geometry and in mechanics.

The argument can be stated in terms of the number of "restraints" imposed on the universe or parent distribution. We seek to know the parameter σ of the parent distribution of infinite population of which the n measurements are a sample. The only thing we know about σ, or indeed of the parent distribution at all, is that the experimental measurements *are a sample*. When we insist that the parent distribution have a characteristic, any characteristic, which is determined from the sample, we impose a restraint on the parent distribution. For example, insisting that the parent distribution have a mean value equal to the sample value m imposes *one* restraint, and the price we pay for this restraint is a sacrifice in s as being the best estimate of σ. In other words, the effective number of measurements useful in the determination of the best estimate of σ is reduced from n to (about) $n - 1$, as in Eq. 2-22; one view is that (about) one of the n measurements is used to determine the mean and the remaining $n - 1$ measurements are left to determine the errors or the dispersion. The best estimate of σ is a little greater than the value of s.

In another view, the reason that the best estimate of σ is greater than s is the following. The sum of the squares of the deviations for the universe population is a minimum only if μ, not m, is used as the reference value in calculating each deviation, whereas the sum for the n sample deviations is a minimum only if m, not μ, is the reference value. This argument is equivalent to the one expressed in the previous paragraph.

The restraint mentioned above, viz., that $m = \mu$, is always unavoidably imposed whenever we try to match a parent distribution, either a model distribution or the one believed to exist in real life (even though it may not be fitted by any model). And it is fairly obvious that a second restraint is imposed if and when we insist that the parent parameter σ be given in terms of s. Then, the factor $n - 2$ enters the statistical formulas as well as $n - 1$. We shall discuss situations of this sort in Chapter 3, and we shall see that the χ^2 test of model match in Chapter 4 involves just this type of argument.

An equivalent way of looking at the restraint is in terms of the ideas of simultaneous equations. The solution of a single equation is said to be unrestrained, but when we require the simultaneous solution of an additional equation we impose a restraint; we impose two restraints with three simultaneous independent equations; etc. The attempt to determine σ from the n experimental measurements, as in Eq. 2-23, involves three simultaneous equations

$$\sigma^2 = \lim_{n \to \infty} \frac{\sum\limits_{i=1}^{n} (x_i - \mu)^2}{n}, \qquad \mu = \lim_{n \to \infty} \frac{\sum\limits_{i=1}^{n} x_i}{n}, \qquad m = \frac{\sum\limits_{i=1}^{n} x_i}{n} \qquad (2\text{-}24)$$

two of which are independent and from which we eliminate μ and solve for σ in terms of the known quantities m, n, and the x_i's. This solution can be carried out statistically but it is not an easy one. The feature of the argument is readily seen when it is pointed out that for $n = 1$ we have *no* deviation; for $n = 2$ we have two deviations but they are identical (except for sign) and therefore are not independent, i.e., we have only $2 - 1$ *independent* deviations. We can generalize the argument to say that for n measurements we have $n - 1$ independent deviations; and the proof of this conclusion lies in the fact that any one of the x_i values is given by Eq. 2-1 in terms of the other x_i values and the value of the mean m. The argument for the $n - 1$ factor in the denominator of Eq. 2-23 is a little more involved than just the number of independent deviations because, with the x_i's as only a sample of the parent distribution, it is not possible from Eq. 2-24 to determine either μ or σ exactly.

Another example of the concept of degrees of freedom is found in curve fitting. A curve may be made to go through *all* the points *if* the equation of the curve has as many constants as there are points. With the curve so fitted, no point deviates at all from the curve, and the sum of the squares of the deviations (i.e., the numerator of the expression for σ) is zero. This is also the same as saying that one degree of freedom is lost for each point fitted, and therefore the number of degrees of freedom left for the determination of error (i.e., the divisor) is zero. The standard deviation σ is thus 0/0 and is indeterminate: there is no information concerning dispersion left in the set of points; there is no freedom left.

Finally, the remark may be made that division in Eq. 2-23 by the number of degrees of freedom, instead of by n, insures that we have the property mentioned earlier, viz., that the standard deviations based on small subsets have statistically the same average value as that computed for the parent set.

Variance: binomial model distribution. The mean and the variance of the binomial model distribution are readily written as the respective moments. Using Eq. 1-20 for p_i in Eq. 2-3, we find

$$\mu = \theta_1{}^0 = \sum_{k=0}^{n} k \, \frac{n!}{k!(n-k)!} \, p^k q^{n-k} \tag{2-25}$$

The factor k in the numerator of the summation tells us that the term for $k = 0$ is zero, so the value of the sum is not altered by changing the lower limit from $k = 0$ to $k = 1$. Then, by dividing both numerator and denominator by k, with $k > 0$,

$$\mu = \sum_{k=1}^{n} \frac{n!}{(k-1)!(n-k)!} \, p^k q^{n-k}$$

Next, n and p are factored out, giving

$$\mu = np \sum_{k=1}^{n} \frac{(n-1)!}{(k-1)!(n-k)!} \, p^{k-1} q^{n-k}.$$

Let $\kappa = k - 1$, and $\eta = n - 1$; then

$$\mu = np \sum_{\kappa=0}^{\eta} \frac{\eta!}{\kappa!(\eta-\kappa)!} \, p^\kappa q^{\eta-\kappa}$$

and we see that the summation is $\Sigma B(\kappa; \, \eta, p)$ which, by Eq. 1-22, is unity. Hence,

$$\mu = np \tag{2-26}$$

The variance of the binomial distribution can be written, with the help of Eq. 2-19, as

$$\sigma^2 = \theta_2{}^\mu = \theta_2{}^0 - \mu^2 = \sum_{k=0}^{n} k^2 \frac{n!}{k!(n-k)!} p^k q^{n-k} - \mu^2 \qquad (2\text{-}27)$$

Now we substitute $[k(k-1) + k]$ for k^2, and, making use of Eq. 2-25, write

$$\sigma^2 = \sum_{k=0}^{n} k(k-1) \frac{n!}{k!(n-k)!} p^k q^{n-k} + \mu - \mu^2$$

Because of the $k(k-1)$ factor in the summation, the summation may just as well begin with $k = 2$. Then, if we cancel the factor $k(k-1)$, and factor out $n(n-1)p^2$, we have

$$\sigma^2 = n(n-1)p^2 \sum_{k=2}^{n} \frac{(n-2)!}{(k-2)!(n-k)!} p^{k-2} q^{n-k} + \mu - \mu^2$$

Let $\delta = k - 2$ and $\nu = n - 2$; then

$$\sigma^2 = n(n-1)p^2 \sum_{\delta=0}^{\nu} \frac{\nu!}{\delta!(\nu-\delta)!} p^\delta q^{\nu-\delta} + \mu - \mu^2$$

and, again, the summation $\Sigma B(\delta;\ \nu, p) = 1$, so

$$\sigma^2 = n(n-1)p^2 + \mu - \mu^2$$

Substituting np for μ from Eq. 2-26, we have

$$\sigma^2 = np(1-p) = npq \qquad (2\text{-}28)$$

In the binomial distribution, δ^2 is always less than $np\ (=\mu)$.

The fractional standard deviation, also called the *coefficient of variation*, can be written for the binomial model distribution as

$$\frac{\sigma}{\mu} = \frac{[np(1-p)]^{\frac{1}{2}}}{np} = \left(\frac{1-p}{np}\right)^{\frac{1}{2}} = \left(\frac{1}{\mu} - \frac{1}{n}\right)^{\frac{1}{2}} \qquad (2\text{-}29)$$

which is especially convenient in those cases for which $n \gg \mu$, as in the Poisson approximation.

Since the normal and the Poisson model distributions are special cases of the binomial, Eqs. 2-26, 2-28, and 2-29 also apply to them. Equations 2-26 and 2-28 are derived again in Chapters 4 and 5 specifically for these distributions.

Standard deviation in the mean (standard error) s_m. If we were to record a *second* set of n measurements, the second value of the mean would in general differ from the first value. But the difference between the two means would be expected to be less than the standard deviation in either set. This expectation could be checked, of course, by a large number N of repetitions of the set of measurements and the frequency distribution of the N means analyzed. We would write for the experimental standard deviation in the mean

$$s_m = \left(\frac{\sum_{j=1}^{N} (m_j - \bar{m})^2}{N} \right)^{1/2} \qquad (2\text{-}30)$$

where $\bar{m}$ is the grand mean of the N values. Very few experimenters are willing to record the Nn measurements required in order to obtain the value of s_m from Eq. 2-30.

Fortunately, statistical theory provides a satisfactory formula for s_m from the n measurements of a *single* set. In Chapter 3 we show in simple fashion that

$$s_m = \frac{s}{\sqrt{n}} \qquad (2\text{-}31)$$

In reference to the parent distribution, the formula is of course for σ_m rather than for s_m, viz.

$$\sigma_m = \lim_{N \to \infty} \left(\frac{\sum_{j=1}^{N} (m_j - \mu)^2}{N} \right)^{1/2} \qquad \text{and} \qquad \sigma_m = \frac{\sigma}{\sqrt{n}} \qquad (2\text{-}32)$$

Combining Eq. 2-32 with Eqs. 2-22 and 2-9, we have

$$\sigma_m \approx \frac{s}{\sqrt{n-1}} = \left(\frac{\sum_{i=1}^{n} (x_i - m)^2}{n(n-1)} \right)^{1/2} \qquad (2\text{-}33)$$

Either s_m or σ_m is often called the standard error in (or of) the mean, or, in experimental sciences, simply the *standard error*.* As a measure of the reliability of the mean, it has more direct significance than has the standard deviation because it includes more vigorously the effect of the number of measurements n.

In one theoretical derivation of the expression for σ_m (see Eq. 3-26) the approximation is made that the hypothetical distribution of the N means, with N very large, is almost a normal distribution irrespective of the shape of the particular parent distribution of which the Nn measurements are samples. This approximation is very good even when the parent distribution is *significantly* different from normal, and it improves as the parent distribution comes closer to being normal. One consequence of this

---

* Unfortunately, many investigators use the term "standard error" as synonomous with "standard deviation" without specifying the particular random variable involved. The phrase "standard deviation in the mean" is awkward; and if the ambiguity in "standard error" persists, a new term should be agreed upon or else the qualifying phrases "in the measurements" and/or "in the mean" respectively must be added.

approximation is that the chance that any one sample mean differs from μ by less than $\pm \sigma_m$ is about 0.683 since this numerical value is a characteristic of the normal distribution (see Table 4-5).

The fractional standard deviation in the mean, or the fractional standard error, is

$$\text{fractional } s_m = \frac{s_m}{m} = \frac{s}{m\sqrt{n}}, \qquad \text{fractional } \sigma_m = \frac{\sigma_m}{\mu} = \frac{\sigma}{\mu\sqrt{n}}$$

$$(2\text{-}34)$$

Equations 2-31, 2-33, and 2-34 are formulas that should be in every scientist's working knowledge of statistics.

Skewness. The first and second moments about the origin and about the mean have been discussed above. Moments about the mean are especially useful as dispersion indices. And it was pointed out that the higher the moment about the mean the greater is the relative weighting of the large deviations. None of the dispersion indices discussed so far gives a measure of the asymmetry of the distribution. Now we introduce the dispersion index called the coefficient of skewness, which is defined in terms of the third moment about the mean. This coefficient is

$$\begin{array}{c} \text{skewness} \\ \text{(experimental)} \end{array} \equiv \frac{\sum\limits_{i=1}^{n} (x_i - m)^3}{ns^3} \qquad (2\text{-}35)$$

and

$$\begin{array}{c} \text{skewness} \\ \text{(universe)} \end{array} \equiv \frac{\sum\limits_{i=1}^{n} (x_i - \mu)^3}{n\sigma^3} \qquad (2\text{-}36)$$

(For a continuous universe distribution, the summation in Eq. 2-36 should be replaced by an integral, etc., as in Eq. 2-21.) The factor s^3 or σ^3 in the denominator makes skewness a dimensionless quantity independent of the scale used. The coefficient of skewness of the measurements in Table 2-2 is $+0.05_1$, but the coefficient of skewness of the distribution in Fig. 2-4(e) is about $+21$. Positive skewness means that more than half of the deviations are on the left (negative) side of the mean but that the majority of the *large* deviations are on the right (positive) side.

Because the skewness is so sensitive to large deviations, its numerical value varies initially rather widely as n increases, and a reasonably stable value is not generally realized until n is rather large. This sensitivity restricts its practical use, but when its experimental value can be relied upon it is a very powerful aid in the fitting of a model distribution. This is particularly true since it is so sensitive in the tail regions where the fit is generally most difficult to check, and since it does allow a comparison of asymmetry.

The expression for experimental skewness in terms of the working mean w is

$$\underset{\substack{\text{skewness} \\ \text{(experimental)}}}{} = \frac{\sum_{i=1}^{n} (x_i - w)^3 - n\Delta^3}{ns^3} - \frac{3\Delta}{s} \qquad (2\text{-}37)$$

where w and Δ are defined in Eqs. 2-4 and 2-14.

The binomial model distribution has a third central moment, i.e., about the mean, given by

$$\theta_3{}^\mu = np(1 - p)(1 - 2p) \qquad (2\text{-}38)$$

which can be easily proved by an extension of the argument used in deriving Eq. 2-28. The binomial skewness is

$$\underset{\substack{\text{skewness} \\ \text{(binomial)}}}{} = \frac{\theta_3{}^\mu}{\sigma^3} = \frac{np(1 - p)(1 - 2p)}{[np(1 - p)]^{3/2}} = \frac{(1 - 2p)}{[np(1 - p)]^{1/2}} \qquad (2\text{-}39)$$

$$= \frac{n - 2\mu}{n\sigma} \qquad (2\text{-}40)$$

Equation 2-38 or 2-39 shows that the binomial distribution is symmetrical only in case $p = \frac{1}{2}$, as was mentioned in Chapter 1.

Other dispersion indices. The fourth central moment, divided by s^4, is called the coefficient of *peakedness* or of *kurtosis*, and is written as

$$\underset{\substack{\text{peakedness} \\ \text{(experimental)}}}{} \equiv \frac{\sum_{i=1}^{n} (x_i - m)^4}{ns^4} \qquad (2\text{-}41)$$

and

$$\underset{\substack{\text{peakedness} \\ \text{(universe)}}}{} \equiv \frac{\sum_{i=1}^{n} (x_i - \mu)^4}{n\sigma^4} \qquad (2\text{-}42)$$

(Again, if Eq. 2-42 is to apply to a continuous universe distribution the summation should be replaced by an integral.) The peakedness, like skewness, is dimensionless and is independent of the scale. The fourth moment, even more so than the third, is restricted in its usefulness with actual measurements unless a very large number of trials have been made. If n is not large, the value of the peakedness is numerically unreliable because of its high sensitivity to fluctuations in the tail regions of the distribution.

Combinations of precision indices are sometimes useful. One such combination is

$$3(\text{skewness})^2 - 2(\text{peakedness}) + 6$$

which is zero for a normal distribution, positive for a binomial or a Poisson distribution, and negative for distributions that are extremely peaked.

Additional indices of dispersion can be defined and evaluated but their practical significance is generally not very great. An exception may be the universe standard deviation in the sample standard deviation, viz., σ_s, which, if σ can be approximated by s, is useful as a guide in determining the number of significant figures with which to express the standard deviation s. This index may be written in general form as

$$\sigma_s = \left(\frac{\theta_4{}^\mu - \sigma^4}{4n\sigma^2}\right)^{1/2} \tag{2-43}$$

where $\theta_4{}^\mu$ is the fourth moment about the universe mean. In special cases, Eq. 2-43 simplifies as

$$\sigma_s = \frac{\sigma}{\sqrt{2n}} \qquad \text{for a normal distribution}$$

and $\hspace{10cm}$ (2-44)

$$\sigma_s = \left(\frac{2\sigma^2 + 1}{4n}\right)^{1/2} \quad \text{for a Poisson distribution}$$

where the effect of the particular shape of the distribution can be seen. It is evident that $\theta_4{}^\mu$ for the normal distribution is $3\sigma^4$, and for the Poisson distribution $\theta_4{}^\mu$ is $\sigma^2 + 3\sigma^4$ expressed in σ units.

As an example of the use of Eq. 2-44 for a normal or approximately normal case, suppose that $n = 8$; then $1/\sqrt{2n} = 0.25$, and, therefore, not more than two significant figures should be used in expressing the standard deviation s, and most likely only one.

It has been mentioned that the probable error is a popular precision index in scientific work, and it may be worthwhile to write the expression for the probable error in the probable error, viz.,

$$pe_{pe} = 0.675 \frac{pe}{\sqrt{2n}} = 0.48 \frac{pe}{\sqrt{n}} \tag{2-45}$$

where the numerical coefficient applies for a normal distribution and is generally a little different for any other distribution (e.g., for a Poisson distribution see Table 5-2).

As a final comment, all the central moments are useful when we are dealing with mathematical or theoretical distributions, i.e., with distributions whose shapes can be expressed exactly. For example, this is the case with the distributions (*e*) and (*f*) in Fig. 2-4. However, for some very interesting distributions the central moments do not exist unless the tails of the distributions are arbitrarily cut off; this is the case for the so-called Cauchy distribution, viz.,

$$f(x) = \frac{1}{\pi[1 + (x - \mu)^2]} \tag{2-46}$$

This expression appears in theoretical physics rather frequently, e.g., in classical dispersion in physical optics, in the shapes of atomic spectral lines, etc. In actual experimental work, distributions whose tails drop off as x^2, or less rapidly than x^2 (the square is the limiting rate for which the moments diverge), are not uncommon.

Conclusions. As stated earlier, the information we would really like to have in the description of a set of measurements is the complete mathematical equation for the distribution histogram or frequency curve. But, in real life, with a limited number n of actual measurements, the distribution is at best defined with some finite vagueness. Then, since obtaining the exact mathematical formulation is impractical, we must content ourselves with one or more of the precision indices. Each index has its own advantages and disadvantages in providing the information we want.

The standard deviation, i.e., the square root of the second central moment, is the index in widest use and the one on which most statistical theory is based. The probable error, the evaluation of which first requires evaluation of the standard deviation, is rather widely used among experimental scientists. There are three excellent reasons for the popularity of the standard deviation: (1) it is statistically efficient and experimentally reliable; (2) the rules of operation in the propagation of errors as based on the standard deviation (rules discussed in the next chapter) are conveniently simple; and (3) the moments higher than the second are usually quantitatively unreliable. Occasionally, a measurement situation is encountered in which the larger deviations are suspect for nonstatistical reasons, and then even the second moment overweights the larger deviations and the mean deviation is used as the dispersion index. The mean deviation, however, is statistically less efficient than is the standard deviation.

The general definitions, concepts, and precision indices discussed in the present chapter apply to sets of measurements having *any* type of frequency distribution. We shall continue with the treatment of empirical data for another chapter, introducing a little more advanced statistical theory, before taking up the mathematical models.

2-12. Problems

Note: A numerical answer to a problem is *not* a complete answer; the student must justify the application of the equation(s) he uses by giving an analysis of the problem, pointing out how the problem meets satisfactorily the conditions on which the equation is based.

1. From the measurements of Table 2-1, determine
   (a) the range,   (ans. 31.7 to 32.3 mm)
   (b) the median,   (ans. 31.9 mm)
   (c) the middle 2 quartiles,   (ans. 31.8 to 31.9 mm; 31.9 to 32.0 mm)
   (d) the mode,   (ans. 31.9 mm)
   (e) the arithmetic mean with and without the device of the working mean,
                                                               (ans. 31.92 mm)
   (f) the mean deviation,   (ans. 0.11 mm)
   (g) the fractional mean deviation,   (ans. 0.0036 or 0.36%)
   (h) the standard deviation with and without the device of the working mean,
                                                               (ans. 0.15 mm)
   (i) the fractional standard deviation,   (ans. 0.004_7 or $0.4_7\%$)
   (j) the standard error, and   (ans. 0.045 mm)
   (k) the skewness with the working mean.   (ans. 1.5)
Express each answer with the proper number of significant figures and indicate the proper dimensions.

2. Make the histogram for the following frequency distribution

$$x = \quad 5 \qquad 6 \qquad 7 \qquad 8 \qquad 9 \qquad 10$$
$$f = 133 \quad 55 \quad 23 \quad 7 \quad 2 \quad 0$$

(where x = petals per flower for ranunculus) and determine
   (a) the mean,
   (b) the median,
   (c) the mode,
   (d) the variance,
   (e) the skewness, and
   (f) the standard error.

3. Sketch on the same graph paper the shape of 2 unimodal frequency distributions A and B matched at the peaks and having the same standard deviations $\pm s$ but such that, in each of 4 cases,
   (a) both have about zero skewness and A has a markedly greater peakedness than B,
   (b) both have about the same peakedness and A has positive and B negative skewness,
   (c) A and B are matched in the central region between about $\pm s$ and A has markedly greater skewness but smaller peakedness than B, and
   (d) A and B are matched in the regions beyond about $\pm s$ but have relative values of skewness and of peakedness as in part (c).

4. If you have a standard deviation of 0.05 ft, what is the smallest number of trials necessary for the standard error to be

(a) <0.003 ft,   (b) >0.03 ft,   and   (c) <0.02 ft?

5. The following observations are made with a comparator on the length of an iron bar:

83.284 cm	83.255	83.310	83.304	83.263
83.302	83.273	83.321	83.295	83.270

Find

(a) the length of the bar,   (ans. mean is 83.2877 cm)
(b) the mean deviation,   (ans. 0.0187 cm)
(c) the standard deviation, and   (ans. 0.021 cm)
(d) the standard error.   (ans. 0.0066 cm)

State each answer with the proper number of significant figures.

6. If the scores on a set of examination papers are changed by either (a) adding 10 points to all scores or (b) increasing all scores by 10%, what effects will these changes have on (i) the mean and (ii) the variance?

[ans. (ai) $m' = m + 10$; (aii) $s'^2 = s^2$; (bi) $m' = 1.1m$; (bii) $s'^2 = (1.1)^2 s^2$]

7. What are the second and third moments about (a) the origin and (b) the mean of the binomial distribution $B(k; 10, \frac{1}{4})$?

8. Find (a) the mean deviation and (b) the standard deviation of the distribution of values of x given by $f = \frac{1}{4}\pi \sin \frac{1}{2}\pi x$ from $x = 0$ to $x = 4$.

[ans. (a) $(\pi - 2)/\pi$;   (b) $(\pi^2 - 8)^{\frac{1}{2}}/\pi$]

9. Calculate the mean and the standard deviation in (a) the position and (b) the speed of an object in simple harmonic motion of amplitude A and of frequency f. Sketch the frequency curves.

[ans. (a) mean position is zero; $s = A/\sqrt{2}$;   (b) mean speed $= 4Af$;
$$s = \sqrt{2}\pi Af]$$

10. Derive the expression for skewness in terms of the working mean.

11. For any binomial distribution, derive the expression for (a) the third central moment, and

(b) the skewness.

12. What is meant by

(a) probable knowledge is the most reliable knowledge devised by man,
(b) the experimental mean is not mathematically convergent,
(c) a sample mean,
(d) a random fluctuation,
(e) the least count in a measurement,
(f) the classification interval,
(g) discrepancy is not an error,
(h) precision is not synonomous with accuracy,
(i) significant figure,
(j) parent or universe propulation,
(k) probability is an "open-ended" concept, and
(l) a set of trial measurements is an example of "random mass-phenomena"?

Why do we prefer

(i) the second central moment rather than the fourth central moment in describing experimental dispersion,

(ii) the arithmetic mean rather than the rms mean as the best location value, and

(iii) in some cases the median rather than mean as a location value?

13. Discuss the relative advantages and disadvantages of the mean deviation vs. the standard deviation as a dispersion index in 8 measurements that approximate a normal distribution except that they are

(a) consistently somewhat higher in the tail regions,

(b) inconsistently higher in the tail regions owing to inconstant systematic errors, or

(c) made with a rather high "background" (as in the intensity measurements of a component line in emission spectra or in a nuclear cross-section measurement).

3

Statistics of Measurements
in Functional Relationships:
Maximum Likelihood,
Propagation of Errors,
Consistency Tests,
Curve Fitting, Etc.

The sole purpose of a measurement in an experimental science is to influence a hypothesis.

Science progresses, as stated earlier, by the constant repetition of three steps: (1) conception of some aspect of nature, i.e., a hypothesis, based on all experience available, (2) calculation of the a priori probabilities for certain events based on this hypothesis, and (3) comparison of the a priori probabilities with actual measurements, i.e., with experimental probabilities. The comparison yields either a confirmation of the hypothesis or a rational basis for modifying it.

The intrinsic difficulty with a hypothesis is that it is perforce formulated with only a limited amount of experience, and the intrinsic difficulty with actual measurements is that they are unavoidably veiled in errors. Each particular property of nature that we would define, and each particular quantity of nature that we would measure, are at best only probabilities.

Our task as scientists is to increase the probability that our current hypotheses are correct, i.e., are confirmed by objective experience.

Elementary but fundamental examples of the function of measurements in improving scientific hypotheses were pointed out in Sections 1-4 and 1-5. These examples arose in the discussion of conditional probability and of the reliability of inferred knowledge. In Chapter 1, however, there was no ambiguity as to the outcome of each experiment; the veil of errors enshrouding each measurement was not involved. Let us continue the line of argument begun in Chapter 1 with emphasis now on the measuremental uncertainties.

First, we continue this specific line of argument with very general equations for a page or two, and then in Section 3-1 we introduce the powerful and useful method of maximum likelihood for dealing with the veil of errors. These discussions are intended to give the reader some insight into or feeling for the subject even though upon first reading he may not understand every step in detail. If he has much trouble in these pages he should not be discouraged at this time but should proceed in cursory fashion on to Section 3-2.

Consider first a discrete set of possible hypotheses; in particular, consider two hypotheses A and B. Suppose that $p_{in}(A)$ and $p_{in}(B)$ are the *initial* or a priori probabilities that hypotheses A and B, respectively, are correct. $p_{in}(A) + p_{in}(B) = 1$. Suppose that an experiment is performed and a set of measurements $x_1, x_2, \cdots, x_i, \cdots, x_n$ is obtained. Suppose also that $p_A(x_i)$ is the probability, on the assumption that A is correct, that the particular set of values x_i would be observed, and that $p_B(x_i)$ is the probability, if B is correct, that the set x_i would be observed. Then, as the consequence of the experiment, the a priori probabilities $p_{in}(A)$ and $p_{in}(B)$ that applied before the experiment are now modified; they become

$$p_{mod}(A) = \frac{p_{in}(A)p_A(x_i)}{p_{in}(A)p_A(x_i) + p_{in}(B)p_B(x_i)} \tag{3-1}$$

$$p_{mod}(B) = \frac{p_{in}(B)p_B(x_i)}{p_{in}(A)p_A(x_i) + p_{in}(B)p_B(x_i)} \tag{3-2}$$

These expressions were written in Chapter 1 where the single observation "head" or "n heads in a row" appeared in the case of the penny-toss experiment in place of x_i, and where "the sun rose" or "the sun rose n times in a row" appeared in place of x_i. Insofar as the experiment yielding x_i is well chosen and well performed, our confidence in A (or B) is increased at the expense of our confidence in B (or A), the increase in confidence being proportional to, say, the difference $p_{mod}(A) - p_{in}(A)$. Of course, this value $p_{mod}(A)$ becomes $p_{in}(A)$ for the next experiment to be performed, etc.

It often happens that the possible hypotheses make up a continuous set rather than a discrete set. As mentioned in Chapter 1, Laplace viewed the problem of the sun's rising as involving a continuous set, whereas the argument in analogy to the coin-tossing experiment presumed a discrete set. In the continuous case, the experiments serve to sort the numerical values of each of the p_{mod}'s into a continuous distribution, and presumably this distribution has in it a single maximum which corresponds to the hypothesis deserving our greatest confidence. (This presumption is an article of faith in experimental science.) The maximum becomes increasingly sharp as good additional experiments are performed and interpreted.

Whether the set of possible hypotheses is discrete or continuous, we are confronted in the evaluation of each p_{mod} with the problem of what to do with the *variety* of x_i values yielded by the experiment. The calculation of $p_A(x_i)$ requires that the hypothesis A be expressible in some analytic functional form. Sometimes the hypothesis refers to the functional form itself, and sometimes it involves the property being measured as either a variable or a parameter in the function. In any case, suppose that the functional form is $\phi(A, x_i)$. Then the probability $p_A(x_i)$ that set x_i is observed is equal to the product of the n factors $\phi(A, x_i)$, each factor being a single experimental observation. Thus,

$$p_A(x_i) = \prod_{i=1}^{n} \phi(A, x_i) \qquad (3\text{-}3)$$

where the product $\Pi\phi(A, x_i)$ is written with the assumption that the n trials are all independent (see Eq. 1-5). A similar expression may be written for each of the other possible hypotheses. To compare the reliability of two different hypotheses A and B, we may write the ratio from Eqs. 3-1, 3-2, and 3-3,

$$\frac{p_{mod}(A)}{p_{mod}(B)} = \frac{p_{in}(A) \cdot \Pi\phi(A, x_i)}{p_{in}(B) \cdot \Pi\phi(B, x_i)} \qquad (3\text{-}4)$$

Equation 3-4 is recognized as the "betting odds" and is often called the likelihood ratio, and $\Pi\phi(A, x_i)$ is known as the likelihood function [if $p_A(x_i)$ is a normalized probability as all proper probabilities are]. Numerical evaluation of the likelihood function is straightforward if the functional form of each hypothesis is known. And, as mentioned in Chapter 1, if we have no a priori knowledge favoring A or B, we usually resort to the desperation-in-ignorance guess that $p_{in}(A) = p_{in}(B)$.

3-1. Method of Maximum Likelihood

As an example of the use of the likelihood ratio, Eq. 3-4, suppose that we wish, from n independent trial measurements of x, to find the most likely estimate (or estimator) g of a true parameter γ in a known mathematical functional form $\phi(x; \gamma)$. Assume that there is only one parameter to be determined. We set up some function $g = g(x_1, x_2, \cdots, x_n)$ of the trial values of x from which the estimate g is to be deduced.

There are several methods for setting up such g functions, and each method gives a different degree of goodness of estimate of g. The statisticians rate these methods in terms of their relative efficiencies. As stated in the discussion of the mean deviation in Section 2-11, the relative efficiency is defined as follows. If N sets of samples each of size n are taken from the parent population, N different values of g are obtained. These N values of g themselves form a distribution, and let us say that the standard deviation of this g distribution is noted. This process is repeated for each of the methods for estimating g, and the standard deviation obtained with the respective method is noted. The relative efficiency of two different methods is taken as the inverse ratio of the squares of the standard deviations. Of many possible methods, that method having the smallest standard deviation has its g values clustered most closely together and is said to be the most efficient. Also, with any method, if the mean of the g distribution for a sample size N tends to a value different from γ, the estimate is said to be biased. If the estimate g converges to the true value γ as $N \to \infty$, the estimate is said to be consistent, i.e., free of bias as the sample size increases without limit. (An example of bias is mentioned presently.) For scientific work, it is generally agreed that a good estimate must have zero (or at most small) bias as well as reasonably high efficiency.

For most parametric estimation problems, the method of estimation known as the method of maximum likelihood is the most efficient; and, if n is large, the estimate is usually satisfactorily consistent. The likelihood function, the product of all n values of $\phi(x_i; \gamma)$, is written

$$L(x_1, x_2, \cdots, x_n; \gamma) = \phi(x_1; \gamma)\phi(x_2; \gamma) \cdots \phi(x_n; \gamma) \qquad (3\text{-}5)$$

Especially in the case of a discrete population, certain values of x_i are observed with a frequency f_i which is greater than unity. In this event, the actual frequency f_i appears as an exponent on the factor $\phi(x_i; \gamma)$, and the total number of factors is r with $r < n$.

Consider the general case in which there is a continuum of possible values for g, i.e., a parameter that is a continuous variable. The relative probability of any two different values of g is given by the likelihood ratio, Eq. 3-4, in which the likelihood functions are of the form given in Eq. 3-5 with one value of g in place of γ for the numerator of the likelihood ratio and with the other value of g in place of γ for the denominator. The ratio $p_{in}(A)/p_{in}(B)$, if nothing is otherwise known about it, may be taken as equal to unity as the desperation-in-ignorance guess. We imagine each of N

possible values of g, viz., $g_1, g_2, \cdots, g_j, \cdots, g_N$, inserted in the L function, and each of the N values of L_j computed. These N values of L_j form a distribution which, as $N \to \infty$, can be shown† to approach a normal distribution and whose mean value at the maximum of the distribution corresponds to the desired estimate g.

To find the value of L_j that makes L a maximum, we differentiate L with respect to γ and set the derivative equal to zero. Since L is a maximum when $\log L$ is a maximum, we may use the logarithmic form when it is more convenient to deal with a sum than with a product. Then,

$$\left(\frac{\partial \log L}{\partial \gamma}\right)_{\gamma = g} = 0 = \sum_{i=1}^{n} f_i \frac{\partial}{\partial g} \log \phi(x_i; g) \qquad (3\text{-}6)$$

and we seek a solution of this expression for g. This value for g is the *most likely* estimate of γ (but as we shall see it is not always an unbiased estimate). Solution of Eq. 3-6 is often explicit and easy without multiple roots; in case of multiple roots the most significant root is chosen.

The procedure can be generalized to treat more parameters than one; there is one likelihood equation for each parameter.

The maximum likelihood method‡ is generally considered to be about the best statistical approach to the majority of measuremental problems encountered in experimental science. This method uses *all* of the experimental information in the most direct and efficient fashion possible to give an unambiguous estimate. Its principal disadvantage is that the functional relationship must be known or assumed.

p in the binomial distribution. To make the above example more specific let us consider a set of n measurements that are known to be fitted by a binomial distribution, and let us find the maximum likelihood estimate of the success probability p. Call p^* this estimate of p. Suppose that "success" is observed w times and "failure" $n - w$ times, so that the likelihood function is, from Eq. 1-20,

$$L = \binom{n}{w} p^w (1 - p)^{n-w} \qquad (3\text{-}7)$$

Then,

$$\left(\frac{\partial}{\partial p} \log L\right)_{p = p^*} = 0 = \frac{w}{p^*} - \frac{n - w}{1 - p^*} \qquad (3\text{-}8)$$

---

† See, e.g., H. Cramér, *Mathematical Methods of Statistics* (Princeton University Press, Princeton, 1946).

‡ This method was used in special applications as early as 1880 by Gauss, but was developed for general applications by Fisher in 1912 to 1935. See, e.g., R. A. Fisher, *Statistical Methods for Research Workers* (Oliver and Boyd, Edinburgh, 1950), 11th ed.

and the most likely estimate of the true value of p is

$$p^* = \frac{w}{n} \tag{3-9}$$

which is the experimental probability as defined in Eq. 1-39.

This method also leads to $\sigma = \sqrt{npq}$; see Problem 27 in Section 3-11.

μ and σ in the normal distribution. To illustrate further the method of maximum likelihood, let us estimate the mean μ and the standard deviation σ of a normal distribution from a sample set of size n. Call the estimates m and s respectively. In this case, using Eq. 1-25 with σ in place of $1/h\sqrt{2}$, Eq. 4-8, the likelihood function is

$$L = \prod_{i=1}^{n} \frac{1}{\sigma\sqrt{2\pi}} \exp\left(-\frac{(x_i - \mu)^2}{2\sigma^2}\right) \tag{3-10}$$

Following the procedure of the maximum likelihood method first for μ,

$$\left(\frac{\partial}{\partial\mu} \log L\right)_{\mu=m} = 0 = \sum_{i=1}^{n} \frac{x_i - m}{\sigma^2} \tag{3-11}$$

from which

$$m = \frac{1}{n} \sum_{i=1}^{n} x_i \tag{3-12}$$

which agrees with Eq. 2-1.

To estimate σ,

$$\left(\frac{\partial}{\partial\sigma} \log L\right)_{\sigma=s} = 0 = \sum_{i=1}^{n} \left(-\frac{1}{s} + \frac{(x_i - \mu)^2}{s^3}\right) \tag{3-13}$$

from which

$$s^2 = \frac{1}{n} \sum_{i=1}^{n} (x_i - \mu)^2 \tag{3-14}$$

which, if we replace μ with our best estimate, viz., m, agrees with Eq. 2-9.†

---

† In the method of maximum likelihood, it is not *necessary* to "replace" μ with m; if we retain μ it can be shown that the estimate $s'^2 = \dfrac{1}{n-1} \sum_{i=1}^{n} (x_i - m)^2$, and this estimate is unbiased. See Eq. 3-98 and the attending discussion.

As a fine point, although $s'^2 = \dfrac{1}{n-1} \sum_{i=1}^{n} (x_i - m)^2$ is an unbiased estimate of σ^2, $\sqrt{s'^2} = s'$ is not an unbiased estimate of $\sqrt{\sigma^2} = \sigma$. Rather, the unbiased estimate of σ is given by

$$\sqrt{\tfrac{1}{2}n} \frac{\Gamma[\tfrac{1}{2}(n-1)]}{\Gamma(\tfrac{1}{2}n)} s$$

if the parent distribution is normal. We shall generally ignore this fine point.

In the case of the mean, the estimate m is an unbiased and consistent estimate of μ; this is true for the estimate of the mean of *any* distribution. But in the case of the standard deviation, s is a biased estimate of σ. s has a negative bias because it is always less than σ; it is on the average less by the fraction $\sqrt{(n-1)/n}$ as stated in Eq. 2-22. When the bias is known, as it is in this case, correction for it can be made. However, the estimate s is a consistent estimate since it converges on the true value asymptotically as $n \rightarrow \infty$ (but s does not converge on σ if we take N samples each of small size even though $N \rightarrow \infty$).

μ in the Poisson distribution. Suppose that the variable k is known to have a Poisson distribution, Eq. 1-26, with the mean μ unknown. The estimate of μ, viz., m, can be obtained from the likelihood function

$$L = \prod_{i=1}^{r} \left(\frac{\mu^{k_i} \bar{e}^{\mu}}{k_i!} \right)^{f_i} \tag{3-15}$$

by differentiating with respect to μ and setting the derivative equal to zero,

$$\left(\frac{\partial}{\partial \mu} \log L \right)_{\mu = m} = 0 = \sum_{i=1}^{r} f_i \left(\frac{k_i}{m} - 1 \right) \tag{3-16}$$

and solving for m,

$$m = \frac{1}{n} \sum_{i=1}^{r} k_i f_i = \frac{1}{n} \sum_{i=1}^{n} x_i \tag{3-17}$$

in agreement with Eq. 2-1. Can this be interpreted in any sense to confirm the statement that the mean is statistically the best location value for an asymmetric distribution?

Instrumental parameter. As a final example in this section of the method of maximum likelihood, suppose that t is the time interval between counts in a Geiger counter measurement of the intensity of cosmic rays, and suppose that the frequency function for t is of the form

$$\phi(t, \theta) = \theta e^{-\theta t} \tag{3-18}$$

where θ is some unknown instrumental parameter whose value we wish to determine. Suppose that a sample set of n measurements of t has been made. The maximum likelihood estimate θ_e is given by the procedure of setting up the likelihood function

$$L = \theta^n \exp \left(-\theta \sum_{i=1}^{n} t_i \right) \tag{3-19}$$

and of finding the value of θ, viz., θ_e, that makes L a maximum,

$$\left(\frac{\partial L}{\partial \theta}\right)_{\theta=\theta_e} = 0 = \theta_e^{n-1} e^{-\theta_e \Sigma t_i}(-\theta_e \Sigma t_i + n) \tag{3-20}$$

$$\theta_e = \frac{n}{\Sigma t_i} \tag{3-21}$$

(Incidentally, in this example the estimate θ_e is the reciprocal of the mean of the recorded times.)

Precision in the maximum likelihood estimate. A graph of the likelihood function $L(g)$ vs. g gives *all* the experimental information contained in the set of measurements x_i that is pertinent to the possible values of g. As discussed above, the estimate g^* of the true value γ corresponds in the graph to the maximum value of L; the precision in this estimate depends upon the details of the spread of $L(g)$ about g^*. This precision may be stated as, say, the standard deviation of the $L(g)$ distribution. As $N \to \infty$, the $L(g)$ distribution becomes normal in shape, and the standard deviation is rather easily deduced; but in real life, with N limited and usually rather small, $L(g)$ may be greatly different from normal, and the problem of finding the precision reliably is more complicated. As a first approximation, however, it may be treated as though it were normal.

For an assumed normal $L(g)$ distribution, we may write the spread of $L(g)$ about the best estimate g^* as

$$L(g) \propto e^{-h^2(g-g^*)^2} \tag{3-22}$$

where the standard deviation is

$$\sigma_g = \frac{1}{h\sqrt{2}} \tag{3-23}$$

from Eq. 4-8. Then,

$$\log L = -h^2(g - g^*)^2 + \text{constant}$$

$$\frac{\partial^2}{\partial g^2} \log L = -2h^2 \tag{3-24}$$

Combining Eqs. 3-23 and 3-24, we find the following very convenient expression,

$$\sigma_g = \left(-\frac{1}{\dfrac{\partial^2}{\partial g^2} \log L}\right)^{\frac{1}{2}} \tag{3-25}$$

Standard error σ_m. As an example of the use of Eq. 3-25, we may point out that differentiating the logarithmic form of Eq. 3-10 twice with respect to μ allows us to write immediately the expression for the standard error (standard deviation in the mean) for the normal distribution, viz.,

$$\sigma_m = \left(\frac{1}{\sum_{i=1}^{n} \frac{1}{\sigma^2}}\right)^{\frac{1}{2}} = \frac{\sigma}{\sqrt{n}} \qquad (3\text{-}26)$$

In this example, g refers to a possible value of the mean in a sample set of n measurements from a normal parent population, but it can be shown that Eq. 3-26 is an exact expression even if the parent distribution is not normal.

In many actual problems, $(\partial^2/\partial g^2) \log L$ cannot be determined analytically. In such cases the distribution $L(g)$ can be approximated numerically by trying several different values of g and by using Eq. 3-5 with each successive value of g written in place of γ. These several values of $L(g)$ are then plotted and the general shape of $L(g)$ sketched in. If it is normal, $(\partial^2/\partial g^2) \log L$ is the same everywhere; if it is not normal but is not far different from normal, the average value $(\partial^2/\partial g^2) \log L$ may be used in Eq. 3-25.

The method of maximum likelihood, and its extension to give the precision of the estimate so obtained, is applicable in many statistical problems in which the functional relationship is known. We shall have occasion to use this method in later discussions.

We have in the above discussion referred several times to the normal distribution and to some of its details; we shall continue to do so throughout the present chapter. For a proper background, the reader is well advised to read at least the first part of Chapter 4.

3-2. Propagation of Errors

In Chapter 2, and in most of the specific examples of the method of maximum likelihood of Section 3-1, the statistics of *direct* measurements was considered. But interest in precision in experimental science extends, of course, beyond direct measurements.

The best value (the mean) of each of several direct measurements is very often used in the computation of the value of another property. For example, velocity is derived from the direct measurements of a distance and of a time, a computation involving simple division. (A critical examination of the measurement of a distance or of a time shows *it* to be really a difference between two location points in space or time—the observed "direct" fluctuations include the component fluctuations in each of the two location points.) Examples of derived properties from more complicated relationships—products, quadratics, exponentials, trigonometric functions, etc.—are very easy to find.

In this section, the rules are discussed for the determination of the precision or reliability of the computed "measurement" in terms of the precision of each directly measured property. This is the subject known as the propagation, or compounding, of errors.

Suppose that the derived property u is related to the directly measured properties x and y by the functional relation

$$u = f(x, y), \qquad u_i = f(x_i, y_i), \qquad u_0 = f(\bar{x}, \bar{y}) \qquad (3\text{-}27)$$

where the bar signifies the mean value, and where the function may be additive, multiplicative, exponential or otherwise, or a combination of these. The function is assumed to be regular as regards continuity and derivability.

First, we must decide whether the measurements of x are entirely independent of those of y. In many cases, the answer is obvious. For example, the distance and time measurements for velocity are independent. The measurements of the two sides of a rectangular table for its area, if in each measurement the observer uses a ruler having a wrong calibration and/or makes the same systematic parallax error, are dependent to the extent that both contain the same systematic error. Such measurements and their errors are also said to be partially correlated (i.e., as discussed later, they have a correlation coefficient between 0 and ± 1). In this case, and in most or all actual cases, the independence is only partial—the errors are of both the random and the systematic types. Both types are obviously present, for example, in the measurement of the area of the table when the parallax errors are random but the calibration error is systematic.

In many actual problems, the functional relation involves parameters that are not independent of each other. For example, the relation may involve two or more of the "fundamental constants" (e.g., electronic charge, electronic mass, velocity of light, Avogadro's number, Planck constant, Boltzmann constant, Faraday constant, Rydberg constant, Bohr magneton, fine structure constant, etc.), and the errors in these parameters from previous experiments propagate along with those in x in the present experiment.

Nonindependent errors: systematic errors. A characteristic of a dependent error is that its algebraic sign generally tends to be the same; i.e., systematic errors cause otherwise independent deviations to be partially correlated as stated above. (See Section 2-7.) Dependent errors propagate to yield the error in u according to the relation

$$\Delta u = \frac{\partial u}{\partial x} \Delta x + \frac{\partial u}{\partial y} \Delta y + \cdots \qquad (3\text{-}28)$$

for all the component direct measurements $x, y, \cdots$ that may be involved in u. The symbol Δ in Eq. 3-28, in contrast with δ which is used for supposedly independent or random errors, is intended to indicate that we are now dealing with a clearly recognized systematic type of error.

In practice the dependent errors are not clearly recognized; they are usually inextricably mixed in with the random errors, and both types of errors together make up the observed frequency distribution of x or y or $\cdots$. Sometimes one can make a test for the presence of dependent errors. The test uses the basic expression for correlation (discussed later). This expression, for n measurements of each variable, with the variables taken a pair at a time, say x and y, is

$$\sum_{i=1}^{n} (\delta x_i \, \delta y_i) \approx 0 \qquad (3\text{-}29)$$

where $\delta x_i = x_i - \bar{x}$, $\delta y_i = y_i - \bar{y}$. If the deviations in the sum are independent, each term in the sum is as likely to be positive as negative, and, as $n \to \infty$, the sum is zero. If n is not very large, the sum may be nearly zero, and the deviations δx_i, δy_i may still be independent; the interpretation becomes a statistical one.

Of course, if a systematic error is present in x and/or y, etc., but is not a dependent error, it will cause a shift in the mean $\bar{x}$ or $\bar{y}$ or $\cdots$, and will not be detected by this correlation test. Later, we discuss some tests for the inconsistency of different means by which, in some instances, the presence of those systematic errors that depend on the variable or on time may be detected. Usually, however, small systematic errors can only be suspected, and the magnitude of each component only estimated.

When dealing with systematic errors in general, the assumption that the algebraic signs of all the component errors are the *same* is not statistically justified. This is especially so if the total number of independent components is greater than, say, three. If the number of components is sufficiently large to justify treating the individual systematic errors as having a significant frequency distribution of their own, with a meaningful mean and standard deviation, then these errors may be treated as though they were random. But if this is not the case, we are generally left with no satisfactory procedure for reckoning the propagation of systematic errors.

Strenuous efforts should be made to recognize and to eliminate any large systematic error. Residual systematic errors are perforce indistinguishable from the random errors, but, if their net effect can be estimated in the mean value, this estimate should be stated as well as, say, the observed standard deviation.

Random errors. Suppose that all errors are independent and may be treated as random. In the general case, in using Eq. 3-27, we have n' trial values of x and n'' trial values of y. It is most likely that $n' \neq n''$ and that u_i is not computed from an associated pair of x_i and y_i. So we imagine an *equivalent* set of n values of x and n values of y such that each of the n values of u is computed from a corresponding imagined pair x_i, y_i. The pairing may be done at random. The imagined x_i or y_i is equivalent to the actual measured values of x_i or y_i if the frequency distribution of the imagined set is the same as of the actual set. With this equivalence, we choose n, the number of "trial" values of u, as large as we please. The argument is easily extended to include more than two independent variables.

Next we assume that all the deviations $\delta x_i = x_i - \bar{x}$ and $\delta y_i = y_i - \bar{y}$ are relatively small. Then, we define the deviation δu_i as

$$\delta u_i = u_i - \bar{u} \approx \frac{\partial u}{\partial x}\,\delta x_i + \frac{\partial u}{\partial y}\,\delta y_i \tag{3-30}$$

which follows from the definition of the partial differential when written for small increments. Or, better, Eq. 3-30 may be obtained from the Taylor expansion from elementary calculus; thus

$$u_i = f([\bar{x} + \delta x_i], [\bar{y} + \delta y_i])$$
$$= f(\bar{x}, \bar{y}) + \frac{\partial u}{\partial x}\,\delta x_i + \frac{\partial u}{\partial y}\,\delta y_i$$

and

$$\delta u_i = u_i - \bar{u} = \frac{\partial u}{\partial x}\,\delta x_i + \frac{\partial u}{\partial y}\,\delta y_i \tag{3-31}$$

which, if the higher order terms are neglected, is the same as Eq. 3-30. Note that we have here taken $\bar{u}$ as $f(\bar{x}, \bar{y})$ rather than as $\bar{u} = \left(\sum_{i=1}^{n} u_i\right)/n$, but these two definitions of $\bar{u}$ are essentially the same *if* all deviations are small.* Note that the partial derivatives are taken at $x = \bar{x}, y = \bar{y}$, hence are constants.

---

* For example, suppose $u(x) = x^2$. It is not true in general that $\overline{x^2} = \bar{x}^2$. However, we can show that this relation is true in the limit as $\delta x_i \to 0$. We write

$$x_i^2 = (\bar{x} + \delta x_i)^2 = \bar{x}^2 + 2\bar{x}\,\delta x_i + \delta x_i^2$$

Then, by definition of the mean square,

$$\overline{x^2} = \frac{1}{n}\sum_{i=1}^{n} x_i^2 = \frac{1}{n}\sum_{i=1}^{n}(\bar{x}^2 + 2\bar{x}\,\delta x_i)$$

neglecting the δx_i^2 term. But it follows from the definition of the mean that

$$\frac{1}{n}\sum_{i=1}^{n}\delta x_i = 0$$

Hence

$$\overline{x^2} = \bar{x}^2$$

as $\delta x_i \to 0$.

Equation 3-30 or 3-31 indicates the procedure by which individual deviations propagate to give an individual deviation in u. We learn from these equations that the effect in u of a deviation in x (or in y, etc.) is multiplied by $\partial u/\partial x$ (or by $\partial u/\partial y$, etc.), hence that, if x (or y, etc.) appears in u with an exponent much greater than unity, the effect may be rather large. In planning an experiment and apportioning relative effort in the measurement of each of the various component quantities, it behooves us to note the exponents on the respective variables.

As an example, consider the relation for the acceleration due to gravity in terms of the length l and the period P of a simple pendulum, viz.,

$$g = 4\pi^2 \frac{l}{P^2}$$

for which

$$\delta g_i = \frac{\partial g}{\partial l}\,\delta l_i + \frac{\partial g}{\partial P}\,\delta P_i = \frac{4\pi^2}{P^2}\,\delta l_i - \frac{8\pi^2 l}{P^3}\,\delta P_i$$

The fractional effect due to the component fractional deviations is

$$\frac{\delta g_i}{\bar{g}} = \frac{\delta l_i}{\bar{l}} - 2\,\frac{\delta P_i}{\bar{P}}$$

where we write $\bar{l}$ for l and $\bar{P}$ for P since the differentiation is carried out at these values. Note the factor -2 in the last term.

We are generally more interested in the rules of propagation of errors when each error is expressed as a mean deviation, as a standard deviation, or as a probable error. Equation 3-31 is not useful in this case because these errors do not have meaningful algebraic signs.

Mean (and fractional mean) deviation. The equations that govern the propagation of mean deviations and fractional mean deviations are

$$\overline{|u_i - \bar{u}|} = \bar{z}_u = \left[\left(\frac{\partial u}{\partial x}\right)^2 \bar{z}_x^2 + \left(\frac{\partial u}{\partial y}\right)^2 \bar{z}_y^2 + \cdots \right]^{1/2} = \left[\sum_{j=1}^{J} \left(\frac{\partial u}{\partial x_j}\right)^2 \bar{z}_{x_j}^2 \right]^{1/2} \quad (3\text{-}32)$$

for J independent variables, and

$$\text{fractional } \overline{|u_i - \bar{u}|} = \text{fractional } \bar{z}_u = \left[\sum_{j=1}^{J} \left(\frac{\partial u}{\partial x_j}\right)^2 \frac{\bar{z}_{x_j}^2}{\bar{x}_j^2} \right]^{1/2} \quad (3\text{-}33)$$

Equation 3-33 usually simplifies to a very convenient expression because of cancellation. The basic relation, the square root of the sum of the squares, is derived presently for the case of propagation of standard deviations, and this relation applies for mean deviations to the extent that the x, y, $\cdots$, and u frequency distributions are all of essentially the same type. In this event, the simple numerical constant relating the mean deviation and the standard deviation cancels out. This numerical constant depends, of course, on the particular shape of the distribution; it is about 0.80 for a normal distribution, i.e., $\bar{z} \approx 0.80s$.

As was pointed out in Chapter 2, the mean deviation is not as statistically efficient as is the standard deviation. The standard deviation, however, as mentioned in Chapter 2, may give too much weight to large deviations in some measurement situations, and also entails a little more computational labor. On the basis of statistical arguments alone, the standard deviation is preferable.

Standard (and fractional standard) deviation. By definition, the square of the standard deviation in u, written s_u, is

$$s_u^{\ 2} = \frac{\sum\limits_{i=1}^{n}(\delta u_i)^2}{n} \tag{3-34}$$

Squaring the binomial in Eq. 3-30 gives

$$(\delta u_i)^2 = \left(\frac{\partial u}{\partial x}\right)^2(\delta x_i)^2 + 2\frac{\partial u}{\partial x}\frac{\partial u}{\partial y}\,\delta x_i\,\delta y_i + \left(\frac{\partial u}{\partial y}\right)^2(\delta y_i)^2$$

Then, placing this expression in Eq. 3-34, we have

$$s_u^{\ 2} = \frac{\left(\dfrac{\partial u}{\partial x}\right)^2\Sigma(\delta x_i)^2 + 2\dfrac{\partial u}{\partial x}\dfrac{\partial u}{\partial y}\Sigma(\delta x_i\,\delta y_i) + \left(\dfrac{\partial u}{\partial y}\right)^2\Sigma(\delta y_i)^2}{n} \tag{3-35}$$

As n increases, the sum $\Sigma(\delta x_i\,\delta y_i)$ goes to zero if x_i and y_i are completely independent (uncorrelated) because any particular product $\delta x_i\,\delta y_i$ is as likely to be positive as negative. Then, since

$$s_x^{\ 2} = \frac{\Sigma(\delta x_i)^2}{n} \qquad \text{and} \qquad s_y^{\ 2} = \frac{\Sigma(\delta y_i)^2}{n}$$

it follows that

$$s_u = \left[\left(\frac{\partial u}{\partial x}\right)^2 s_x^{\ 2} + \left(\frac{\partial u}{\partial y}\right)^2 s_y^{\ 2}\right]^{1/2} \tag{3-36}$$

Note that n does not appear in Eq. 3-36 and, as may be expected, s_u does not depend upon either the actual or the imaginary number of x's or the actual or the imaginary number of y's.

Generalization of the derivation of Eq. 3-36 to cases where more than two variables are involved is obvious. The general expression for J independent variables may be written

$$s_u = \left[\sum_{j=1}^{J}\left(\frac{\partial u}{\partial x_j}\right)^2 s_{x_j}^{\ 2}\right]^{1/2} \tag{3-37}$$

It also follows from Eq. 3-37 and from arguments leading to Eq. 3-45 that the standard deviation in the mean $\bar{u}$, or the standard error, is

$$s_{\bar{u}} = \left[\sum_{j=1}^{J} \left(\frac{\partial u}{\partial x_j} \right)^2 s_{\bar{x}_j}^2 \right]^{1/2} \tag{3-38}$$

where $s_{\bar{x}_j}$ is the standard deviation in the mean value of the jth component property.

The fractional standard deviations in u, and then in $\bar{u}$, are written as

$$\text{fractional } s_u = \frac{s_u}{\bar{u}} = \frac{\left[\sum_{j=1}^{J} \left(\frac{\partial u}{\partial x_j} \right)^2 s_{x_j}^2 \right]^{1/2}}{\bar{u}} \tag{3-39}$$

$$\text{fractional } s_{\bar{u}} = \frac{s_{\bar{u}}}{\bar{u}} = \frac{\left[\sum_{j=1}^{J} \left(\frac{\partial u}{\partial x_j} \right)^2 s_{\bar{x}_j}^2 \right]^{1/2}}{\bar{u}} \tag{3-40}$$

and are usually expressed in per cent. As with the fractional mean deviation, Eq. 3-39 or 3-40 should not be used unless the zero of each of the x_j and the u scales is physically significant. Equations 3-39 and 3-40 generally simplify to very convenient expressions.

Equations 3-36 through 3-40 are the really fundamental equations in the subject of propagation of errors and are well worth memorizing.

It was mentioned in Chapter 2 that scientists frequently use the "probable error," pe, as a precision index. For any given distribution, the probable error, discussed in detail in Chapters 4 and 5, is linearly proportional to the standard deviation. For a normal or near-normal distribution, $pe \approx 0.675s$; for any other distribution the constant of proportionality is different. But irrespective of the numerical value of the constant, it follows that

$$pe_u = \left[\sum_{j=1}^{J} \left(\frac{\partial u}{\partial x_j} \right)^2 pe_{x_j}^2 \right]^{1/2} ; \quad pe_{\bar{u}} = \left[\sum_{j=1}^{J} \left(\frac{\partial u}{\partial x_j} \right)^2 pe_{\bar{x}_j}^2 \right]^{1/2} \tag{3-41}$$

and

$$\text{fractional } pe_u = \frac{\left[\sum_{j=1}^{J} \left(\frac{\partial u}{\partial x_j} \right)^2 pe_{x_j}^2 \right]^{1/2}}{\bar{u}} ;$$

$$\text{fractional } pe_{\bar{u}} = \frac{\left[\sum_{j=1}^{J} \left(\frac{\partial u}{\partial x_j} \right)^2 pe_{\bar{x}_j}^2 \right]^{1/2}}{\bar{u}} \tag{3-42}$$

if all the u and the x_j distributions are of the same type so that the constant of proportionality cancels out.

Sum or difference. Referring to Eq. 3-27, let

$$u = x \pm y \pm \cdots$$

then

$$\frac{\partial u}{\partial x} = 1, \qquad \frac{\partial u}{\partial y} = \pm 1, \text{ etc.}$$

and, by Eq. 3-37,

$$s_u = \sqrt{s_x^2 + s_y^2 + \cdots} \tag{3-43}$$

and, if the proportionality constant between s and pe cancels out,

$$pe_u = \sqrt{pe_x^2 + pe_y^2 + \cdots} \tag{3-44}$$

Note that the standard deviation (or the probable error) of the sum is *less* than the sum of the standard deviations (or probable errors) of the components; it is the square root of the sum of the squares.

A very important example of the compounding of errors in a sum is the following one. We wish to determine the reliability of the mean value m which is defined by Eq. 2-1 from n trial measurements of x. It readily follows from the definition of the mean that

$$\frac{\partial m}{\partial x_1} = \frac{\partial m}{\partial x_2} = \frac{\partial m}{\partial x_3} = \cdots = \frac{1}{n}$$

The standard deviation of a single measurement x_i is s_{x_i}. Then by the use of Eq. 3-37, the standard deviation in the mean, i.e., the standard error, is

$$s_m = \left[\sum_{i=1}^{n} \left(\frac{\partial \bar{x}}{\partial x_i} \right)^2 z_i^2 \right]^{1/2} = \left[\frac{1}{n^2} \sum_{i=1}^{n} z_i^2 \right]^{1/2}$$

$$s_m = \frac{s}{\sqrt{n}} \tag{3-45}$$

and this has already appeared as Eq. 2-31. Also, if the proportionality constant cancels out,

$$pe_m = \frac{pe}{\sqrt{n}} \tag{3-46}$$

Equation 3-45 applies, of course, to any one of the independent x_j measurements in Eq. 3-37. Hence, we can immediately write Eqs. 3-38 and 3-39.

Product or quotient: factors raised to various powers. Let

$$u = x^a y^b \tag{3-47}$$

where a and b are assumed to be exact constants. Then,

$$\frac{\partial u}{\partial x} = ax^{a-1}y^b, \qquad \frac{\partial u}{\partial y} = bx^a y^{b-1}$$

and, by Eq. 3-37,

$$s_u = \sqrt{a^2 x^{2(a-1)} y^{2b} s_x^{\,2} + b^2 x^{2a} y^{2(b-1)} s_y^{\,2}} \qquad (3\text{-}48)$$

Because the partial differentiation in the Taylor expansion is carried out at the values $\bar{x}$ and $\bar{y}$, the values of x and y in this expression are taken as the mean values $\bar{x}$ and $\bar{y}$. Likewise, the probable error may be written with pe_u for s_u, pe_x for s_x, pe_y for s_y, and also the standard error $s_{\bar{u}}$ and the probable error in the mean $pe_{\bar{u}}$ may be written with the appropriate changes in notation, assuming, of course, that when pe is used the proportionality constant cancels out.

The expression for the fractional standard deviation (or fractional probable error) is especially convenient,

$$\text{fractional } s_u = \left(\frac{a^2 s_x^{\,2}}{\bar{x}^2} + \frac{b^2 s_y^{\,2}}{\bar{y}^2} \right)^{\!\! \frac{1}{2}} ;$$

$$\text{fractional } s_{\bar{u}} = \left(\frac{a^2 s_{\bar{x}}^{\,2}}{\bar{x}^2} + \frac{b^2 s_{\bar{y}}^{\,2}}{\bar{y}^2} \right)^{\!\! \frac{1}{2}} \qquad (3\text{-}49)$$

and

$$\text{fractional } pe_u = \left(\frac{a^2 pe_x^{\,2}}{\bar{x}^2} + \frac{b^2 pe_y^{\,2}}{\bar{y}^2} \right)^{\!\! \frac{1}{2}} ;$$

$$\text{fractional } pe_{\bar{u}} = \left(\frac{a^2 pe_{\bar{x}}^{\,2}}{\bar{x}^2} + \frac{b^2 pe_{\bar{y}}^{\,2}}{\bar{y}^2} \right)^{\!\! \frac{1}{2}} \qquad (3\text{-}50)$$

if, in the formulas involving pe, all the frequency distributions are of the same type. It is obvious, since a and b are squared in Eqs. 3-49 and 3-50, that the sign of a or b in Eq. 3-47 may be either positive or negative and Eqs. 3-49 and 3-50 are unaltered. Thus we have treated the case of either a product or a quotient.

As a special case of Eq. 3-47, consider

$$u = A x^a \qquad (3\text{-}51)$$

where A is a constant. With Eq. 3-48, we write

$$s_u = \sqrt{A^2 a^2 x^{2(a-1)} s_x^{\,2}} = A a x^{a-1} s_x ; \qquad \text{fractional } s_u = \frac{a s_x}{\bar{x}} \qquad (3\text{-}52)$$

Note that we have assumed that the errors in all the components are independent. We must be careful that this assumption is satisfied. A case in which it is not satisfied is the following one. Let $u = x_1 + x_2$, where $x_1 = x_2$. From Eq. 3-43 we obtain $s_u = \sqrt{2} s_x$. But from Eq. 3-52, with $A = 2$ and $a = 1$, we find $s_u = 2 s_x$, which is different from the previous value by the factor $\sqrt{2}$. The latter calculation is the correct one; the former improperly presumes δx_1 to be independent of δx_2, whereas in fact they are the same quantity. Inclusion of the correlation term in Eq. 3-35 corrects for the dependence and brings the results into agreement.

Other functions. If the functional relation is that of a logarithm,

$$u = B \ln x \qquad (3\text{-}53)$$

we write $\partial u / \partial x = B/x$; then, with Eq. 3-37, the standard deviation in u is

$$s_u = \left(\frac{B^2}{x^2} s_x^{\,2}\right)^{\!\frac{1}{2}} = \frac{Bs_x}{\bar{x}} \;; \qquad \text{fractional } s_u = \frac{Bs_x}{\bar{x}\bar{u}} \qquad (3\text{-}54)$$

As another example, consider a trigonometric relation,

$$u = A \sin x \qquad (3\text{-}55)$$

where x is not near $\pi/2$. It is important to realize that for *any* function whose first derivative in the region of interest is very small, the higher terms in the Taylor expansion cannot be neglected. In the present trigonometric example,

$$s_u = As_x \cos \bar{x}; \qquad \text{fractional } s_u = s_x \cot \bar{x} \qquad (3\text{-}56)$$

In expressing s_x, note that the units should be radians, not degrees, since the trigonometric functions and the derivatives are in radians.

3-3. Different Means

It often happens that in a series of direct measurements the individual values are not all equally good. Some values should be given more weight than others in the determination of the mean; otherwise the mean is not the "best" value. And often we are interested in comparing two different means for consistency.

Weighted mean. If measurement x_i is assigned a weight w_i, the weighted mean m^w is written as

$$m^w = \frac{w_1 x_1 + w_2 x_2 + \cdots + w_i x_i + \cdots + w_n x_n}{w_1 + w_2 + \cdots + w_i + \cdots + w_n} = \frac{\displaystyle\sum_{i=1}^{n} w_i x_i}{\displaystyle\sum_{i=1}^{n} w_i} \qquad (3\text{-}57)$$

With the standard deviation s_i of each measurement x_i known, the weight w_i is properly expressed in terms of s_i; w_i is replaced by $1/s_i^{\,2}$, a relation shown presently to follow from the principle of least squares (if all the errors are small). Or, if the grand weighted mean of N different means is desired, we may write the weight of the ith mean as $1/s_{\bar{x}_i}^{\,2}$. Then,

$$\text{weighted grand mean} = \bar{\bar{x}}^w = \frac{\displaystyle\sum_{i=1}^{N} \bar{x}_i / s_{\bar{x}_i}^{\,2}}{\displaystyle\sum_{i=1}^{N} 1 / s_{\bar{x}_i}^{\,2}} \qquad (3\text{-}58)$$

To show that w_i should be replaced by $1/s_i^2$ according to the principle of least squares (if all the errors are small), consider for simplicity only two values of x_i. Then,

$$m^w = \frac{w_1 x_1 + w_2 x_2}{w_1 + w_2} = \frac{x_1 + w x_2}{1 + w}$$

where $w = w_2/w_1$. Write $u = m^w$ and, with Eq. 3-37,

$$s_{m^w} = \left(\frac{s_1^2 + w^2 s_2^2}{(1 + w)^2}\right)^{1/2}$$

We proceed to solve for the particular value of w, call it $w_{\min}$, for which $\partial s_{m^w}/\partial w = 0$; we find

$$w_{\min} = \frac{s_1^2}{s_2^2}$$

This argument is easily generalized to show that each of many weights w_i is inversely proportional to s_i^2, i.e.,

$$w_1 s_1^2 = w_2 s_2^2 = w_3 s_3^2 = \cdots, \qquad w_i \propto \frac{1}{s_i^2} \tag{3-59}$$

The value of $(pe_i)^2$ can alternatively be used in place of s_i^2.

One immediate consequence of Eq. 3-57 or Eq. 3-58, whether for the weighted mean of a simple set of n measurements or for the weighted grand mean of different component means, is that, if one or more of the standard deviations is much smaller than the others, the less precise values of x_i or of $\bar{x}_i$ can be neglected. This is a feature of great interest in designing experiments in which several different direct measurements are involved to yield a computed result. (This does not say, however, that large deviations, $x_i - \bar{x}$, can be neglected; see Section 4-6.)

Note that Eq. 3-59 followed from placing $\partial s_{m^w}/\partial w$ equal to zero and solving for w; this is equivalent to finding the value of w_i for which the sum

$$\frac{1}{n} \sum_{i=1}^{n} w_i (x_i - m^w)^2$$

is a minimum. Thus, the weighting $1/s_i^2$ is based on the principle of weighted least squares. Strictly speaking, we should point out that this principle is valid only if the frequency distribution in question is normal or if all the deviations are sufficiently small that the higher powers in the Taylor expansion are negligible.

It is instructive to apply the method of maximum likelihood to the case of the normal distribution. The likelihood function is written as in Eq.

3-10 except that now the standard deviation is considered as being possibly different for each measurement x_i. Thus,

$$L = \sum_{i=1}^{n} \frac{1}{\sigma_i \sqrt{2\pi}} \exp \left(- \frac{(x_i - \mu)^2}{2\sigma_i^2} \right)$$

and

$$\left(\frac{\partial}{\partial \mu} \log L \right)_{\mu = m^w} = 0 = \sum_{i=1}^{n} \frac{x_i - m^w}{\sigma_i^2}$$

from which

$$m^w = \frac{\sum_{i=1}^{n} x_i / \sigma_i^2}{\sum_{i=1}^{n} 1 / \sigma_i^2} \tag{3-60}$$

Comparison of Eq. 3-60 with Eq. 3-57 shows that for the normal case the weight $w_i \propto 1/\sigma_i^2$.

Equation 3-45 may now be derived directly from an argument of weighting. The reliability (in terms of the standard deviation) with n measurements, each of unit weight, is the same as the reliability of one measurement (the mean) having weight n. Thus,

$$s^2 = n s_m^2 \quad \text{or} \quad s_m = \frac{s}{\sqrt{n}}$$

This derivation is really equivalent to the one leading to Eq. 3-45 in which the condition was made that all deviations must be small.

Weighted dispersion indices. It is more or less obvious that $w_i/(\Sigma w_i)$ is equivalent to the relative frequency, f_i/n, in the expression for the mean, Eq. 2-2. Also, with this change in notation, the weighted standard deviation is written

$$s_x^w = \left(\frac{\Sigma w_i (x_i - m^w)^2}{\Sigma w_i} \right)^{1/2} = \left(\frac{\Sigma w_i (x_i - m^w)^2}{n} \right)^{1/2} \tag{3-61}$$

if the weights are so chosen that $\Sigma w_i = n$.

The weighted probable error pe^w is given by the product of the appropriate constant times s_x^w, the appropriate constant being 0.675 in the case of a normal distribution, as stated earlier.

Note that by allowing different weights to be assigned to individual measurements x_i, we distort the condition of random trials, and if a weighted location index or precision index is used it should be stated as such. However, different *means* may be weighted with impunity.

Consistency of two means: the t test. One important test for the existence of a systematic error in a mean value is afforded by comparison with another mean value determined on a different day, or by a different observer, or with modified or different apparatus. This comparison is an involved statistical problem because each mean, even in the absence of systematic errors, is only a sample of the infinite parent population of possible means. The two samples are expected to disagree to a certain extent simply because they are merely samples; and the problem is to decide whether or not the observed disagreement is "reasonable" on the basis of random sampling.

Several criteria for consistency have been proposed. The simplest is that two means may be considered consistent (no "evidence" for a significant systematic error in either mean) if they agree within about the sum of their standard deviations. The criterion for "agreement" is entirely arbitrary; some conservative investigators take twice the sum of the standard deviations.

A better criterion for consistency is that the two means are consistent if the difference between them, $\bar{x}_1 - \bar{x}_2$, is less than the standard deviation in the difference. This standard deviation is given with the aid of Eq. 3-43 as

$$s_{(\bar{x}_1 - \bar{x}_2)} = \sqrt{s_{\bar{x}_1}{}^2 + s_{\bar{x}_2}{}^2} \qquad (3\text{-}62)$$

In case the two means have equal precision, $s_{(\bar{x}_1 - \bar{x}_2)} = \sqrt{2}s_{\bar{x}}$. (This test is further developed in Section 5-8 as a quantitative test to determine whether or not a measured signal is "really" above the background noise.)

An even better criterion for consistency is the following one. Assume that the two sets of measurements, n_1 of x_1 and n_2 of x_2, are consistent and are pooled. Then, the best estimate of the standard deviation of the parent population, of which the $n_1 + n_2$ measurements are a compound random sample, is

$$\sigma_{(x_1 + x_2)} = \left(\frac{\Sigma x_i{}^2 - (\Sigma x_i)^2/n_1 + \Sigma y_i{}^2 - (\Sigma y_i)^2/n_2}{(n_1 - 1) + (n_2 - 1)} \right)^{1/2} \qquad (3\text{-}63)$$

where $n_1 + n_2 - 2$ is the number of degrees of freedom. As a working parameter in this test, which is called the t test, we write

$$t \equiv \frac{\bar{x}_1 - \bar{x}_2}{\sigma_{(x_1 + x_2)}} \left(\frac{n_1 n_2}{n_1 + n_2} \right)^{1/2} \qquad (3\text{-}64)$$

In the special case for which $n_1 = n_2$, Eq. 3-64 becomes

$$t_{n_1 = n_2} = \frac{\bar{x}_1 - \bar{x}_2}{\sigma_{(x_1 + x_2)}} \sqrt{\tfrac{1}{2}n}$$

On our assumption that the sets x_1 and x_2 are consistent, the value of t, as different pairs of sample sets are considered, is expected to fluctuate for the reason that they are *sample* sets each of finite size. If an infinite

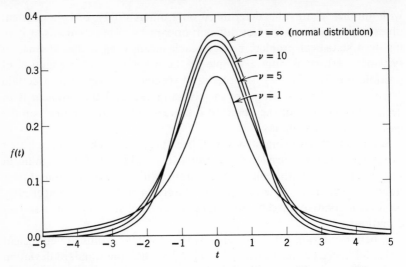

Fig. 3-1. t distribution curves for different numbers of degrees of freedom ν. For $\nu = \infty$ the distribution is normal.

number of pairs of sample sets are imagined, the corresponding values of t constitute a t distribution. This distribution can be expressed in rather simple analytic form (not easily derived, however) if the x_i and y_i are from a normal parent distribution, viz., as

$$f(t) = c\left(1 + \frac{t^2}{\nu}\right)^{-[\frac{1}{2}(\nu+1)]} \tag{3-65}$$

where c is a constant chosen to make the integral of $f(t)$ equal unity, and ν is the number of degrees of freedom. This t distribution, illustrated in Fig. 3-1, is symmetrical in shape about the mean $t = 0$ and, for $\nu < \infty$, is relatively higher in the tails than is the normal distribution. Knowing the analytic form of the t distribution, we can calculate the probability that the value of t of the next sample pair of sets will fall outside a specified range, e.g., outside a range set by the values $\pm t_c$ in Fig. 3-1. This calculation is made by integrating Eq. 3-65 over the set range. The specification of $\pm t_c$ to bound this range is arbitrary. Commonly, t_c is chosen so that the calculated probability is 0.05, i.e., that out of 100 sample values of t only 5 on the average will fall outside the bounds of $\pm t_c$. Note that the calculated probability is based on the assumption that $\bar{x}_1$ and $\bar{x}_2$ *are* consistent. If it turns out that the magnitude of the experimental value of t as deduced from Eq. 3-64 is larger than the magnitude of t_c, this fact does not *prove* that the two means are inconsistent but it argues rather strongly in favor of a suspicion that they are inconsistent. The argument is even stronger if t_c is set at any limit less than the 5% limit, e.g., the 1% limit. Inconsistency would be caused by the presence of any significant systematic error affecting the observed deviations differently in one set of measurements than in the other set.

Values of t that are exceeded only 1 (or 5) in 100 times on the average, if no significant nonconstant systematic errors are present, are listed in Table 3-1 for several different numbers of degrees of freedom $n_1 + n_2 - 2$.

Table 3-1. Values of t_c in the t Test, 1% and 5% Limits

$n_1 + n_2 - 2$	2	4	6	8	10	12	20	30	∞
t_c (1% limit)	9.92	4.60	3.71	3.36	3.17	3.06	2.85	2.75	2.58
t_c (5% limit)	4.30	2.78	2.45	2.31	2.23	2.18	2.09	2.04	1.96

The general principles of the t test as described above are applicable to many types of consistency problems in statistics with but rather minor changes in the terminology.*

In a third test for consistency, each mean $\bar{x}_i$ is assigned the weight $w_i = 1/s_{\bar{x}_i}^2$, and the grand mean of the N means is calculated by Eq. 3-58. The standard deviation in the weighted grand mean is, by Eq. 3-61 appropriately modified,

$$
s_{\bar{\bar{x}}} = \left(\frac{\sum\limits_{i=1}^{N} w_i (\bar{x}_i - \bar{\bar{x}})^2}{\sum\limits_{i=1}^{N} w_i} \right) \tag{3-66}
$$

Then the value $s_{\bar{x}_i}$ for each mean is compared with the value of $s_{\bar{\bar{x}}}$. The interpretation of this comparison is placed on a quantitative basis with the assumption that the ratios $s_{\bar{\bar{x}}}/s_{\bar{x}_i}$ are normally distributed with a "width" (standard deviation) equal to $\sqrt{N/2}$. Again, by a method detailed in Chapter 4, the particular ratio $(s_{\bar{\bar{x}}}/s_{\bar{x}_i})_p$ is computed such that the probability that it or a larger value will occur is less than, say, 0.01. If the observed ratio does not exceed $(s_{\bar{\bar{x}}}/s_{\bar{x}_i})_p$, the ith mean is said to be consistent with the grand mean.† The procedural details in the calculation for normal probability, an integration of Eq. 1-25 with the particular limits, are discussed in detail in Chapter 4.

Comparison of precisions in two sets of measurements: the F test. Often we have two or more sets of measurements of a given property, and

---

* The t distribution was introduced in 1908 by W. S. Gosset, who wrote under the pseudonym of "Student," and the arguments were completed by R. A. Fisher in 1925.

† This test was proposed by R. T. Birge, *Phys. Rev.*, **40**, 213 (1932).

we would like to pool them so as to increase the total number of measurements and thereby increase the reliability of the mean according to Eq. 3-45. The pooling of such sets of measurements requires that the sets be consistent not only in regard to their means but also in regard to their standard deviations. Or, we may wish to test the internal consistency of the precision of two sets of measurements (rather than of merely the means) recorded on different days, with different apparatus, or by different observers. Again, the standard deviations of the various sets or samples are expected to differ *somewhat* among themselves, even if they are consistent, because of the fact that they are merely samples. We seek a test, probabilistic of course, for consistency of standard deviations.

In the *t* test for consistency of two different means, as just described, the assumption is made that both sample sets of measurements are from the same population (from a normal population if Eq. 3-65 is used). Then the probability of the validity of this assumption is tested. We shall make this assumption again, but this time use the so-called *F* ratio as the working parameter which is defined in terms of the standard deviations of the two sets. (The *t* parameter was defined in terms of the difference in the means.)

Suppose that s_{x_1} and s_{x_2} are the respective sample standard deviations in the n_1 measurements of x_1 and in the n_2 measurements of x_2. Then, σ_{x_1} and σ_{x_2} are the best estimates of the standard deviations of the parent populations. The *F* ratio is defined as

$$F \equiv \frac{\sigma_{x_1}^{\ 2}}{\sigma_{x_2}^{\ 2}} = \frac{\dfrac{n_1}{n_1 - 1} s_{x_1}^{\ 2}}{\dfrac{n_2}{n_2 - 1} s_{x_2}^{\ 2}} \tag{3-67}$$

As in the method of the *t* test, an infinite number of pairs of sample sets are imagined, and the corresponding values of *F* constitute an *F* distribution. This is a continuous distribution whose analytic form, if the two sets of measurements are from the same normal parent distribution, is

$$f(F) = cF^{\frac{1}{2}(v_1 - 2)}(v_2 + v_1 F)^{-[\frac{1}{2}(v_1 + v_2)]} \tag{3-68}$$

where c is a constant and where $v_1 = n_1 - 1$ and $v_2 = n_2 - 1$ are the respective numbers of degrees of freedom. The shape of the *F* distribution is asymmetric, as shown in Fig. 3-2 for a typical pair of values of v_1 and v_2. As in the *t* test, we can calculate with Eq. 3-68 the probability that the value of *F* of the next sample pair of sets will fall outside a specified range, e.g., outside the range set by the arbitrary values F_1 and F_2 indicated in Fig. 3-2. This calculation is an integration of Eq. 3-68 with the particular limits F_1 and F_2.

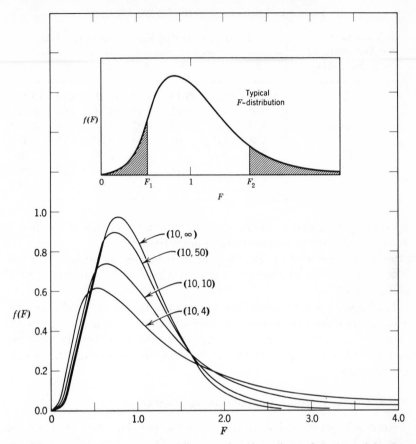

Fig. 3-2. *F* distribution curves for different pairs of numbers of degrees of freedom (ν_1, ν_2).

Now, however, since $f(F)$ is not symmetric, it is convenient further to define F as being greater than unity, i.e., to have the larger standard deviation always in the numerator of Eq. 3-67. Suppose F_2 is chosen so that the probability is the arbitrary value 0.05, i.e., that out of 100 sample values of F only 5 on the average will be larger than F_2. Note that the calculated probability is based on the assumption that σ_{x_1} and σ_{x_2} are consistent, i.e., estimates of the true value σ_x of a comon parent population. If it turns out that the experimental value of F as deduced from Eq. 3-67 is larger than F_2, we may say that, statistically, the standard deviations are not consistent.

Table 3-2 lists the limits for F, if the chances that it will not exceed the limit are 5%, for different numbers of degrees of freedom in determining

Table 3-2. Limits for F in the F Test, 5% Level

$\nu_1(=n_1-1)$ (for Denominator in Eq. 3-67)	$\nu_2\,(=n_2-1)$ (for Numerator in Eq. 3-67)						
	2	3	5	8	12	20	∞
2	19.00	19.16	19.30	19.37	19.41	19.44	19.50
3	9.55	9.28	9.01	8.84	8.74	8.66	8.53
5	5.79	5.41	5.05	4.82	4.68	4.56	4.36
8	4.46	4.07	3.69	3.44	3.28	3.15	2.93
12	3.88	3.49	3.11	2.85	2.69	2.54	2.30
20	3.49	3.10	2.71	2.45	2.28	2.12	1.84
50	3.18	2.79	2.40	2.13	1.95	1.78	1.44

σ_{x_1} and σ_{x_2} respectively. In each case, the number of degrees of freedom is given by the number of trial measurements less one.

As in the case of the t test, the general principles underlying the F test have rather wide applicability in many problems in the statistical tests of consistency.*

In Chapter 4, the χ^2 test is introduced, a test for the probability that an assumed mathematical model frequency distribution fits a set of measurements. The arguments in this test are very similar to those in the t test and in the F test, the principal difference being the use of a different working parameter.

3-4. Curve Fitting: Least-Squares Method

Among experimental scientists the most popular application of the principle known as least squares is in curve fitting. We shall first discuss the formulas and their applications, and then we shall give the justification for the principle of least squares in general. This justification, if the deviations are normally distributed and properly weighted, is by the method of maximum likelihood.

Experiments are often performed for the purpose of evaluating a fundamental constant or for calibrating an instrument. For example, by measurements of the voltage V and the frequency ν, we may determine the numerical value of the constants h/e and ϕ in Einstein's photoelectric equation $V = (h/e)\nu - \phi$. Or, by using the relation $s = s_0 + v_0t + \frac{1}{2}gt^2$, the acceleration of gravity g may be found in an experiment with a freely falling body. In each such case, the problem is to determine the constants

* The F test was developed by R. A. Fisher and first published in 1924. See R. A. Fisher, *Statistical Methods for Research Workers* (Oliver and Boyd, Edinburgh, 1950), 11th ed.

in a specified functional relationship between the dependent and the independent variables. The importance of the problem often justifies considerable effort in the analysis of the measurements.

If there are K constants to be determined and if there are K pairs of measurements, then there are K simultaneous equations which may be solved for each constant. This is a so-called "exact" determination with no degrees of freedom for the evaluation of the precision. But if more than K pairs of measurements are available, the constants are said to be "over-determined"; the errors in the measured values of the variables prevent an "exact" determination but *do* provide a basis for evaluating the precision.

The usual procedure is to make a graph of the measured quantities and to "fit" a curve to the data as best we can. If we rely chiefly upon the eye in making this fit, there is a strong tendency to give undue weights to the end points. As a matter of fact, the end points are often the least reliable because of experimental factors in the extremes of the range. By the method of least squares, however, we can give either equal or unequal weights, as desired, to the various points of the graph.

The method of least squares does not tell us in a practical way the best functional relationship; it does tell us precisely the best values of the constants appearing in the equation. Also, it does allow us to choose between two different functional relations, as is seen presently.

Best fit of a straight line. Many functional forms can be expressed as a linear relation,

$$y = a + bx \qquad (3\text{-}69)$$

The photoelectric equation cited above is an example of this form. The constant that relates the variations in electrical resistivity ρ with the temperature T is given by the expression $\alpha = (T/\rho)\,(\partial\rho/\partial T)$, and this expression can be put in the linear form $\log \rho = A + \alpha \log T$. The Cauchy equation for the refractive index of a substance is $n = a + b/\lambda^2$, which is seen to be linear when x is written for $1/\lambda^2$. The exponential decay law, $I = I_0 e^{-\mu x}$, can be rephrased to be $\log I = \log I_0 - \mu x$.

It usually turns out that, of the two general constants a and b in Eq. 3-69, we are more interested in b than in a, but this is not always so. b gives the slope of the graph and a the intercept.

Consider the graph of measured values of x and y, such as in Fig. 3-3, and a straight line

$$y_0 = a + bx_0 \qquad (3\text{-}70)$$

such that the sum of the squares of the deviations from it shall be a minimum. In what direction should the deviations be reckoned? Ideally,

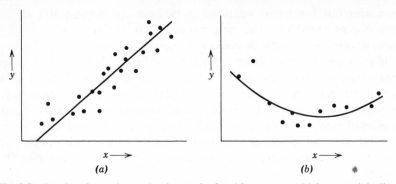

Fig. 3-3. Graphs of experimental points to be fitted by a curve: (*a*) by a straight line, (*b*) by a parabola.

if only random errors are present in both x and y, the deviations should be reckoned perpendicular to the straight line. But the arithmetic involved in the determination of the constants a and b is rather formidable in this case and, in general, the result depends upon the choice of the scale of each coordinate axis; correction for even this effect is possible but is very laborious. The usual procedure is to choose either the x or the y direction for the deviations, recognizing that the price paid for the simpler arithmetic is a sacrifice, usually negligibly small, in the accuracy of the best fit of the line. The choice between the x and the y direction is made in favor of that direction in which the larger standard deviation is found; in order to make this comparison in the same dimensions and units, s_y is compared with bs_x. In almost all cases in experimental science, x is taken as the independent variable whose values are selected with practically negligible error, and in these cases the deviations are reckoned along the y axis.

We shall assume in the following text that all the deviations are taken along the y axis, i.e., that $b^2 s_x{}^2 \ll s_y{}^2$. Then, $a + bx_i$ is always taken as the exact value of y, viz., y_0. Accordingly, a deviation is written as

$$\delta y_i = y_i - y_0 = y_i - (a + bx_i) \tag{3-71}$$

Graphically, δy_i is the length of a vertical line drawn between y_i and y_0 $(= a + bx_i)$ at the x_i abscissa position. (Remember that if $\delta x_i \neq 0$, δy_i is not an observed deviation in y, i.e., $y_i - \bar{y}$; rather, δy_i may be greater or less than the observed deviation because δy_i also includes the observed deviation in x_i.)

Let us assume initially that all δy_i's are equally weighted. In accord with the principle of least squares, we seek those values of a and b that make the sum of the squares of the n deviations δy_i a minimum. Thus,

$$\sum_{i=1}^{n} (\delta y_i)^2 = \sum_{i=1}^{n} (y_i - a - bx_i)^2$$

$$\frac{\partial[\Sigma(\delta y_i)^2]}{\partial a} = 2na - 2\Sigma y_i + 2b\Sigma x_i = 0 \tag{3-72}$$

$$\frac{\partial[\Sigma(\delta y_i)^2]}{\partial b} = 2b\Sigma x_i^2 + 2a\Sigma x_i - 2\Sigma(x_i y_i) = 0 \tag{3-73}$$

from which

$$a = \frac{\begin{vmatrix} \Sigma y_i & \Sigma x_i \\ \Sigma x_i y_i & \Sigma x_i^2 \end{vmatrix}}{\begin{vmatrix} n & \Sigma x_i \\ \Sigma x_i & \Sigma x_i^2 \end{vmatrix}} = \frac{\Sigma x_i^2 \Sigma y_i - \Sigma x_i \Sigma(x_i y_i)}{n\Sigma x_i^2 - (\Sigma x_i)^2} = \frac{\bar{y}\Sigma x_i^2 - \bar{x}\Sigma(x_i y_i)}{\Sigma(x_i - \bar{x})^2} \tag{3-74}$$

$$b = \frac{\begin{vmatrix} n & \Sigma y_i \\ \Sigma x_i & \Sigma x_i y_i \end{vmatrix}}{\begin{vmatrix} n & \Sigma x_i \\ \Sigma x_i & \Sigma x_i^2 \end{vmatrix}} = \frac{n\Sigma(x_i y_i) - \Sigma x_i \Sigma y_i}{n\Sigma x_i^2 - (\Sigma x_i)^2} = \frac{\Sigma(x_i - \bar{x})(y_i - \bar{y})}{\Sigma(x_i - \bar{x})^2} \tag{3-75}$$

where $\bar{x}$ and $\bar{y}$ are the mean values of the observed x_i's and y_i's. These values for a and b respectively are to be inserted in Eq. 3-70 to give the straight line that best fits the measurements. This line generally does not pass through *any* of the actual experimental points, but this is of no consequence.

If the labor of calculating the quantities in Eqs. 3-74 and 3-75 for a and b becomes excessive, computational shortcuts can be devised. A short cut commonly used is based on the same idea as that of the working mean discussed in Chapter 2 for computing the values of the mean and of the standard deviation, but we shall not give the details here.

Now consider that the n measurements should *not* be weighted equally. Assign weight w_i to the ith point. Then, the best fit of the line is such that $\sum_{i=1}^{n} w_i(\delta y_i)^2$ is a minimum. After performing the same sort of algebra as above, we find that

$$a^w = \frac{\Sigma w_i x_i^2 \Sigma w_i y_i - \Sigma w_i x_i \Sigma w_i x_i y_i}{\Sigma w_i \Sigma w_i x_i^2 - (\Sigma w_i x_i)^2} = \frac{\bar{y}\Sigma w_i x_i^2 - \bar{x}\Sigma w_i x_i y_i}{\Sigma w_i(x_i - \bar{x})^2} \tag{3-76}$$

$$b^w = \frac{\Sigma w_i \Sigma w_i x_i y_i - \Sigma w_i x_i \Sigma w_i y_i}{\Sigma w_i \Sigma w_i x_i^2 - (\Sigma w_i x_i)^2} = \frac{\Sigma w_i(x_i - \bar{x})(y_i - \bar{y})}{\Sigma w_i(x_i - \bar{x})^2} \tag{3-77}$$

where $\bar{x}$ and $\bar{y}$ are the weighted means, $(\Sigma w_i x_i)/\Sigma w_i$ and $(\Sigma w_i y_i)/\Sigma w_i$, respectively. The proper statistical weight to be assigned to each point is $w_i = 1/s_i^2$.

It must be noted that when a nonlinear relation is put in linear form by a change in one or both variables, e.g., an exponential equation to logarithmic form, etc., such a change always involves an alteration of scale which is equivalent to a gradual change of weights along the scale. Such a change of weights, unless properly corrected for, always results in a different value of a and b. (An example is given as Problem 12 in Section 3-11.) The "best" values of a and b depend on the "best" form of the relationship between x and y. It is important to note that, in case the y values for each x are normally distributed, the proper correction is made *automatically*, irrespective of the functional form, *if* weight $1/s_i^2$ is consistently assigned to the ith point; this is shown by the method of maximum likelihood (and is also part of Problem 12, Section 3-11).

The standard deviations in the values for a and b may be deduced as follows. Draw the n straight lines through the n points x_i, y_i and the common point $\bar{x}$, $\bar{y}$. This gives n values of a_i and n values of b_i. These n values, however, are not equally weighted; the standard deviation in a_i and in b_i is proportional to $1/(x_i - \bar{x})$, and thus the weight is proportional to $(x_i - \bar{x})^2$. The standard deviation in a_i and b_i is determined with Eq. 3-37, for which $J = 1$, viz.,

$$s_{a_i} = \left| \frac{\partial a_i}{\partial y_i} \right| s_{y_i} = \frac{\bar{x}}{x_i - \bar{x}} s_{y_i}$$

$$s_{b_i} = \left| \frac{\partial b_i}{\partial y_i} \right| s_{y_i} = \frac{1}{x_i - \bar{x}} s_{y_i}$$

Then, with the weighting factors

$$w_{a_i} \propto \frac{1}{s_{a_i}^2} \quad \text{and} \quad w_{b_i} \propto \frac{1}{s_{b_i}^2}$$

we can write, using Eq. 3-61, if all the s_{y_i}'s are the same (all y_i's equally weighted),

$$s_a = \left(\frac{1}{n} \frac{\Sigma w_{a_i}(a_i - a)^2}{\Sigma w_{a_i}} \right)^{1/2} = \left(\frac{1}{n} \frac{\Sigma (x_i - \bar{x})^2 (a_i - a)^2}{\Sigma (x_i - \bar{x})^2} \right)^{1/2} \tag{3-78}$$

and

$$s_b = \left(\frac{1}{n} \frac{\Sigma w_{b_i}(b_i - b)^2}{\Sigma w_{b_i}} \right)^{1/2} = \left(\frac{1}{n} \frac{\Sigma (x_i - \bar{x})^2 (b_i - b)^2}{\Sigma (x_i - \bar{x})^2} \right)^{1/2} \tag{3-79}$$

where a_i and b_i are given implicitly by $\bar{y} = a_i \bar{x} + b_i$ and $y_i = a_i x_i + b_i$, or explicitly by

$$a_i = \frac{\bar{y}x_i - \bar{x}y_i}{x_i - \bar{x}} \quad \text{and} \quad b_i = \frac{\bar{y}_i - y}{x_i - \bar{x}}$$

and a and b by Eqs. 3-74 and 3-75.

Or, each standard deviation may be expressed in terms of the standard deviation s_y from equally weighted y_i values,

$$s_y = \left(\frac{\Sigma(y_i - a - bx_i)}{n} \right)^{\frac{1}{2}} \tag{3-80}$$

viz.,

$$s_a = \left(\frac{\Sigma x_i^2}{n\Sigma x_i - (\Sigma x_i)^2} \right)^{\frac{1}{2}} s_y \tag{3-81}$$

and

$$s_b = \left(\frac{n}{n\Sigma x_i^2 - (\Sigma x_i)^2} \right)^{\frac{1}{2}} s_y \tag{3-82}$$

These expressions may be derived by using Eq. 3-37, viz.,

$$s_a^2 = \sum_{i=1}^{n} \left(\frac{\partial a}{\partial y_i} \right)^2 s_{y_i}^2$$

and

$$s_b^2 = \sum_{i=1}^{n} \left(\frac{\partial b}{\partial y_i} \right)^2 s_{y_i}^2$$

Substitute a and b from Eqs. 3-74 and 3-75 and take all s_{y_i}'s to be the same. For example, in the b case,

$$\frac{\partial b}{\partial y_i} = \frac{nx_i - \Sigma x_i}{n\Sigma x_i^2 - (\Sigma x_i)^2}$$

and

$$\sum_{i=1}^{n} \left(\frac{\partial b}{\partial y_i} \right)^2 = \frac{n}{n\Sigma x_i^2 - (\Sigma x_i)^2}$$

from which Eq. 3-82 readily follows. The argument is essentially the same for Eq. 3-81.

Note that Eq. 3-80 would give σ_y if n were replaced by $n - 2$; the number of degrees of freedom is here *two* less than n because of the two arbitrary parameters, a and b, in the definition of each deviation.

The probable error in a or b is given by multiplying Eq. 3-81 or 3-82 by the constant 0.675 if the distribution of the weighted values of a or b is normal.

Straight line through origin. If the intercept a in the equation for the straight line, Eq. 3-69, is known to be zero, it is not meaningful to differentiate with respect to a, as in Eq. 3-72. In this case, the expression for b is obtained directly from Eq. 3-73 with a put equal to zero. Then,

$$b = \frac{\Sigma x_i y_i}{\Sigma x_i^2} \quad \text{or} \quad b^w = \frac{\Sigma w_i x_i y_i}{\Sigma w_i x_i^2} \tag{3-83}$$

The expression for the correlation coefficient, defined presently, is based on Eq. 3-83.

Best fit of a parabola. The equation of a parabola is

$$y = a + bx + cx^2 \qquad (3\text{-}84)$$

Again, if the number n of pairs of measurements x_i, y_i is greater than three, i.e., the number of constants now to be determined, the method of least squares gives the best fit of the parabola.

The argument is the same as for the case of the straight line. Assume that all the error is in y_i, and write the deviation of each point from the best parabolic curve as

$$\delta y_i = y_i - a - bx_i - cx_i^2 \qquad (3\text{-}85)$$

The best values of the constants a, b, and c are those for which

$$\frac{\partial[\Sigma(\delta y_i)^2]}{\partial a} = \frac{\partial[\Sigma(\delta y_i)^2]}{\partial b} = \frac{\partial[\Sigma(\delta y_i)^2]}{\partial c} = 0$$

The algebra for the simultaneous solution of these three equations for a, b, and c is straightforward.

Likewise, if the x_i, y_i measurements are not equally weighted, and if the weights are known, the weighted values of a^w, b^w, and c^w can be calculated. The expressions for the weighted precision indices also follow.

Perhaps the most important aspect of the method of least squares in curve fitting is that it allows determination of the precision of the constants, and this part of the problem must not be neglected; the procedures are similar to those detailed above in the discussion of the best fit of a straight line.

It should be pointed out that calculations of a, b, and c are greatly simplified if the values of x are chosen to have equal interval spacings Δx and to be symmetrical with respect to the median, and if the x variable is changed so that the zero of the scale is at the median value and is measured in Δx units. In this case, all summations of odd powers of the new variable x' are equal to zero. Denoting this case with primes also on a, b, and c, we write*

$$a' = \frac{\Sigma x_i'^4}{n\Sigma x_i'^4 - (\Sigma x_i'^2)^2}\Sigma y_i - \frac{\Sigma x_i'^2}{n\Sigma x_i'^4 - (\Sigma x_i'^2)^2}\Sigma x_i'^2 y_i$$

$$b' = \frac{n\Sigma x_i'^4 - (\Sigma x_i'^2)^2}{n\Sigma x_i'^2\Sigma x_i'^4 - (\Sigma x_i'^2)^3}\Sigma x_i' y_i \qquad (3\text{-}86)$$

$$c' = \frac{n}{n\Sigma x_i'^4 - (\Sigma x_i'^2)^2}\Sigma x_i'^2 y_i - \frac{\Sigma x_i'^2}{n\Sigma x_i'^4 - (\Sigma x_i'^2)^2}\Sigma y_i$$

* See, e.g., G. C. Cox and M. Matuschak, *J. Phys. Chem.*, **45**, 362 (1941).

In these equations, x' is measured from the median value and x' values are integers if $x' \equiv (x_i - x_{\text{median}})/\Delta x$ for n even and if $x' \equiv 2(x_i - x_{\text{median}})/\Delta x$ for n odd.

The expression for a' forms the basis of the least-squares parabolic method for the smoothing of data, as discussed later.

Best fit of a sine curve. The function

$$y = a \sin (\phi - b) \tag{3-87}$$

cannot be converted to the form of a straight line or to a power series in which a and b appear as coefficients of the power terms. The fitting of this type of function illustrates additional interesting features.

From a graph of the measurements y_i, ϕ_i, estimate a value ϵ for b and let $\delta = b - \epsilon$, which must be rather small. Let $\theta = \phi - \epsilon$, and $A = 1/a$. Then, $\sin (\phi - b) = \sin (\theta - \delta)$, and, after expanding $\sin (\theta - \delta)$, Eq. 3-87 becomes

$$Ay - \sin \theta + \delta \cos \theta = 0$$

Assume all the error in the ith point to be $\delta(Ay_i)$ and write the deviation as

$$\delta(Ay_i) = Ay_i - \sin \theta_i + \delta \cos \theta_i$$

The first approximation to the best values of A and δ, hence for a and b, is that for which $\Sigma(Ay_i - \sin \theta_i + \delta \cos \theta_i)^2$ is a minimum, i.e., for which

$$A\Sigma y_i^2 - \Sigma y_i \sin \theta_i + \delta \Sigma y_i \cos \theta_i = 0$$
$$A\Sigma y_i \cos \theta_i - \Sigma \cos \theta_i \sin \theta_i + \delta \Sigma \cos^2 \theta_i = 0 \tag{3-88}$$

by writing $\partial/\partial A = 0$ and then $\partial/\partial \delta = 0$. If the approximation given by the solution of these two simultaneous equations is not satisfactory, a better estimate of ϵ is then found by making δ smaller and repeating the process.

Likewise, the weighted values a^w and b^w and the precision indices s_a, s_b, $s_a{}^w$, and $s_b{}^w$ may be computed with the same type of argument that was given for the straight-line case.

The cases of the straight line, the parabola, and the sine curve are illustrative of the curve-fitting aspect of statistical precision; the reader is referred to the literature for the fitting of functional relationships that cannot be expressed in one of these three forms.*

Criterion for choice of functional relation. As stated earlier, the method of least squares in curve fitting does not tell us directly the *best* functional relation $y = f(x)$, only the best values of the constants. But it can be used to tell which of two relations is the better. Thus, for example,

---

* For example, see F. S. Acton, *Analysis of Straight-Line Data* (John Wiley & Sons' New York, 1959).

we may choose between a straight-line relation and a parabolic relation, or between a parabolic relation and a power series which has terms higher than the second power.

Let the two relations to be compared be α and β, having a number of constants c_α and c_β respectively. For each value of x_i, which is assumed to be exact, let $y_{\hat\alpha}$ or y_β be the value of y computed from the respective relation. Then, calculate

$$\Omega_\alpha = \frac{\Sigma(y_i - y_\alpha)^2}{n - c_\alpha} \quad \text{and} \quad \Omega_\beta = \frac{\Sigma(y_i - y_\beta)^2}{n - c_\beta} \qquad (3\text{-}89)$$

The relation which has the smaller value of Ω is the one that better fits the measurements.

Table 3-3. A Differences Table

x	y	Δy	$\Delta^2 y$	$\Delta^3 y$	$\Delta^4 y$
x_1	y_1				
		Δy_1			
$x_2 = x_1 + \Delta x$	y_2		$\Delta^2 y_1$		
		Δy_2		$\Delta^3 y_1$	
$x_3 = x_1 + 2\Delta x$	y_3		$\Delta^2 y_2$		$\Delta^4 y_1$
		Δy_3		$\Delta^3 y_2$	
$x_4 = x_1 + 3\Delta x$	y_4		$\Delta^2 y_3$	$\cdot$	$\cdot$
		Δy_4		$\cdot$	$\cdot$
$x_5 = x_1 + 4\Delta x$	y_5	$\cdot$	$\cdot$	$\cdot$	
$\cdot$	$\cdot$	$\cdot$	$\cdot$		
$\cdot$	$\cdot$	$\cdot$			
$\cdot$	$\cdot$				

It follows of course that, of *all* possible relations, that relation for which Ω is a minimum is the best one. Comparison of the ratio $\Omega_\alpha/\Omega_\beta$ with Eq. 3-67 shows that this test may be properly called an F test for the best relation.

If the values of x are chosen so that the x intervals are all the same, Δx, and if each x_i may be considered as exact, then a relatively quick way of testing the suitability of a functional relation is the following one. Construct a "differences table," such as Table 3-3, in which the definitions of first-order and second-order differences are

$$\Delta y_i \equiv y_{i+1} - y_i, \qquad \Delta^2 y_i \equiv \Delta y_{i+1} - \Delta y_i \qquad (3\text{-}90)$$

and the definitions of higher-order differences are self-evident. If the nth-order difference is constant (or is within the standard deviation of their differences), a function consisting of an nth order power series approximation is required.

The scheme works for all functional forms that can be converted to a power series by a change of variable,* even though the highest power is unity as in the case of the straight line.†

3-5. Justification of Least-Squares Method from Maximum Likelihood

We have encountered so far several applications of the principle of least squares. The first was met in the definition of the mean with the deviations equally or unequally weighted (whichever applies) as the location index for which the sum of the squares of the deviations is a minimum; then, the principle was implied (but not specifically discussed) in the high statistical efficiency of the standard deviation as a dispersion index based on the sum of the squares of the deviations; it was also implied (but not discussed) in the high efficiency of t, F, and, later, the χ^2 tests for consistency; the least squares method was used explicitly in the determination of the least-squares values of constants in known functional relationships; and, finally, the principle was used in the criterion for choosing the better of two different functional forms for the representation of a set of measurements. A popular method of data smoothing (mentioned presently) is

---

* Note that a change of variable implies a change of relative weights, as was discussed in connection with the best fit of a straight line; see Problem 12, Section 3-11.

† Incidentally, if we ignore errors and precision altogether, the average of the "constant" values of the nth-order difference allows a determination of the value of the intercept in the power series relation. Furthermore, if Δx is small, the other constants may be approixmated with a trivial bit of computation. For example, if the function is a second-order power series,

$$y = a + bx + cx^2$$

we may write

$$y + \Delta y = a + b(x + \Delta x) + c(x + \Delta x)^2$$

$$\Delta y = b \, \Delta x + c \, \Delta x^2 + 2cx \, \Delta x = a' + b'x$$

where, since Δx is constant, a' and b' are constants. Repetition of this procedure gives

$$\Delta y + \Delta^2 y = a' + b'(x + \Delta x)$$

$$\Delta^2 y = b' \, \Delta x = b''$$

Hence, knowing Δx, we can determine b' from the second-order difference "constant"; then, knowing b', the average $\frac{1}{2}(x_i + x_{i+1})$, and Δy_i, we can compute a'; then, from a' and b', we can compute b and c; then, knowing y_i and x_i, we can compute a. The difficulty with these approximations is that we must assume that a Δy_i and a pair x_i, y_i are exactly known. Of course, what appears to be the best values are chosen. As stated in the first sentence of this footnote, this procedure ignores errors and all questions of precision.

also based on this principle. And, errors propagate according to convenient rules based on the sum of the squares, viz., based on the simple addition rule for the variances, if all the errors are sufficiently small that, in the Taylor expansion, the terms of powers higher than the first may be neglected.

Strictly, the least-squares method is valid only in case the errors are normally distributed, but the method is frequently invoked for near-normal distributions and indeed for distributions in general in which the errors are all small. The validity in the case of normal errors is easily shown by the method of maximum likelihood.

Suppose that we have a single independent variable x and that we are concerned with values of y given by

$$y = f(x, \alpha, \beta, \cdots)$$

where $\alpha, \beta, \cdots$ are fixed parameters whose values we wish to determine. Suppose that the deviations are essentially all in y, viz., that

$$\delta y_i = y_i - f(x)$$

as was discussed in connection with Eq. 3-71, and are normally distributed. For given values of $\alpha, \beta, \cdots$ and of x_i, the probability of a measurement yielding a result between y_i and $y_i + dy_i$ is given by

$$p(y_i, y_i + dy_i) = \frac{1}{\sqrt{2\pi}} \frac{dy_i}{\sigma_i} \exp\left(-\frac{(\delta y_i)^2}{2\sigma_i^2}\right) \tag{3-91}$$

The probability of observing y_1 in the interval dy_1, y_2 in dy_2, $\cdots$, and y_n in dy_n is the likelihood function

$$L = \prod_{i=1}^{n} \frac{1}{\sqrt{2\pi}} \frac{dy_i}{\sigma_i} \exp\left(-\frac{(\delta y_i)^2}{2\sigma_i^2}\right) \tag{3-92}$$

if the deviations are independent.

It is convenient to think of "error space" which is an n-dimensional space in which the ith coordinate is $z_i = y_i/\sigma_i$. Then, Eq. 3-92 can be written as

$$L = \frac{1}{(2\pi)^{\frac{1}{2}n}} \exp\left[-\tfrac{1}{2}\Sigma(\delta z_i)^2\right] dv \tag{3-93}$$

where dv is the elementary volume in error space. The relative likelihood of any set of errors or deviations in dv depends only on $\Sigma(\delta z_i)^2$, i.e., on the square of the radius vector R in error space. It is immediately apparent that the value of α (or of $\beta, \cdots$) that corresponds to the maximum value of L is that for which the sum of the squares of the deviations is a minimum. This is a proof of the validity of the principle of least squares for normally distributed errors.

Note that it is $\Sigma[(\delta y_i)^2/\sigma_i^2]$ that is to be minimized where σ_i^2 is the weighting factor to be associated with each y_i. (Such weighting was discussed earlier for the special case of the weighted mean in connection with Eq. 3-60.) The derivation of the principle of least squares, therefore, *requires* that, in application of the principle, each value δy_i be *properly* weighted. In many measurement problems, all that is known about σ_i is that its expected value is the same for all i; in such cases all deviations are properly equally weighted and we write simply σ for σ_i.

If many different samples each of size n are taken from the infinite parent y population, many different values of $\Sigma(\delta z_i)^2 \ (= R^2)$ are obtained. Analysis of the R^2 distribution gives further interesting information regarding the principle of least squares.

We can rewrite Eq. 3-93 in terms of R, with $R^{n-1} \, dR = dv$, as

$$L(R) \, dR = Ce^{-\frac{1}{2}R^2}R^{n-1} \, dR \tag{3-94}$$

where the constant C can be evaluated as follows. Let

$$u = \tfrac{1}{2}R^2 \tag{3-95}$$

then $du = R \, dR$; and let $R^{n-2} = (2u)^{\frac{1}{2}(n-2)}$; then,

$$L(u) \, du = Ce^{-u}2^{\frac{1}{2}(n-2)}u^{\frac{1}{2}(n-2)} \, du$$

Since the sum of all probabilities $L(u)$ must equal unity,

$$\int L(u) \, du = 1 = C[\tfrac{1}{2}(n-2)]! \, 2^{\frac{1}{2}(n-2)}$$

and therefore

$$C = \frac{1}{2^{\frac{1}{2}(n-2)}[\frac{1}{2}(n-2)]!}$$

Then,

$$L(u) \, du = \frac{1}{[\frac{1}{2}(n-2)]!} \, e^{-u}u^{\frac{1}{2}(n-2)} \, du \tag{3-96}$$

Equation 3-96 forms the basis of the χ^2 distribution and of the χ^2 test for the goodness of fit of a mathematical model frequency distribution to a set of actual measurements. Specifically, Eq. 3-96 allows calculation of the probability that the sum of the squares of n observed deviations will fall in an arbitrarily selected range, a range that is set by the choice of the limits of integration. This is discussed further in Chapter 4.

The derivation of Eq. 3-96 has not specifically included the effect of the parameters α, β, $\cdots$ in the function $y = f(x, \alpha, \beta, \cdots)$. If there are q parameters whose values are to be estimated from the n measurements at hand, then proper account of the effect of these parameters in the minimization of R^2 [i.e., of $(\delta z_i)^2$ in Eq. 3-93] reduces n to $n-q$; i.e., there are $n-q$ degrees of freedom left for the estimation of the characteristics of the R^2 distribution. $(\alpha, \beta, \cdots$ may refer to functional constants, instrumental parameters, distribution characteristics such as $\bar{y}$ and σ_y, etc.) The pertinent error space then has $n - q$ dimensions.

In regard to the R^2 distribution, it is interesting to note that the most likely value of R^2, viz., R^{*2}, is readily obtained from Eq. 3-94 by the method of maximum likelihood.† Thus,

$$\left(\frac{\partial}{\partial R} \log L(R)\right)_{R = R^*} = 0 = \frac{n - 1}{R^*} - R^*$$

and the most likely value is

$$R^{*2} = n - 1, \quad \text{or, generally, } R^{*2} = n - q - 1 \quad (3\text{-}97)$$

It was asserted, for a normal distribution of errors, that the best estimate of the variance of the parent distribution is $[n/(n - 1)]s^2$. Equation 3-97 reiterates this for the case in which no additional parameters $\alpha, \beta, \cdots$ are to be estimated. Write

$$R^2 = \frac{1}{\sigma^2} \Sigma(\delta y_i)^2 = \frac{n}{\sigma^2} s^2 = n - 1 \Big|_{R^2 = R^{*2}} \quad (3\text{-}98)$$

Also, the mean value of R^2, viz., $\overline{R^2}$, may be obtained from either Eq. 3-94 or Eq. 3-96. By definition of the mean value of u,

$$\bar{u} = \int u L(u) \, du = \int u \frac{1}{[\frac{1}{2}(n - 2)]!} e^{-u} u^{\frac{1}{2}(n-2)} \, du$$

which, upon integration, is $\bar{u} = \frac{1}{2}n$. Hence, with Eq. 3-95,

$$\overline{R^2} = n, \quad \text{or, generally,‡ } \overline{R^2} = n - q \quad (3\text{-}99)$$

In case nothing is known specifically about the proper weight to be assigned to each y_i value, Eq. 3-99 and the definition of R^2 $[= \Sigma(\delta y_i/\sigma_i)^2]$ tell us that the proper *average* weight is

$$\sigma_{i_{av}}^2 = \frac{\Sigma(\delta y_i)^2}{n - q}$$

† The most likely value of R can also be obtained from $L(u)$. To do this we note that $L(R) \, dR = L(u) \, du = L(u) \sqrt{2u} \, dR$, and we must use the function $\sqrt{2u} \, L(u)$, not $L(u)$ alone. Then,

$$\left(\frac{\partial}{\partial u} \log \sqrt{2u} L(u)\right)_{u = u^*} = 0 = \frac{1}{2u^*} - 1 + \frac{1}{2}(n - 2)\frac{1}{u^*}$$

from which

$$R^{*2} = 2u^* = n - 1$$

‡ The function $L(u)$, rather than $2uL(u)$, suffices here because no differentiation is involved.

3-6. Data Smoothing

Let us discuss briefly another problem in the treatment of experimental data, a problem closely related to curve fitting. This is known as data smoothing. Data smoothing always presumes *some* knowledge of the analytic form of the best-fitted curve $y = f(x)$, although this presumption is not always recognized by investigators who try to smooth their data.

It must be emphasized at the beginning of this discussion that, in general, we should *not* indulge in data smoothing unless we have a clear a priori assurance of the order of magnitude of at least the first and second derivatives of the appropriate function $y = f(x)$ throughout the region of interest. Furthermore, because of the inherent arbitrariness in any data-smoothing operation, it is practically impossible to treat the measurements statistically *after* they have been smoothed, and any quantitative interpretation of the results is likewise open to some question.

We shall mention two popular methods of data smoothing. In the first method, smoothing is accomplished graphically, a portion of the data at a time, by arbitrarily drawing a smooth curve "through" the experimental points. This method is improved if the first-order differences between adjacent x values are smoothed, and is further improved if second-order differences are smoothed. (First- and second-order differences have been described earlier in connection with Table 3-3.) By successive applications, this method is capable of very satisfactory results (except for the end points) but the procedure is usually slow and inefficient. The fact deserves repetition that this and any method of data smoothing require that the unknown relation $y = f(x)$ be a slowly varying function over each small portion of the curve being treated; otherwise, any short-range real "structure" in the curve would be undesirably smoothed out.

A second smoothing method is based on the principle of least squares. This method, for convenience, presumes that the values of x are chosen with equal interval spacings Δx, that the error is entirely in the y values, and that each small portion, e.g., four adjacent intervals each of size Δx, of the unknown $f(x)$ curve agrees reasonably well with a small portion of a parabola. Consider the five measured values y_{-2}, y_{-1}, y_0, y_{+1}, y_{+2} corresponding to the values $x_0 - 2\Delta x$, $x_0 - \Delta x$, x_0, $x_0 + \Delta x$, $x_0 + 2\Delta x$. We wish to find y, the smoothed value, to replace y_0.

First, let x be replaced by x', defined as

$$x' \equiv \frac{x - x_0}{\Delta x} \tag{3-100}$$

as used also in Eq. 3-86, so that x_0 is the central value and the unit of x'

is Δx. If the parabolic relation fits the unknown relation satisfactorily well over the range $4\Delta x$, the value of y we seek is

$$y = a' + b'x' + c'x'^2 \qquad (3\text{-}101)$$

and, because of the shifted zero of the x' scale to x_0, this value of y we seek is just a'. The value of a' is given by Eq. 3-86, which for five points becomes

$$y_{x_0} = a' = \tfrac{1}{35}[17y_0 + 12(y_{+1} + y_{-1}) - 3(y_{+2} + y_{-2})]$$

This method of smoothing is used by starting at one end of the range of x_i's and working systematically and consecutively through the values of x_i to the other end. The method does not do well at the ends, and the end regions should be repeated, working toward the respective end. It is also important that the unknown function have no real "structure," of a size comparable to the range $4\Delta x$, which should not be smoothed out.*

3-7. Correlation

So far in this chapter we have considered relations $y = f(x)$ in which x is the only variable. Additional variables are often involved, and if so we say that y is correlated to x and correlated to each of the other variables. Or, we say that y is functionally related stochastically rather than exactly to x. The cases of correlation most frequently encountered in practice are those for which the other variables are not specifically known; in fact, their existence is suspected only because the observed fluctuations in y for a given value of x are too great to be attributed to experimental error alone.

Examples of correlated properties are (1) the heights of mothers and of adult daughters in the United States, (2) the grades of college students in mathematics courses and in physics courses, (3) the longevity of men past age 60 years and their weight at age 50 years, and (4) the mass of the atomic nucleus and the number of nuclear fragments into which the nucleus breaks in fission by slow-neutron bombardment.

Correlation coefficient. Let the graph of Fig. 3-4 of a set of student grades in mathematics and physics represent two correlated properties. We shall define an index or coefficient to express the degree of correlation. This coefficient is such that it would be zero if the points were distributed

---

* It is possible, in this method, to accentuate rather than to smooth a periodic component in the experimental "jitter" of the measurements if this period is equal to or less than about $4\Delta x$. If this is suspected, try a different x interval. (The smoothing operation is like a filter that attenuates waves of some frequencies and resonates with some others.)

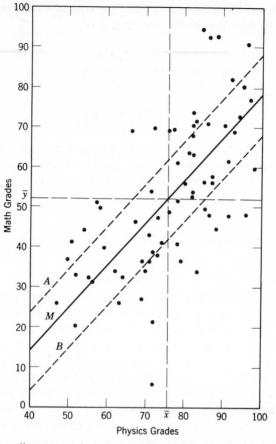

Fig. 3-4. Scatter diagram to show correlated variables: mathematics and physics grades of a group of students. M is the linear regression line; A and B are the probable error lines on the assumption of equal weights and normal distribution.

completely at random in the plane of the graph, and would be unity if the points fell exactly on some curve given by $y = f(x)$.

For simplicity, let $y = f(x)$ be the equation of a straight line whose origin, by adjustment of the scales, is at the point $\bar{x}, \bar{y}$, where $\bar{x}$ and $\bar{y}$ are the means of the n observed values of x and y respectively. Denote the variables on the adjusted scale by primes, $y' = bx'$. The sign of b, i.e., the slope of the line, is chosen so that the line follows the general trend of the points. The correlation is conventionally expressed with the assumption that x_i is exact and that all the error is in y_i. Then, the numerical value of b is determined from Eq. 3-83.

Assume first that all the points x_i, y_i are equally weighted. With this assumption the equation of the straight line is

$$y'_{sl} = bx'_i = \frac{\sum_{i=1}^{n} x'_i y'_i}{\Sigma x'^2_i} x_i \qquad (3\text{-}102)$$

Introduce the quantity

$$S_{y'_{sl}} \equiv \left(\frac{\Sigma(y'_i - y'_{sl})^2}{n}\right)^{\frac{1}{2}} \qquad (3\text{-}103)$$

which is a measure of the dispersion of the measured values y'_i with respect to the least-squares fitted straight line. ($S_{y'_{sl}}$ is called the standard error of estimate.) The standard deviation in the y'_i values is

$$s_{y'} = \left(\frac{\Sigma y'^2}{n}\right)^{\frac{1}{2}} \qquad (3\text{-}104)$$

The correlation coefficient r is defined in terms of $S_{y'_{sl}}$ and $s_{y'}$ as follows:

$$r \equiv \left(1 - \frac{S^2_{y'_{sl}}}{s^2_{y'}}\right)^{\frac{1}{2}} \qquad (3\text{-}105)$$

From Eq. 3-105, the value of r may be anywhere in the range 1 to -1; by convention, the negative values correspond to an inverse correlation, i.e., to a situation in which the general trend of the points is such that the slope of the straight line is negative (see also Eq. 3-107 and Fig. 3-5). For $r = 0$, $S_{y'_{sl}} = s_{y'}$, and this is possible only if $y'_{sl} = 0$. It follows, if $y'_{sl} = 0$, that (1) the least-squares straight line, Eq. 3-102, has zero slope; and (2) the sum $\Sigma x'_i y'_i$ is zero, which, as discussed in Section 3-1, is the condition encountered in the propagation of errors that the deviations δx_i ($= x_i - \bar{x} = x'_i$) and δy_i ($= y_i - \bar{y} = y'_i$) be entirely independent.

The ratio $S_{y'_{sl}}/s_{y'}$ decreases in magnitude as r increases, and this ratio is sometimes called the alienation coefficient.

Computation of the correlation coefficient r is generally easier with a modified form of Eq. 3-105 obtained as follows. From Eqs. 3-102 and 3-103,

$$S^2_{y'_{sl}} = \frac{\Sigma y'^2_i - 2\Sigma y'_i y'_{sl} + \Sigma y'^2_{sl}}{n} = s^2_{y'} - \frac{(\Sigma y'_i x'_i)^2}{n\Sigma x'^2_i} \qquad (3\text{-}106)$$

hence, noting also that $s_{x'}^2 = (\Sigma x'^2_i)/n$,

$$r = \left(1 - \frac{S^2_{y'_{sl}}}{s^2_{y'}}\right)^{\frac{1}{2}} = \frac{\Sigma x'_i y'_i}{ns_{x'}s_{y'}} = b\frac{s_{x'}}{s_{y'}} \qquad (3\text{-}107)$$

using Eq. 3-83. Or, better, in terms of the weighted means $\bar{x}^w$ and $\bar{y}^w$,

$$r = \frac{\Sigma w_i(x_i - \bar{x}^w)(y_i - \bar{y}^w)}{\sqrt{\Sigma w_i(x_i - \bar{x}^w)^2 \Sigma w_i(y_i - \bar{y}^w)^2}} \qquad (3\text{-}108)$$

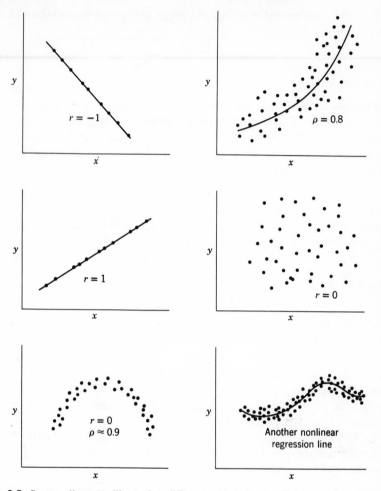

Fig. 3-5. Scatter diagrams illustrating different correlation coefficients and regression lines.

Covariance. The term covariance is commonly used. This is a characteristic of the parent population of which x_i and y_i are individual samples. It may be written σ_{xy} and the best evaluation of it from n actual observations is

$$\sigma_{xy} \approx \frac{\Sigma(x_i - \bar{x})(y_i - \bar{y})}{n - 1} = \frac{\Sigma x_i' y_i'}{n - 1} \qquad (3\text{-}109)$$

The covariance may be divided by the product of $\sigma_{x'}$ and $\sigma_{y'}$ to give the best determination of the parent or universe correlation coefficient.

It is often convenient in statistics to speak of the experimental covariance which is given by

$$s_{xy} = \frac{\Sigma x'_i y'_i}{n} = r s_{x'} s_{y'} \qquad (3\text{-}110)$$

from Eq. 3-107.

Interpretation. The usefulness of the correlation coefficient is in the help it provides in answering such questions as: "If a student's grade in mathematics is 75, what grade may he expect in physics?" The answer to such a question can be worked out simply if r, $\bar{y}$, $\bar{x}$, s_y, and b are known. The equation of the least-squares fitted straight line is

$$y'_{sl} = bx' \qquad (3\text{-}111)$$

This is the line M indicated in Fig. 3-4. The expected value of y for a given value of x is readily obtained from Eq. 3-111. Then, the value of $S_{y'_{sl}}$ is computed from Eq. 3-105 as

$$S_{y'_{sl}} = s_{y'}\sqrt{1 - r^2} \qquad (3\text{-}112)$$

and the answer to the question is simply

$$\bar{y} + [y'_{sl}]_{x'} \pm S_{y'_{sl}} \qquad (3\text{-}113)$$

where the plus or minus value is the standard deviation in the expected physics grade. If the x' and y' frequency distributions are normal, the probable error in the expected value is $0.675 S_{y'_{sl}}$, i.e., the chances are 50–50 that the student's physics grade would be $\bar{y} + [y'_{sl}]_{x'} \pm 0.675 S_{y'_{sl}}$. Lines A and B in Fig. 3-4 are parallel to the line M and mark the 50–50 limits; calculation of lines A and B also presumes that the parent y distribution is independent of x.

In the question as posed, the student's grade in mathematics is 75. To make the calculated answer numerical, suppose that $r = 0.60$, $\bar{y} = 80$, $\bar{x} = 70$, $s_{y'} = 10$, and $b = \bar{y}/\bar{x}$. Then,

$$\bar{y} + [y'_{sl}]_{x'=5} = 80 + \tfrac{8}{7}(75 - 70) \pm 10\sqrt{1 - (0.60)^2} = 85.7 \pm 8$$

if the reliability is expressed as the standard deviation, and as

$$\bar{y} + [y'_{sl}]_{x'=5} = 85.7 \pm 0.675 \times 8 = 85.7 \pm 5.4$$

if the reliability is expressed as the probable error and if the x' and y' distributions are normal. (If they are not normal, the factor 0.675 must be changed appropriately; and if the distributions are asymmetrical, lines such as A and B in Fig. 3-4 do not have the same graphical significance as for symmetrical distributions.)

Another useful feature of the correlation coefficient is the following. If $r = 0.60$, we may infer that the effect of the x variable *may* be about 60% of the net effect of all the correlated variables including x. However,

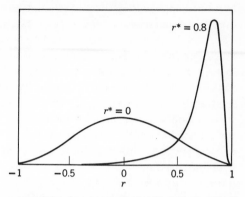

Fig. 3-6. r distributions for two different values of maximum likelihood r^*.

an interpretation of this sort is very risky because of the fact that *all* of the common effect in x and y may be due to other variables.†

Each of these physical interpretations of the correlation coefficient presumes that the unspecified as well as specified correlated variable have distributions that are somewhere near normal.

Calculation of the standard deviation in r can be made by the rather impractical procedure of recording many sample sets of x_i, y_i measurements, computing r_i for each sample set, and the mean value of r, viz., $\bar{r}$, and then calculating s_r in the usual experimental manner with an equation of the form of Eq. 2-9. The distribution of all the sample values of r_i is essentially normal about the mean $\bar{r}$ *if* $\bar{r}$ is small, but the distribution is increasingly skewed as $\bar{r}$ approaches ± 1, i.e., as x and y become strongly correlated either positively or negatively. This is illustrated in Fig. 3-6. No simple formula, therefore, can be given for the standard deviation in a single measurement of r for any value of $\bar{r}$.

In the above discussion of correlation, a straight line is taken as the least-squares fitted curve $y = f(x)$, the so-called regression‡ curve, on which all the points would lie if the correlation coefficient were unity.

---

† For example, tuition fees for students at Cornell University and liquor consumption in the state of New York have quite a positive correlation as studied over the past 90 years.

‡ The line M, or in general the curve $y = f(x)$, is often called the regression line. This term comes originally from studies of the correlation of heights of sons and heights of fathers: It was found that sons' heights, compared with fathers' heights, tended to regress toward the symmetrical or mean line M. Regression is another word to express the fact that additional uncontrolled variables are involved.

The slope of the regression line M, viz., the constant b, and the mean value of y, viz., $\bar{y}$, are sometimes called the regression coefficients.

The regression curve discussed here is based on the assumption that x is exact and all the error is in y; a slightly different regression line or curve is obtained if error is allowed in x.

It often happens that the straight line is not the most reasonable curve, but that a curve of a higher power series, or whatnot, is better. For example, the points on a graph of "distance in feet to stop" vs. "speed in miles per hour" for a random selection of 100 automobiles are better fitted by a parabola by the argument attending Eq. 3-89, and it is preferable to use the squared relation rather than to change the variable to make the relation linear.* (This point is treated in Problem 29 of Section 3-11.) In this nonlinear event, the quantity $S_{y'_{st}}$ is, as before, the measure of the y spread about the curve in general, and a correlation coefficient (often called the correlation index ρ to distinguish it from r for a straight line), is defined by Eq. 3-105. But the magnitude of ρ is different from r, and the physical interpretation of the numerical value of correlation in the nonlinear case is more complicated than in the linear case. It is, of course, important in speaking of correlation to specify the particular least-squares regression line involved.

3-8. Inefficient Statistics

Throughout this book, emphasis is placed on the procedures that use *all* of the experimental information; such procedures are often loosely referred to as *efficient* statistics. However, it is often convenient to use *inefficient* statistics to obtain quickly at least an order of magnitude of some desired feature of the measurements. The quick-and-easy formulas of inefficient statistics frankly have in them almost no attempt to use much of the imformation actually available in the measurements. In this quick-and-easy interest, their discussion may logically have appeared earlier in this book, somewhere in the latter part of Chapter 2. But the understanding of the concepts of efficiency vs. inefficiency involves a considerable degree of statistical sophistication. We have in the present chapter at least touched upon the types of arguments basic to this understanding. However, in this brief section, these arguments will not now be rehearsed: Suffice it to say that in each case mentioned tersely below† (1) the numerical efficiency of a location value is relative to the efficiency of the mean, and the efficiency of a dispersion index is relative to that of the standard deviation, and (2) the measurements are presumed to be from a parent normal distribution.‡

---

* Each case of this sort must be judged on its own merits. In the example cited, the parabolic relation is preferable because of the role of the other correlated variables, e.g., variables such as the weight of the car, the size and type of brakes and tires, reaction time of different drivers, etc.

† See, e.g., W. Dixon and F. Massey, Jr., *Introduction to Statistical Analysis* (McGraw-Hill Book Co., New York, 1951), for more complete discussion of inefficient statistics.

‡ For an asymmetrical parent distribution, the quantitative use of these particular inefficient statistics depends of course upon the degree of asymmetry.

Location index. The median has been described as being 64% efficient in a large set of measurements whose parent distribution is normal. Thus, 36% of the information contained in the data is ignored if the median is taken as an estimate of the value of the mean. But, when the number n of trial measurements is very large, this inefficiency may not be serious. The efficiency of the median increases as n becomes smaller; for example, the efficiency is 69% for $n = 5$, and 74% for $n = 3$.

In general, however, the median is more efficient as a location value than is the mid-range which approaches 0% for very large n, and is 54% for $n = 10$, 77% for $n = 5$, 92% for $n = 3$.

If only two of the large number n of measurements are to be averaged to give an estimate of the mean, again if the parent distribution is approximately normal, the best two measurements for this purpose are those at the points 29% and 71% along the range. This estimate of the mean is 81% efficient. The 25% and 75% points are practically as good and are easier to remember.

If three measurements are used, the average of those at the 20%, 50%, and 80% points in the range give an 88% efficiency in estimating the mean value, and these three are also about the best three.

When n is only about 7 to 10, the average of the third measurement from each end of the range gives an estimate of the mean with an efficiency of about 84%.

Dispersion indices. Attention has already been called to the fact that, in a normal distribution, the mean deviation, as a dispersion index, is only 88% efficient.

When the number n of measurements is very large and the parent population is approximately normally distributed, the standard deviation is estimated with about 65% efficiency from

$$s \approx \frac{(93\%) \text{ point} - (7\% \text{ point})}{3} \tag{3-114}$$

or with about 80% efficiency from

$$s \approx \frac{(97\% \text{ point} + 85\% \text{ point} - 15\% \text{ point} - 3\% \text{ point}}{6} \tag{3-115}$$

These respective points are the best if only two or four points are to be used.

When n is small, 2 to 20 or so from a near-normal parent distribution, the standard deviation is estimated simply from the range as

$$s \approx \frac{\text{range}}{\sqrt{n}} \tag{3-116}$$

with an efficiency that falls from 99% for $n = 3$ to about 85% at $n = 10$. As n increases, we should use, instead of $\sqrt{n}$ in Eq. 3-116, the following: 3.5 for $n = 15$, 3.7 for $n = 20$, 4.1 for $n = 30$, 4.5 for $n = 50$, and 5.0 for $n = 100$. The efficiency, however, progressively decreases as n increases.

Standard deviation in the mean (standard error). When n is small, the simplest estimation is

$$s_m \approx \frac{\text{range}}{n} \tag{3-117}$$

where, again, for $n \gtrsim 10$, n should be replaced with the respective numerical values given in the previous paragraph.

Examples. As examples with the measurements listed in Table 2-2, the inefficient estimates of the mean, of the standard deviation, and of the standard error are compared with the efficient values in Table 3-4.

Table 3-4. Comparison of Inefficient Estimates with the Efficient Values from Measurements of Table 2-2

		m	s		s_m	
Inefficient	median	128	Eq. 3-114	1.3		
	2 points	128.5	Eq. 3-115	1.7	Eq. 3-117	0.14
	3 points	128	Eq. 3-116	1.5		
Efficient	Eq. 2-1	128.2$_7$	Eq. 2-9	1.4$_7$	Eq. 2-31	0.20$_6$

3-9. Conclusions and Design of Experiments

Many of the illustrations of statistical treatment of measurements in this chapter presume a larger number of measurements than most experimenters care to record. The small number of measurements in typical experiments is often due to (a) the fact that most experimenters have a sort of "intuitive" judgment about the reliability of measurements as a consequence of their laboratory training, perhaps a sense of some possibly poorly formulated inefficient statistics, (b) the experimenter's indifference toward wringing the last bit of precision from the measurements, and/or (c) an inadequate appreciation of the possibilities of statistical analysis. It is perhaps the first fact, coupled with his belief that the systematic errors are never quite eliminated, a situation that requires some guessing anyway, that prompts the experimenter to prefer the probable error, the 50–50 chance, to the statistician's standard deviation (or its square) as a statement of reliability.

However, there comes a time when every scientist is acutely aware of the need of a quantitative analysis of precision as free as possible from ambiguity. This need may come in the stating of the precision of his own measurements or in the interpretation of another's. This need is more frequently and more acutely felt as the pertinent facet of science progresses and the residual uncertainties in the pertinent scientific facts and concepts become smaller. The continuing tests of a generalization or of a theory depend more and more upon small differences.

After systematic errors have been eliminated as far as possible, the remaining inherent ambiguity in precision and in its interpretation is reduced to a minimum *only by a statistical argument*.

The design of an experiment, as the phrase is used in the subject of statistics, refers generally to the process of determining a priori the most economical sample size or sizes to give a specified precision, where economical refers to both time and financial cost. It usually does not involve any changes in the apparatus or in the general measurement operations; but it does specify the order of taking measurements and the groupings of measurements. One purpose of the order or grouping has to do with the possible detection of sources of constant or systematic error in the measurements. Design features that are obviously pertinent are easily stated in broad general terms:*

(1) The number of measurements must be sufficiently large to give the necessary number of degrees of freedom for the determination of the desired precision.

(2) If subsets of measurements (including controls or background) are involved, they should be of approximately equal size and grouped in such a way as to reveal inconstant effects (such as a zero drift in the apparatus).

(3) If measurements or subsets are of unequal precisions, each should be weighted inversely as the square of the standard deviation (or, alternatively, if the distributions allow, as the square of the probable error).

(4) Before subsets recorded at different times, with different apparatus, or by different observers, are pooled to form a grand set, the subsets should be tested for consistency.

(5) If one or more measurements or subsets has a high precision, s_h, the measurements or subsets having low precision s_l may be neglected as a consequence of weighting if, say, $s_l \geqslant 4s_h$.

(6) All component direct measurements to be used in computing the value of a derived property should have precision roughly in accord with the relative magnitude of the final propagated error in the computed value—it serves little purpose to spend time and effort improving the

---

* For fuller discussions, see, e.g., W. G. Cochran and G. M. Cox, *Experimental Designs* (John Wiley & Sons, New York, 1950), and R. A. Fisher, *The Design of Experiments* (Oliver and Boyd, Edinburgh, 1949), 5th ed.

precision of one component if the precision of the derived measurement is heavily dominated by another component.

(7) And, finally, the fluctuations in the direct measurements, or in the subsets of measurements, must be as nearly random as possible; this often involves a rather rigid discipline on the part of the experimenter in order to avoid systematic errors and bias.

3-10. Summary

The topics discussed in many parts of this chapter and in Chapter 2 serve the pedagogical purpose of emphasizing the difference between the properties of a sample set of measurements and those of the parent or universe frequency distribution. For example, the mean and its precision are at best related stochastically to the corresponding mean and precision of the parent distribution. This is essentially the problem in the reliability of inferred knowledge of any sort, including measurements and hypotheses, the basic phenomena of any experimental science.

This chapter has been concerned with direct or derived measurements that have parent distributions of unknown shape. This is the situation commonly found for derived measurements, but, fortunately, many of the direct measurements in experimental science have parent distributions of one of two general types, and each of these types is fitted reasonably well by a simple mathematical model. With the model, once its parameters are satisfactorily determined (albeit only stochastically since the determination is by means of the sample), predictions of future measurements can be made and the reliability of any characteristic of the parent distribution can be established with many fewer measurements than is possible when we must rely on the sample knowledge alone. Some examples of this convenience, in the case of specialized types of derived quantities (e.g., the means and precisions of successive subsets) that are fitted reasonably well by the normal distribution, have been shown in the discussions of many of the topics of this chapter. In Chapter 4, the normal model is explored in some detail, and then in the final chapter the Poisson model and typical Poisson measurements are discussed.

3-11. Problems

The student should test his intuitional feeling with the correct answer to each problem.

1. Given the measurements:

10.01 ± 0.25 gm	9.98 ± 0.04 gm
10.00 ± 0.12	9.97 ± 0.06
9.99 ± 0.05	9.96 ± 0.15

(a) Find the weighted mean if the weights are taken as inversely proportional (i) to the ± values, (ii) to the squares of the ± values as they should be.

(b) Find the standard error (standard deviation in the mean) if each ± value is interpreted as the standard deviation.

2. The standard deviation in the reading of a given voltmeter is 0.20 v; the corresponding quantity for a given ammeter is 0.015 amp. What are the percentage standard deviations of single determinations of wattages of lamps operated at approximately their rated wattages, obtained from readings on these instruments for the case of

(a) a 500-w, 115-v lamp,   (ans. 0.39%)

(b) a 60-w, 115-v lamp,   (ans. 2.9%)

(c) a 60-w, 32-v lamp, and   (ans. 1.0%)

(d) a 60-w, 8-v lamp?   (ans. 2.5%)

3. With what precision may the density of a 10-g steel ball bearing of approximate density 7.85 g/cm^3 be obtained if the standard deviation of the determination of its average radius is 0.015 mm, and of its mass, 0.05 mg?   (ans. 0.67%)

4. What is the standard deviation in u, where $u = 3x$, in terms of the standard deviation in x?

5. One of the radiation constants is given by the formula

$$\alpha = \frac{2\pi^5 k^4}{15 h^3 c^2}$$

where $k = 1.38049 \times 10^{-16}(1 \pm 0.000,05)$ erg/(molecule °K),
  $h = 6.6254 \times 10^{-27}(1 \pm 0.000,2)$ erg-sec,
  $c = 2.997928 \times 10^{10}(1 \pm 0.000,004)$ cm/sec,

where the ± values are probable errors.

(a) Solve for α and express it with the proper number of significant figures.

(b) What is its probable error expressed with the proper number of significant figures?

6. What is the standard deviation in u, where $u = 3x + 5y^2$, from the measurements

$$x = 12 \quad 13 \quad 11 \quad 12 \quad 10 \quad 14 \quad 13 \quad 12 \quad 14 \quad 13 \quad 12$$
$$y = 35 \quad 37 \quad 34 \quad 37 \quad 34 \quad 37 \quad 36 \quad 35 \quad 38 \quad 34 \quad 35$$

(a) when x and y are assumed to be completely independent, and

(b) when they are recognized as being partially dependent?

7. (a) What is the correlation coefficient in Problem 6?

(b) What is the equation, with constants evaluated, of the linear regression line?

8. p is the pull required to lift a weight w by means of a pulley block, and the following measurements are made:

$$p \text{ (lb)} = 12 \quad 15 \quad 21 \quad 25$$
$$w \text{ (lb)} = 50 \quad 70 \quad 100 \quad 120$$

(a) Find a linear law of the form $p = a + bw$.

(b) Compute p when $w = 150$ lb.

(c) Find the sum of the deviations.

(d) Find the sum of the squares of the deviations of the given values of p from the corresponding computed values.

Note significant figures in all parts of this problem.

9. In a determination of h/e by the photoelectric method, the following stopping potentials were found, after correction for the contact potential difference, corresponding to the various wavelengths of incident light:

λ (A) =	2535	3126	3650	4047	4339	5461
V (v) =	+0.520	−0.385	−0.915	−1.295	−1.485	−2.045

Using the least-squares method, determine h/e and its standard deviation. Assume errors in V only, a fractional standard deviation of 0.5%.

10. If R is the resistance to motion of a car at speed V, find a law of the form $R = a + bV^2$ from the following data:

(a) weighted equally, and

(b) weighted in proportion to the speed V:

$$V \,(\text{mi/hr}) = 10 \quad 20 \quad 30 \quad 40 \quad 50$$
$$R \,(\text{lb/ton}) = 8 \quad 10 \quad 15 \quad 21 \quad 30$$

11. The α-ray activity of a sample of radon, expressed in terms of its initial activity as unity, is measured after each succeeding 24-hr interval to be: 0.835, 0.695, 0.580, 0.485, 0.405, 0.335, 0.280, and 0.235. On the assumption that the activity obeys an exponential decay law, find the equation that best represents the activity, and determine the decay constant and the half-life.

(ans. $y = 1.000,36e^{-0.1815t}/\text{day}$, 0.1815/day, 3.82 days)

12. What is the expression for the best value of α in the blackbody law relating radiant energy and temperature, $E = \alpha T^4$, from n pairs of measurements?

(a) Solve this problem first without knowledge of the precision of the measurements by writing the relation in each of the following forms:

(i) $E = \alpha T^4$

(ii) $\ln E = \ln \alpha + 4 \ln T$

(iii) $E/(T^4) = \alpha$

and give a qualitative reason for the differences in the answers.

$$\left[\text{ans. (i) } \Sigma E_i T_i^4/(\Sigma T_i^8), \text{ (ii) } \ln^{-1}(\Sigma \ln E_i - 4\Sigma \ln T_i)/n, \text{ (iii) } \frac{1}{n} \Sigma \frac{E_i}{T_i^4} \right]$$

(b) Solve the problem in terms of the standard deviations s_E and s_T constant for all pairs of measurements.

13. Calculate the value of the correlation coefficient r for the following data on the heights x (in inches) and weights y (in pounds) of 12 college students:

$x =$	63	72	70	68	66	69	74	70	63	72	65	71
$y =$	124	184	161	164	140	154	210	164	126	172	133	150

14. Are the stars that are easily visible with the naked eye randomly distributed in the sky? Divide the entire sky into many equal small solid angles, and discuss a method for finding the answer in terms of sample means and standard deviations.

15. A quantity y is expressed in terms of a measured quantity x by the relation $y = 4x - 2/x$. What is the percentage mean deviation in y corresponding to an error of 1% in x?

(ans. depends upon x; about 1% when x is large, ∞ when $x = 1/\sqrt{2}$)

16. The viscosity η of a liquid is calculated using Poiseuille's formula for the quantity of liquid Q flowing through a cylindrical tube of length l and of radius a in time t under a pressure difference p. Write the expression for

(a) the mean deviation,
(b) the fractional mean deviation,
(c) the fractional standard deviation

in η in terms of the errors in the measured quantities Q, l, a, and p, where

$$\eta = \frac{\pi p a^4 t}{8lQ} .$$

17. The viscosity η of a liquid is measured by a rotation viscometer. The cylinders are of radii a and b, and a torque G is applied to the rotating cylinder so that $\eta = \dfrac{G}{4\pi\omega}\left(\dfrac{1}{a^2} - \dfrac{1}{b^2}\right)$, where ω is the angular velocity of rotation. Calculate

(a) the fractional mean deviation, and
(b) the fractional standard deviation

in η when $a = 4$ cm and $b = 5$ cm, and when the mean deviation in both a and b is 0.01 cm and the standard deviation in both a and b is 1.25×0.01 cm, assuming that the error in G/ω may be neglected.

18. A coil of n turns of radius r carries a current I. The magnetic field at a point on its axis at a distance x from its center is $H = 2nr^2I(r^2 + x^2)^{-3/2}$. If the error in measuring x is ϵ, find the value of x for which the error in H is greatest

(a) when ϵ is the standard deviation, and
(b) when ϵ is the mean deviation.   (ans. $r/2$)

19. The mean of 100 observations is 2.96 cm and the standard deviation is 0.12 cm. The mean of a further 50 observations is 2.93 cm with a standard deviation of 0.16 cm. Find

(a) the mean,
(b) the standard deviation, and
(c) the standard error

for the two sets of observations taken together as a single set of 150 observations.

20. Derive Eq. 3-36.

21. Prove that the frequency function of the variable t, Eq. 3-65, approaches the frequency function of the normal variable z, Eq. 1-25, as the number of degrees of freedom $\nu \to \infty$. Assume that the constant approaches $1/\sqrt{2\pi}$.

22. Consider the accompanying data on the yield of corn in bushels per plot on 22 experimental plots of ground, half of which were treated with a new type of fertilizer. Does the fertilizer increase the yield?

Treated	6.2	5.7	6.5	6.0	6.3	5.8	5.7	6.0	6.0	5.8
Untreated	5.6	5.9	5.6	5.7	5.8	5.7	6.0	5.5	5.7	5.5

Table 3-5

Gap (cm)	Sparking Potential (kv)	Gap (cm)	Sparking Potential (kv)
5	137	35	720
10	263	40	775
15	382	45	825
20	483	50	870
25	573	55	908
30	650	60	937

Table 3-6

x (mi/hr)	y (ft)
4	2, 10
7	4, 22
8	16
9	10
10	18, 26, 34
11	17, 28
12	14, 20, 24, 28
13	26, 34, 34, 46
14	26, 36, 60, 80
15	20, 26, 54
16	32, 40
17	32, 40, 50
18	42, 56, 76, 84
19	36, 46, 68
20	32, 48, 52, 56, 64
22	66
23	54
24	70, 92, 83, 120
25	85

23. Prove that the variable t^2 in Eq. 3-65 with v degrees of freedom is a special case of the variable F in Eq. 3-68 with $v_1 = 1$ and $v_2 = v$.

24. Ten rats were fed protein from raw peanuts and another 10 rats received theirs from roasted peanuts. The weight gains of the rats are shown in the accompanying data. Did roasting the peanuts have any effect on their protein value as judged by weight gain?

| Raw | 61 | 60 | 56 | 63 | 56 | 63 | 59 | 56 | 44 | 61 |
| Roasted | 55 | 54 | 47 | 59 | 51 | 61 | 57 | 54 | 62 | 58 |

25. Samples of sizes 10 and 20 taken from two normal populations give $s_1 = 12$ and $s_2 = 18$. Test the hypothesis that the standard deviations are internally consistent.

26. The curve to be fitted is known to be a parabola. There are 4 experimental points at $x = -0.6, -0.2, 0.2,$ and 0.6. The experimental y values are $5 \pm 2, 3 \pm 1, 5 \pm 1,$ and 8 ± 2. Find the equation of the best fitted curve.

[ans. $y(x) = (3.685 \pm 0.815) + (3.27 \pm 1.96)x + (7.808 \pm 4.94)x^2$]

27. Differentiate $(\partial/\partial p) \log L$, Eq. 3-8, with respect to p and, using Eq. 3-9, solve for $(p - p^*)^2$ and then show that the standard deviation in p, with the reference value as the estimate p^*, is $\sigma_p = \sqrt{p^*(1 - p^*)/n}$. Show that this result obtained by the method of maximum likelihood for the binomial distribution is equivalent to writing $\sigma_w = \sqrt{npq}$, Eq. 2-28, where w is the number of "wins."

28. Smooth the measurements given in Table 3-5 of the sparking potentials in air between spheres of 75-cm diameter as a function of sphere separation.

29. Measurements were made on the distance-to-stop as a function of speed with a group of 50 different automobiles of various manufacture and with different drivers. The measurements are given in Table 3-6. The speed is presumed to have been very accurately known in each case, the parent y distribution is presumed to be independent of x, and all the distance measurements to have equal weighting. Which of the following relations best represents the measurements and what are values of the constants:

(a) $y = ax$, (b) $y = b + cx$, (c) $y = dx^2$, or (d) $y = ex + fx^2$?

(ans. $e = 1.24, f = 0.082$).

4

Normal Probability Errors

The normal (Gauss) probability distribution is the mathematical model most commonly invoked in statistics and in the analysis of errors. For example, as was pointed out in the last chapter, it can be demonstrated analytically that this model fits very well the distribution of each of certain special parameters of empirical distributions: (a) the likelihood functions L_j of Section 3-1 approach a normal distribution; (b) in the tests of consistency of Section 3-3, the t distribution is normal if the number of degrees of freedom is very large; and (c) the ratios $s_{\bar{x}}/s_{\bar{x}_i}$ can be assumed to be normally distributed.

And it was pointed out that the analysis of the errors in direct measurements is greatly simplified if it can be assumed that the parent distribution is normal. Examples of such simplification are (a) the weight to be assigned to each measurement x_i is $1/s_{x_i}^2$ if the x_i's are normally distributed; (b) the method of least squares is strictly valid if the normal distribution applies; and (c) errors propagate according to convenient rules if the parent distributions are normal.

Indeed, the "theory of errors" as developed during the early years of the subject, i.e., the theory of probability as applied to direct measurements, was based almost exclusively on the assumption that the normal distribution fits the measurements. Nowadays, however, especially in view of the popularity of measurements made with Geiger counters, etc. (see Chapter 5), the Poisson distribution takes its place alongside the normal distribution in the analysis of errors in direct measurements. But even so, when the expectation value μ in the Poisson distribution (Eq. 1-26) is rather large, the simpler algebraic expression that describes the normal case is a convenient and satisfactory approximation to the Poisson expression.

4-1. Derivation of the Normal (Gauss) Probability Density Function

It is apparent in the binomial distribution, Eq. 1-21, that, if the "success" probability p is constant, the expectation or mean value μ and the neighboring region of interest shift to larger and larger values of k as the number of trials n increases. This is shown in Fig. 4-1. When n becomes *very* large, two significant features appear: (1) the mean value μ becomes of dominant importance as the reference value, i.e., we become much more interested in the *deviations* than in the values of k reckoned from the origin (at $k = 0$), and (2) the unit interval between adjacent k values becomes relatively very small, i.e., the distribution loses much of its practical

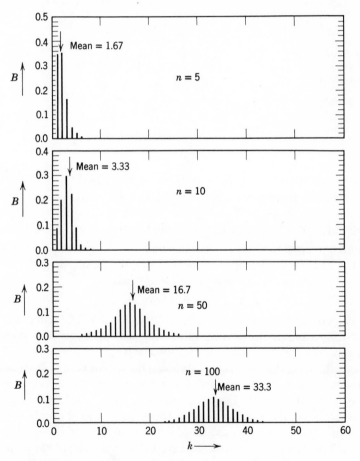

Fig. 4-1. Binomial probability $B(k; n, \frac{1}{3})$ vs. k; p constant, n varied.

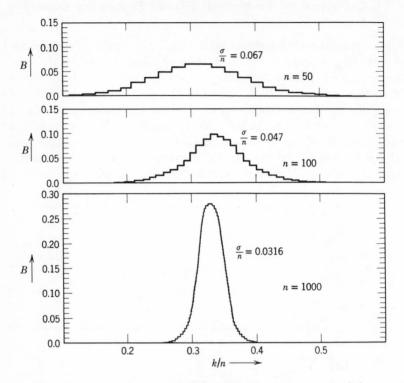

Fig. 4-2. Binomial probability $B(k; n, \frac{1}{3})$ vs. k/n; p constant, n varied.

discrete character. In regard to the second feature, if $n \to \infty$, the ratio of the unit k interval to the standard deviation $\sigma \ (= \sqrt{npq})$ approaches zero, and the distribution becomes continuous in the limit. In other words, adjacent values of the deviation variable z, where

$$z \equiv k - \mu = k - np \approx k - k_0 \qquad (4\text{-}1)$$

can be written, in the limit, as separated by the differential dz. In Eq. 4-1, k_0 is the most probable value of k as is discussed in connection with Eq. 1-24; and, in the limit, $k_0 - np = 0$.

As we shall see, the normal distribution is the special case of the binomial distribution when n becomes infinite and p remains of moderate value.

It is instructive to plot binomial distributions, as n increases, with k/n (instead of k) as the abscissa values. In such plots, as shown in the step curves of Fig. 4-2, the mean value of k/n is constant if p is constant, but the width of the curve decreases and the individual steps become smaller.

To derive the formula for the normal probability distribution, we use the first term of Stirling's approximation, Eq. 1-14, to represent each factorial number in the binomial expression. Thus,

$$B(k; n, p) = \frac{n!}{k!(n-k)!} p^k q^{n-k}$$

$$\approx \frac{\sqrt{2\pi n} n^n e^{-n}}{\sqrt{2\pi k}\, k^k e^{-k} \sqrt{2\pi(n-k)}(n-k)^{n-k} e^{-(n-k)}} p^k q^{n-k} \quad (4\text{-}2)$$

$$\approx \left(\frac{n}{2\pi k(n-k)}\right)^{1/2} \frac{n^n}{k^k(n-k)^{n-k}} p^k q^{n-k} \quad (4\text{-}3)$$

and, writing $n^n = n^k n^{n-k}$,

$$B(k; n, p) \approx \left(\frac{n}{2\pi k(n-k)}\right)^{1/2} \left(\frac{np}{k}\right)^k \left(\frac{nq}{n-k}\right)^{n-k} \quad (4\text{-}4)$$

Let us now change the variable k to z according to Eq. 4-1 and also write $n - k = nq - z$ (the latter follows from Eq. 4-1 and from $p + q = 1$). Then, Eq. 4-4 becomes

$$\begin{array}{l} B(z; n, p) \approx \\ n \text{ large} \end{array} \frac{1}{\left[2\pi npq\left(1 + \dfrac{z}{np}\right)\left(1 - \dfrac{z}{nq}\right)\right]^{1/2}} \left(\frac{1}{1 + \dfrac{z}{np}}\right)^{np+z} \left(\frac{1}{1 - \dfrac{z}{nq}}\right)^{nq-z}$$

Since, for n large, the quantities $z/(np)$ and $z/(nq)$ are small compared to unity, we may neglect them in the first factor; but they cannot be neglected in the parenthesized factors that are raised to high powers. In treating the parenthesized factors, it is convenient to rewrite the expression in logarithmic form so as to take advantage of the power series expansion of a logarithm. This expansion, for any x such that $2 > x > 0$, is

$$\log_e x = (x - 1) - \tfrac{1}{2}(x - 1)^2 + \tfrac{1}{3}(x - 1)^3 - \cdots \quad (4\text{-}5)$$

Hence,

$$\begin{array}{l} \log_e B(z; n, p) \approx -\left(\frac{1}{2}\right) \log_e (2\pi npq) - (np + z)\left[\frac{z}{np} - \frac{z^2}{2n^2 p^2} + \frac{z^3}{3n^3 p^3} - \cdots\right] \\ n \text{ large} \end{array}$$

$$+ (nq - z)\left[\frac{z}{nq} + \frac{z^2}{2n^2 q^2} + \frac{z^3}{3n^3 q^3} + \cdots\right]$$

$$\approx -\left(\frac{1}{2}\right) \log_e (2\pi npq) - \frac{z^2}{2n}\left(\frac{1}{p} + \frac{1}{q}\right) + \frac{z^3}{6n^2}\left(\frac{1}{p^2} - \frac{1}{q^2}\right)$$

$$- \frac{z^4}{12n^3}\left(\frac{1}{p^3} + \frac{1}{q^3}\right) + \cdots \quad (4\text{-}6)$$

For n small, several approximations have been made up to this point in the derivation; but for n large, the most serious approximation is the one to be made now, viz., that

$$\frac{z^3(q^2 - p^2)}{6n^2p^2q^2} - \frac{z^4(p^3 + q^3)}{12n^3p^3q^3} \approx 0$$

or, since $\sigma = \sqrt{npq}$ from Eq. 2-28, that

$$\frac{z^3(q^2 - p^2)}{6\sigma^4} - \frac{z^4(p^3 + q^3)}{12\sigma^6} \approx 0 \qquad (4\text{-}7)$$

Which of these two terms is the more important depends on the values of p and q. With this approximation, it is seen that, with p of moderate value, we neglect the net effect of all z terms of powers higher than the second in Eq. 4-6. Then, as an approximation, we change $B(z; n, p)$ to $G(z; n, p)$, with G symbolizing "Gauss", note that $p + q = 1$, and write

$$\log_e G(z; n, p) = -\left(\frac{1}{2}\right) \log_e (2\pi npq) - \frac{z^2}{2npq}$$

and

$$G(z; n, p) = \frac{1}{\sqrt{2\pi npq}} e^{-[z^2/(2npq)]}$$

An important feature of this expression is that the parameters n, p, and q of the binomial distribution appear always as a triple product. Hence, some simplification is afforded by writing

$$h \equiv \frac{1}{\sqrt{2npq}} = \frac{1}{\sigma\sqrt{2}} \qquad (4\text{-}8)$$

and then

$$G(z; h) = \frac{h}{\sqrt{\pi}} e^{-h^2 z^2} \qquad (4\text{-}9)$$

or

$$G(z; h) \Delta z = \frac{h}{\sqrt{\pi}} e^{-h^2 z^2} \Delta z \qquad (4\text{-}10)$$

Equation 4-9 is the normal (Gauss) probability density function. It is also called the normal differential probability distribution, or the law of the normal frequency distribution.

As seen in Eq. 4-9, $G(z; h)$ is only one value in a continuum of values, and $G(z; h)$ does not have the significance of probability until it is multiplied by Δz, as in Eq. 4-10. $G(z; h) \Delta z$ is the probability of observing a deviation z within the small interval Δz.

The function

$$\frac{h}{\sqrt{\pi}} \int_{-\infty}^{z} e^{-h^2 z^2} dz = \Phi(z) \qquad (4\text{-}11)$$

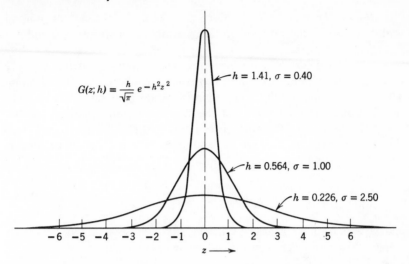

$$G(z; h) = \frac{h}{\sqrt{\pi}} e^{-h^2 z^2}$$

$h = 1.41, \sigma = 0.40$

$h = 0.564, \sigma = 1.00$

$h = 0.226, \sigma = 2.50$

$z \longrightarrow$

Fig. 4-3. Normal (Gauss) density function (normalized frequency distribution) for each of three values of the parameter h.

is called the normal (Gauss) probability distribution function or the cumulative probability distribution. (Note the difference between the terms "probability density function" and "distribution function.") Equation 4-11 gives the probability of observing a deviation z in the range $-\infty$ to z.

Shape of the normal frequency curve. Three graphs of the normal density function, Eq. 4-9, are shown in Fig. 4-3. The normal (Gauss) curve is symmetrical, since z appears to the second power only, and the curve approaches the z axis asymptotically at both extremes. The curve is shown as continuous as is appropriate for the normal distribution which is based on the assumption that the limits $n \to \infty$ and $\Delta z \to 0$ have been reached. The maximum ordinate and the shape of the curve are determined by the single parameter h. The peak ordinate value is $h/\sqrt{\pi}$, and the relative width of the curve increases as h decreases. h is a precision index that varies inversely with the standard deviation σ (Eq. 4-8).

Normalization. In order that Eq. 4-10 or 4-11 give a probability, it is necessary that the probability function be normalized, i.e., that the sum of *all* possible outcomes equal unity:

$$\frac{h}{\sqrt{\pi}} \int_{-\infty}^{\infty} e^{-h^2 z^2} \, dz = 1 \qquad (4\text{-}12)$$

This normalization has been assured in the derivation inasmuch as

$\sum_{k=0}^{n} B(k; \ n, p) = 1$, Eq. 1-22. Since the area under the curve is normalized, the inverse relation between the maximum ordinate and the width of the curve is obvious.

We shall have need later for the type of integration indicated in Eq. 4-12, so let us carry it out now and at the same time check the normalization. The usual method for this integration is based on geometrical considerations. Consider $y = G(z; \ h)$ in the z, y plane, and a similar function $y = G(x; \ h)$ in the perpendicular x, y plane. Let $A/2$ be the area under the curve in the z, y plane from $z = 0$ to ∞, and also the area under the curve in the x, y plane from $x = 0$ to ∞. Thus,

$$A = 2\frac{h}{\sqrt{\pi}} \int_0^\infty e^{-h^2 z^2} \, dz = 2\frac{h}{\sqrt{\pi}} \int_0^\infty e^{-h^2 x^2} \, dx \qquad (4\text{-}13)$$

and we wish to show that the coefficient $2(h/\sqrt{\pi})$ is such that the area $A=1$.

Since the x and z variables are independent,

$$A^2 = 4\frac{h^2}{\pi} \int_0^\infty e^{-h^2 z^2} \, dz \int_0^\infty e^{-h^2 x^2} \, dx = 4\frac{h^2}{\pi} \int_0^\infty \int_0^\infty e^{-h^2(z^2 + x^2)} \, d\bar{z} \, dx$$

Evaluating the double integral corresponds to determining the volume of the solid obtained by rotating the $G(z; \ h)$ curve about the y axis. To perform this integration, it is convenient to change to polar coordinates in the x, z plane. So, place $r^2 = z^2 + x^2$. The element of area $dz \, dx$ becomes $r \, d\theta \, dr$, and this is $(\pi/2)r \, dr$ in one quadrant. Hence,

$$A^2 = 4\frac{h^2}{\pi}\frac{\pi}{2} \int_0^\infty e^{-h^2 r^2} r \, dr$$

and the integration is in an easy form. Integration gives $A^2 = 1$, which proves that the normal probability density function is normalized as it is written in Eqs. 4-9 and 4-12.

In a measurement problem, we are concerned with an experimental frequency distribution of n trial measurements. This experimental distribution may be normalized by dividing the ordinate (frequency) scale by n. An alternative procedure, if use of the normal frequency distribution is involved in the analysis or predictions of the experimental values, is to multiply $G(z; \ h) \, \Delta z$, or $\int_{z_1}^{z_2} G(z; h) \, dz$, by n. The normal expression, multiplied by n, is properly called the normal frequency distribution; but this product is not a probability because it is no longer normalized. With the significance and procedure of normalization well understood, careful distinction is usually not explicitly made between the terms frequency distribution and probability distribution.

4-2. Errors in the Normal Approximation

The essential approximation made in the derivation of Eq. 4-9 was the neglect of the terms of powers higher than the second in the logarithmic expansion. This approximation, represented by Eq. 4-7, is valid only if n is very large or if all the deviations are very small. A quick inspection of Eq. 4-7 shows that the deviations should be at least smaller than about $\pm 3\sigma$ if $n \sim 10$, or about $\pm 4\sigma$ if $n \sim 100$. (Note that n is the number of *Bernoulli* trials.)

Table 4-1. Errors in $G(z; h) \Delta z$

k	$B(k; 10, 0.2)$	$G(z; h) \Delta z$
0	0.1074	0.0904
1	0.2684	0.2307
2	0.3020	0.3154
3	0.2013	0.2307
4	0.0880	0.0904
5	0.0264	0.0189
6	0.0055	0.0021

As an example of the errors introduced for large deviations, consider the calculations shown in Table 4-1 for $n = 10$ and $p = 0.2$. The agreement between $G(z; h) \Delta z$ and the correct $B(k; n, p)$ is not alarmingly bad for small k even though n in this case is not large. The magnitude of Δz is taken as unity in these calculations. In the comparison, the normal reference value ($z = 0$) is taken at $\mu = np = 2$. In this case in which μ is an integer, μ is also the most probable value k_0 of the binomial distribution. It should be pointed out, however, that the normal distribution formula is derived on the condition not only that $n \to \infty$ but also that the integration is carried out from $-\infty$ to $+\infty$. The latter condition is not well met in these calculations; this means that here $G(z; h)$ is not normalized and that the mean is not at $z = 0$. The central part of the normal distribution, as represented by the values in Table 4-1, is symmetrical and, with it for comparison, the skew in the binomial distribution is apparent.

As another example, this time with $n = 100$, $p = 0.3$, i.e., with a larger value of $\mu (= 30)$, compare the calculations listed in Table 4-2. The percentage error is seen to be rather small for all those deviations less than about $\pm 3\sigma$, but the percentage error becomes rapidly large for those deviations greater than about $\pm 4\sigma$, especially on the side of negative z. This is in agreement with the prediction made earlier from the quick inspection of Eq. 4-7. It should be pointed out that almost all, about 95%, of the area under the normal density curve is contained within $\pm 2\sigma$,

Table 4-2. Errors in $G(z; h) \Delta z$

k $\Delta k = 3$	z $\Delta z = 3$	$B(k; 100, 0.3) \Delta k$	$G(z; h) \Delta z$	% Error
10	−20	0.000 006	0.000 03	+400
13	−17	0.000 15	0.000 33	+100
16	−14	0.002 01	0.002 83	+40
19	−11	0.014 30	0.015 99	+12
22	−8	0.059 07	0.058 95	0
25	−5	0.148 87	0.144 47	−3
28	−2	0.237 94	0.234 05	−2
32	2	0.230 13	0.234 05	+2
35	5	0.140 86	0.144 47	+3
38	8	0.058 89	0.058 95	0
41	11	0.017 02	0.015 99	−6
44	14	0.003 43	0.002 83	−18
47	17	0.000 49	0.000 33	−33
50	20	0.000 05	0.000 03	−40

and about 99.7% is contained within $\pm 3\sigma$. Incidentally, much of the error in the central region, viz., $z \lesssim \pm 2\sigma$, is due to the arbitrarily adjusted position of the normal origin at μ. Also, the skewness of the binomial distribution is still quite noticeable even when μ is as large as 30.

As a final example of the errors due to the normal approximation, consider $n = 100$ and $p = 0.5$. Taking $p = 0.5$ gives the special binomial case of symmetry, and in this case the errors are independent of the finite skewness of the typical ($p \neq 0.5$) binomial distribution. Note also in this case, $p = 0.5$, that the third-order term in Eq. 4-6 is equal to zero, hence, that the worst approximation is that the fourth-order term be taken as equal to zero. This example is illustrated by the numerical values in Table 4-3.

4-3. Significance of the Bernoulli Trials in Actual Measurements

Elementary Errors: The normal (Gauss) probability distribution function has been derived on the basis of n Bernoulli trials with a constant success probability p per trial. Now we wish to apply this function in the analysis of trial measurements of, say, the length of a table. What is the significance of the n Bernoulli trials? And what do we mean in the table-measurement problem when we say that n must be large and p constant in order that the actual measurements "fit" the normal distribution? The answers to these questions are in terms of the so-called elementary errors mentioned in the discussion of random errors in Section 2-7.

Table 4-3. Errors in $G(z; h)$ Δz Independent of Skewness

All odd-order terms in Eq. 4-6 are zero

k $\Delta k = 3$	z $\Delta z = 3$	$B(k; 100, 0.5)\,\Delta k$		$G(z; h)\,\Delta z$		% Error
52	2	0.221	26	0.220	96	−0.14
55	5	0.145	88	0.145	18	−0.41
58	8	0.067	43	0.066	55	−1.3
61	11	0.021	39	0.021	28	−0.52
64	14	0.004	69	0.004	75	1.3
67	17	0.000	70	0.000	74	5.7
70	20	0.000	07	0.000	08	14
73	23	0.000	00	0.000	01	20

We assume that the variations among actual trial measurements (e.g., of the length of the table) are caused by the many elementary errors that unavoidably enter in each measurement. The elementary errors are *never specifically recognized*—if any such error were recognized the experiment would (or should) be modified to eliminate it or at least to reduce it drastically. In general, we may list as examples of such errors:

(1) Extremely small disturbances and fluctuations due to such things as mechanical vibrations, changes in the line voltage, variations in temperature (fluctuations caused perhaps by thermal expansion or contraction or even by Brownian motion, as is very likely the case in Fig. 2-3), "pickup" from other electrical operations in the environment, irregularities in instrument calibration, molecular motion in an electrical resistor, "shot effect" in an electronic vacuum tube, cosmic rays or residual radioactivity in the background, etc.

(2) Human judgment, as in interpolating beyond the smallest division of a scale of an instrument, position of the eye which introduces an inconstant parallax, fluctuations in the response of the eye or of the nervous system in general, etc.

(3) Uncertainty in the definition of the property being measured as, for example, in the length of a table whose edges are not exactly parallel or perfectly smooth, or in the intensity of cosmic rays or of β-particles in nuclear disintegrations, etc.

This list is not intended to be exhaustive, merely illustrative. And it may be pointed out that, if we are so inclined, each imagined elementary error may be subdivided into more elementary errors. The number of such errors, all presumed now to be random and independent, is very large indeed.

With measurements in continuous sample space, each elementary error is to be identified with a basic Bernoulli trial. We assume that the effect of each elementary error is a very small increment, either positive or negative, in the actual measurement; we assume that the elementary errors so conspire that the observed deviation is their algebraic sum. With measurements in discrete sample space, as in counting experiments, the elementary errors are grouped into bundles that correspond to "yes, a count is observed" and "no, a count is not observed" in a specified sample. In this case, as discussed in Chapter 5, the basic Bernoulli trial is identified with "a count" vs. "no count."

Mechanical analog for Bernoulli-type elementary errors in continuous sample space. Referring to Fig. 4-4, suppose that many identical small spherical steel balls are dropped one at a time vertically from the nozzle at the top. Each ball filters down through the symmetrical array of steel pins (represented by solid circles in the figure) and comes to

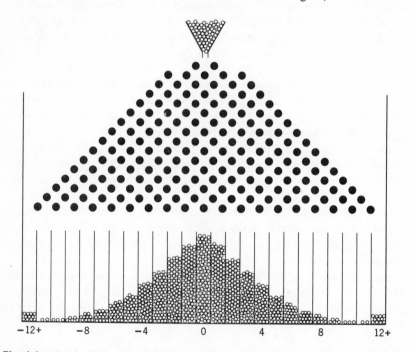

Fig. 4-4. Model of elementary errors underlying the normal distribution. Each ball dropped from the nozzle finds its way to a bin at the bottom and corresponds to one measurement. (After Galton.)

rest in one of the many identical bins at the bottom. Whether the ball, as it encounters a pin, goes to the right or to the left is presumed to be determined entirely by chance. As drawn, the pins are arranged in an array of quincunxs (one side of a face-centered cubic structure). If each ball is only slightly smaller than the clearance distance between pins, it falls practically head on to the next pin and has a constant chance, perhaps a 50–50 chance, of being deflected to the right or to the left. It is not necessary that this chance be 50–50, but it must be constant, the same for each pin encountered; a noneven chance might be realized in this model if pins of an asymmetrical shape were used. There are numerous possible paths through the array and some balls will find their way to each of many different bins.

In analogy, each operation of a ball filtering through to a bin is a measurement. The horizontal position of the nozzle represents the supposedly "true" value for the case of the 50–50 pin chance; each deflection caused by a pin encountered in the filtering process corresponds to a small elementary error; and the position of the bin into which the ball finally comes to rest represents the measured value.*

If the chance is 50–50, then the central bins, directly under the nozzle, have the best chance of receiving the largest number of balls, and the frequency with which a ball enters a particular bin decreases with the distance of the bin from the central position. If the right-left deflection chance per pin is constant but is not 50–50, the shape of the histogram is essentially the same and symmetrical but its maximum ordinate is shifted to one side; this corresponds to the effect of a systematic error.

As mentioned in Chapter 3, there is no practical way of distinguishing between an undetected systematic error and one or more random elementary errors since, in real life, we *never truly know* the "position of the nozzle."

To be a good analog for the normal distribution, the number of horizontal rows of pins and the number of balls dropped must be increased indefinitely, and the geometrical size of the balls, the pin spacing, and the bin size must be reduced indefinitely (conditions that, in combination, correspond to the infinite number of Bernoulli trials and to continuous sample space). These extensions can be easily imagined.†

* The "true" value is merely supposed because, unfortunately, our *best* view of it is through the thick veil of elementary errors. Also, in some measurements, the property itself is altered by the very process of measurement, a complication enshrined in Heisenberg's uncertainty principle. In any case, the "true" experimental value is usually taken as the mean value resulting from the measurements.

† The ball filtering down through the array of pins is solving the popular random-walk problem in one dimension. If the deflection chance is 50-50, the ball performs a symmetric random walk. The physicist takes this as the simplest model for one-dimensional diffusion.

Characteristics of elementary errors. In the derivation of the normal distribution we assumed that the magnitude of the increment per elementary error is constant (only *two* possible outcomes of a Bernoulli trial, viz., positive and negative), and that the probability p that the magnitude is positive is constant for all elementary errors. In an actual measurement, it is most unlikely that all the elementary errors contribute in accord with these two assumptions. However, those elementary errors making extremely small incremental contributions are presumed to be less important than those making larger contributions. In essence, then, we assume the existence of a very large number n of important elementary errors all of about the same incremental size, and all of about the same positive sign probability p. p may be reasonably presumed to be $\frac{1}{2}$ but this value is not necessary.

In support of the just-mentioned relaxation of the rigid Bernoulli requirements of the elementary errors, we may point out that the normal distribution function can be derived on the basis of elementary errors having somewhat different characteristics from those of the Bernoulli trials in our derivation.*

Two other sets of characteristics are as follows: (1) If $p = \frac{1}{2}$, the incremental contributions need not be rigidly constant in magnitude for all elementary errors; if they are very small, they may be merely of the same order of magnitude. (2) If the sizes of all the possible increments of a given elementary error are themselves normally distributed, the number of errors n need not be specified, n may be either large or small, and, furthermore, the standard deviation in the distribution due to *any one* elementary error may be large or small.

In conclusion, it is reasonable to suppose that numerous elementary random errors of the various imagined causes actually do exist and are indeed responsible for the observed variations in the trial measurements in continuous sample space. And it is reasonable to suppose that these elementary errors conspire in such fashion as to cause the trail measurements to fit in more or less good approximation to the normal (Gauss) distribution, even though we are not able to fix in detail their special characteristics. Also, it is reasonable that the region of greatest misfit of a set of trial measurements is in the tails, say $|z| \gtrsim 2\sigma$, for which a few elementary errors of relatively large contributions but of nonnormal shape would have the greatest effect.

It is significant that, at least to the author's knowledge, *no* experimental situation leads to a truly normal distribution, and that the

---

* All these derivations are special cases in probability theory of the proof of the so-called central limit theorem. See H. Cramér, *Mathematical Methods of Statistics* (Princeton University Press, Princeton, 1946), pp. 213–232.

deviations from normal are greatest in the tail regions beyond about $\pm 2\sigma$.

In the application of the normal distribution function to actual measurements, the Bernoulli-trial parameters n, p, and q have no individual significance beyond the concepts of the elementary errors. These parameters always appear as the product npq and this product, which does have practical significance, we refer to in terms of the precision index h or σ [$\sigma = 1/(h/\sqrt{2}) = \sqrt{npq}$]. In the application of the normal distribution, we shall generally determine (best estimate) σ and h from the actual measurements themselves rather than from the Bernoulli parameters. Having no further need of n as a symbol of the number of Bernoulli trials, we use it as the symbol for the number of actual trial measurements. It is hoped that this double use of the symbol n will not be confusing.

4-4. The Error Function

The probability of observing a deviation z in the range from $-z_1$ to $+z_2$, where z_1 and z_2 are arbitrarily chosen, is found by integrating the normal density function, Eq. 4-9, between these particular limits. This integration is carried out by expanding the exponential term in a power series and by integrating term by term, but it is a tedious process. Fortunately, integral values for most problems can be found in reference tables. In the tables, we generally find the integral value as integrated from either 0 to z or from $-z$ to $+z$ (where the numerical value of z is the parameter of the table), and it is necessary to make simple additions or subtractions to deduce the integral value between two arbitrary limits of integration such as z_1 and z_2. This is easily done with comprehension if we remember that the integral between any two limits is the area under that part of the normal density curve bounded by the two limits.

Standardized variables. The function $\Phi(z)$ given in Eq. 4-11 is not in a satisfactory form for general tabular listing because h has a different numerical value for each different specific set of measurements. It is convenient to standardize the variable, i.e., to use either hz or z/σ ($= \sqrt{2}\,hz$) instead of just z; then, in terms of either of these forms of the variable, the error function is invariant to different values of h (or of σ).

The two most popular forms of the invariant function for computational purposes are

$$\Phi(x) = \frac{2}{\sqrt{\pi}} \int_0^x e^{-x^2} dx \qquad (4\text{-}14)$$

where $x = hz$, and

$$\operatorname{erf}(t) = \operatorname{erf}\left(\frac{z}{\sigma}\right) = \frac{1}{\sqrt{2\pi}} \int_{-t}^{+t} e^{-t^2/2}\, dt \qquad (4\text{-}15)$$

where $t = z/\sigma = \sqrt{2}\,hz$. The term "error function" is used specifically in reference to Eq. 4-15. To aid in the ready use of the tables,* we point out that, in Eq. 4-14 where $x = hz$, $\Phi(x) = 0.8427$ for $x = 1$; in Eq. 4-15, where $x = z/\sigma = \sqrt{2}\,hz$, erf $(t) = 0.6827$ for $t = 1$; and also in Eq. 4-15, if the integration limits are 0 to t instead of from $-t$ to $+t$, $\frac{1}{2}$ erf $(t) = 0.3413$, viz., $0.6827/2$, for $t = 1$. (Note that x here is not the value of a single measurement, as in Chapters 1, 2, and 3, but is a standardized deviation.) Table 4-4 lists some values of $\frac{1}{2}$ erf (t) from 0 to t.

4-5. Precision Indices

To use Eq. 4-14 or 4-15 in a typical measurement problem, we must know two parameters. First, we must know the central location value, the value at which $z = 0$. This is usually taken as at the arithmetic mean of the set of n observed trial measurements. Then, we must know one or more of the dispersion precision indices. For example, if the standard deviation s is known from the n observed measurements, a satisfactory estimate of the universe standard deviation σ is obtained from the relation

$$\sigma = \left(\frac{n}{n-1}\right)^{1/2} s$$

as discussed in connection with Eqs. 2-22 and 3-98. Knowing the numerical value of σ we may proceed with the change of the variable z to the standard variable z/σ, or to zh since we know that $\sigma = 1/(h\sqrt{2})$, and make use of Eq. 4-15 or 4-14 respectively.

Dispersion indices other than σ and h are common, e.g., the mean deviation $\bar{z}$ and the probable error (or some other confidence limit). For a mathematical model of the frequency distribution, such as the normal distribution, a simple numerical relation exists between each pair of the various dispersion indices.

Mean deviation. The mean deviation $\bar{z}$ is taken without regard to the algebraic sign of the individual deviations, as discussed in Chapter 2

---

* B. O. Peirce, *A Short Table of Integrals* (Ginn & Co., Boston, 1956), 4th ed., p. 128, uses the form of Eq. 4-14.

H. B. Dwight, *Tables of Integrals* (Macmillan Co., New York, 1957), 3rd ed., p. 275, uses the form of Eq. 4-15.

The Handbook of Chemistry and Physics (Chemical Rubber Publishing Co., 1956), 38th ed., uses the form of Eq. 4-15 with the integration from 0 to t instead of from $-t$ to $+t$.

Tables of Probability Functions, Vol. 1 (Federal Works Agency, Work Projects Administration, 1941, sponsored by the National Bureau of Standards), uses Eq. 4-14.

Table 4-4. Error Function $\frac{1}{2}$ erf (t) from 0 to t and Ordinate Values
$$G(t) = (1/\sqrt{2\pi})\, e^{-t^2/2}$$

t	$\frac{1}{2}$ erf (t) Area	$G(t)$ Ordinate	t	$\frac{1}{2}$ erf (t) Area	$G(t)$ Ordinate
0	0	0.3989	2.0	0.4773	0.0540
0.1	0.0398	0.3970	2.1	0.4821	0.0440
0.2	0.0793	0.3910	2.2	0.4861	0.0355
0.3	0.1179	0.3814	2.3	0.4893	0.0283
0.4	0.1554	0.3683	2.4	0.4918	0.0224
0.5	0.1915	0.3521	2.5	0.4938	0.0175
0.6	0.2258	0.3332	2.6	0.4953	0.0136
0.7	0.2580	0.3123	2.7	0.4965	0.0104
0.8	0.2881	0.2897	2.8	0.4974	0.0079
0.9	0.3159	0.2661	2.9	0.4981	0.0060
1.0	0.3413	0.2420	3.0	0.4987	0.0044
1.1	0.3643	0.2179	3.1	0.4990	0.0033
1.2	0.3849	0.1942	3.2	0.4993	0.0024
1.3	0.4032	0.1714	3.3	0.4995	0.0017
1.4	0.4192	0.1497	3.4	0.4997	0.0012
1.5	0.4332	0.1295	3.5	0.4998	0.0009
1.6	0.4452	0.1109	3.6	0.4998	0.0006
1.7	0.4554	0.0941	3.8	0.4999	0.0003
1.8	0.4641	0.0790	4.0	0.5000	0.0001
1.9	0.4713	0.0656	4.4	0.5000	0.0000

and stated in Eq. 2-7. This index for the normal distribution is written with the subscript "th" to indicate that it is theoretical or universe rather than experimental. Thus,

$$\bar{z}_{th} = \frac{\dfrac{2h}{\sqrt{\pi}} \displaystyle\int_0^\infty z e^{-h^2 z^2}\, dz}{\dfrac{h}{\sqrt{\pi}} \displaystyle\int_{-\infty}^\infty e^{-h^2 z^2}\, dz} = \frac{2h}{\sqrt{\pi}} \int_0^\infty z e^{-h^2 z^2}\, dz \tag{4-16}$$

Dividing by the area under the distribution curve, as in the middle part of Eq. 4-16, is a routine normalization procedure but is not necessary in this case because we already know that the probability distribution is properly normalized, Eq. 4-12. The remaining integral in Eq. 4-16 is an easy one to evaluate, and we find that

$$\bar{z}_{th} = \frac{1}{h\sqrt{\pi}} = \frac{0.564}{h} \tag{4-17}$$

Our best estimate as to the value of $\bar{z}_{th}$ from $\bar{z}$, the experimental value, is usually taken to be

$$\bar{z}_{th} \approx \left(\frac{n}{n-1}\right)^{\frac{1}{2}} \bar{z} \tag{4-18}$$

As mentioned in Chapter 2, the mean deviation $\bar{z}$ is rather commonly used by experimenters, not only because it is the easiest dispersion index to calculate. It was also stated in Chapter 2 that the mean deviation is an inefficient index. And, as mentioned before, in addition to its inefficiency, the mean deviation does not lead to a useful general rule for the propagation of errors in a derived measurement. The standard deviation is generally a preferable index.

Standard deviation. The square root of the mean squared deviation for the normal distribution is written as

$$\sigma = \left(\frac{\dfrac{h}{\sqrt{\pi}}\displaystyle\int_{-\infty}^{\infty} z^2 e^{-h^2 z^2} dz}{\dfrac{h}{\sqrt{\pi}}\displaystyle\int_{-\infty}^{\infty} e^{-h^2 z^2} dz}\right)^{\frac{1}{2}} = \left(\frac{h}{\sqrt{\pi}}\int_{-\infty}^{\infty} z^2\, e^{-h^2 z^2} dz\right)^{\frac{1}{2}} \tag{4-19}$$

where, again, the indicated normalization is not actually necessary in this case. This expression may be altered slightly,

$$\sigma = \left(-\frac{1}{h\sqrt{\pi}}\int_{0}^{\infty} e^{-h^2 z^2}(-2h^2 z^2)\, dz\right)^{\frac{1}{2}}$$

and the integration performed by parts. (Write $u = z$ and $dv = z e^{-h^2 z^2}\, dz$.) Then,

$$\sigma = \left\{-\frac{1}{h\sqrt{\pi}}\left[\left[z e^{-h^2 z^2}\right]_0^{\infty} - \int_0^{\infty} e^{-h^2 z^2} dz\right]\right\}^{\frac{1}{2}}$$

The first term on the right vanishes at both limits; the second term is the definite integral we encountered in Eq. 4-13. After carrying out the integration, we have

$$\sigma = \frac{1}{h\sqrt{2}} = \frac{0.707}{h} \tag{4-20}$$

This expression we already knew, Eq. 4-8, from the derivation of the normal frequency distribution; its derivation here merely checks the various arguments and gives us practice in their use.

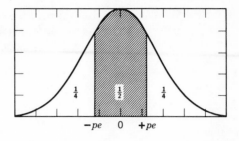

Fig. 4-5. The particular deviation known as the probable error, *pe*, divides the area $\frac{1}{4}:\frac{1}{2}:\frac{1}{4}$.

Probable error. The probable error, *pe*, is defined as the particular deviation that divides the left (or right) half of the area under a frequency distribution curve into two equal parts. Thus, the probability of observing a deviation within $\pm pe$ is $\frac{1}{2}$. This is indicated in Fig. 4-5. In other words, for a normal distribution, *pe* is the particular value of *z* for which erf $(x) = \frac{1}{2}$, viz.,

$$\text{erf}\,(x) = \frac{1}{2} = \frac{2}{\sqrt{\pi}} \int_0^{x=h(pe)} e^{-x^2} dx$$

This integral is easily evaluated from a table of values of error functions, and we find

$$pe = \frac{0.4769}{h} = 0.6745\sigma \tag{4-21}$$

The probable error, having equal positive and negative magnitudes, is a dispersion index that can be indicated on the graph of *symmetrical distributions only*. It is hardly the less useful, although not pictorial, as a dispersion index for asymmetrical distributions. Indeed, the probable error is an index rather commonly used by experimental scientists, although statisticans always prefer the standard deviation. It is important to note that the numerical relation between the probable error and any other index depends specifically upon the shape of the distribution; the numerical relation in Eq. 4-21 between *pe* and σ holds specifically for the normal distribution.

Confidence limits in general. The probable error is the 50% confidence limit by definition; see Fig. 4-5. Any other confidence limit, e.g., the 90% confidence limit, may be deduced in the same manner as that for the probable error. Thus, for the 90% limit,

$$0.90 = \frac{2}{\sqrt{\pi}} \int_0^{x=h(90\%\text{c.l.})} e^{-x^2} dx, \qquad 90\% \text{ c.l.} = \frac{1.164}{h} \tag{4-22}$$

In terms of confidence limits in the normal distribution, the precision indices correspond to the per cent limits as listed in Table 4-5.

Table 4-5. Numerical Relationships between Various Dispersion Indices
and the Confidence Limits for the Normal Distribution

Dispersion Index	Confidence Limit (%)
$\sigma/2$	38.3
pe	50
$\bar{z}_{th}$	57.6
σ	68.3
$2pe$	82.2
$1/h$	84.2
2σ	95.45
$3pe$	95.69
3σ	99.73

In summary, for the normal distribution,

$$pe : \bar{z}_{th} : \sigma : \frac{1}{h} = 0.477 : 0.564 : 0.707 : 1.000$$

$$\approx 3\tfrac{1}{2} : 4 : 5 : 7$$

and these ratios are valid, of course, whether the variable is taken as z
or as hz or as $\sqrt{2}\,hz$. The relative positions of these indices, and the
corresponding ordinate values, are indicated on the normal frequency
curve of Fig. 4-6.

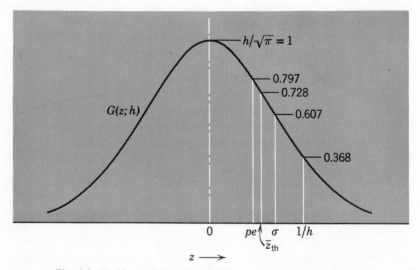

Fig. 4-6. Positions of dispersion indices in the normal distribution.

4-6. Probability for Large Deviations

In a normal distribution the probability that a deviation $|z|$ will be observed equal to or greater than some particular deviation $|z_1|$ is given by

$$G(|z| > |z_1|) = \frac{2h}{\sqrt{\pi}} \int_{z_1}^{\infty} e^{-h^2 z^2} \, dz$$

This probability may be more easily evaluated, depending on the particular tables available, if the limits of integration are changed and the expression written as

$$G(|z| > |z_1|) = 1 - \frac{2h}{\sqrt{\pi}} \int_{0}^{z_1} e^{-h^2 z^2} \, dz \qquad (4\text{-}23)$$

A few calculations with Eq. 4-23 are listed in Table 4-6. In this table, for convenience, the independent variable is listed as $|z_1/\sigma|$. Note from the

Table 4-6. Probability for Large Deviations

$\|z_1/\sigma\|$	$G(\|z\| > \|z_1\|)$ (%)	Odds against, to 1	$\|z_1/\sigma\|$	$G(\|z\| > \|z_1\|)$ (%)	Odds against, to 1
0.6745	50.0	1.00	2.4	1.64	59.99
0.8	42.37	1.36	2.6	0.932	106.3
1.0	31.73	2.15	2.8	0.511	194.7
1.2	23.01	3.35	3.0	0.270	369.4
1.4	16.15	5.19	3.5	0.0465	2,149.
1.6	10.96	8.12	4.0	0.0063	15,772.
1.8	7.19	12.92	5.0	5.73×10^{-5}	1.7×10^6
2.0	4.55	20.98	6.0	2.0×10^{-7}	5.0×10^8
2.2	2.78	34.96	7.0	2.6×10^{-10}	3.9×10^{11}

table that the probability for observing a deviation greater than $|2\sigma|$ is small, and for a deviation greater than $|3\sigma|$ is *very* small.

Rejection of a "bad" measurement. It often happens in a trial series that one measurement differs from the others by a relatively large amount. It is *possible*, of course, that such a widely divergent value should occur even if the number of measurements n is small. And if n is large, we should *expect* a few large deviations. The probability for a large deviation is independent of n but the frequency of occurrence of such a deviation is directly proportional to n.

The appearance of a widely divergent measurement places the experimenter in a difficult position. The relative influence of this one measurement is distressingly large on the magnitude of the mean and on the standard deviation (or on the probable error; this error is computed from the standard deviation). The experimenter is faced with the question: In order to do "justice" to his measurements as a whole, should the "bad' measurement be rejected?

Before seriously considering rejection, the experimenter should do the following. First, he should make additional measurements if at all possible so as to lessen the relative influence of the divergent value or else to reveal it more convincingly as being "bad." Second, he should make every effort to find a blunder or a transient systematic error that might be responsible for the discordant value. Many important discoveries have been made in searches for possible valid reasons for the divergence beyond that owing to randomness. There is, for example, the famous case of the discovery of argon by Lord Rayleigh. He noted a discrepancy between the density of a sample of nitrogen prepared from air and that of a sample produced chemically. It would have been easy for him to reject immediately one of his results as having been caused by some unidentified mistake.

Sometimes, confronted with the question of what to do with a divergent value, the experimenter uses the median instead of the mean as the better location value and also as the reference value in computing the dispersion index, e.g., the "standard deviation from the median." However, a price is paid for the safety afforded by this scheme—the median is less efficient than the mean, i.e., more measurements are needed to obtain the same precision. Also, this procedure is very unconventional in experimental science, and if it is used the reported measurements may be misunderstood.

This problem of what to do with a large deviation is so common that, as a general policy, some investigators take the mean of all but the highest and lowest values in each set of trial measurements. To resort to this device is obviously less than honest, and, in fact, it denies the fundamental basis of statistical interpretations of precision.

Chauvenet's criterion for rejection. Rejection on the basis of a hunch or of general fear is not at all satisfactory, and some sort of objective criterion is better than none. Many objective criteria have been proposed, all of them arbitrary. The one due to Chauvenet seems to be the most widely accepted. This criterion states that a measurement in a set of n trials shall be rejected if its deviation (reckoned from the mean) is such that the probability of occurrence of all deviations equally large or larger does not exceed $1/(2n)$. On this criterion, some rather *small* deviations are unreasonably discarded if n is not very large.

If the parent distribution is normal, the critical rejection size z_{ch} (subscript "ch" for Chauvenet) can be computed for any value of n from the equation

$$G(|z| \geqslant |z_{ch}|) = \frac{2h}{\sqrt{\pi}} \int_{z_{ch}}^{\infty} e^{-h^2 z^2} \, dz = \frac{1}{2n} \qquad (4\text{-}24)$$

For this calculation, h is computed (from s) before the measurement in question is rejected. The need for the factor 2 in the coefficient of the integral in Eq. 4-24 is readily recognized if the rejection criterion is restated as follows: The deviation, to be acceptable, must fall with the range bounded by $\pm z_{ch}$; if it falls ouside of this range, *on either side*, it is rejected.

Note that as n increases the critical rejection size z_{ch} also increases, and, for very large n, rejection of any measurement becomes very improbable, as it should. The dependence of z_{ch} on n up to 500 is shown in Table 4-7.

Table 4-7. Dependence on n of Chauvenet's Limiting Values hz_{ch}, z_{ch}/σ, z_{ch}/pe

n	hz_{ch}	z_{ch}/σ	z_{ch}/pe	n	hz_{ch}	z_{ch}/σ	z_{ch}/pe
5	1.16	1.68	2.44	20	1.58	2.24	3.32
6	1.22	1.73	2.57	30	1.69	2.39	3.55
7	1.27	1.79	2.68	40	1.77	2.50	3.70
8	1.32	1.86	2.76	50	1.82	2.58	3.82
9	1.35	1.92	2.84	100	1.98	2.80	4.16
10	1.39	1.96	2.91	200	2.14	3.02	4.48
14	1.49	2.10	3.12	500	2.33	3.29	4.88

In this table, for convenience of interpretation, the critical deviation is standardized in each of three ways.

If Chauvenet's criterion is used and a measurement rejected, and if a second measurement is also suspected of being "bad," the same criterion may be applied to the second measurement. Before applying the criterion to the second measurement, the first measurement must be discarded and the new value of the mean and of the standard deviation must be computed for use in Eq. 4-24 from the remaining measurements. To be consistent, this procedure should be repeated until no measurement remains in the set if it falls outside the limit. If as many as several per cent of the measurements are rejected, this fact should arouse suspicion that the parent distribution is *not* normal, that the tails are indeed higher than normal. A test of the goodness of fit of the normal distribution should be made (Section 4-8). In any case, if rejection is made, the best practice is to compute the mean value after the final rejection, but the standard deviation, as the measure of precision, *before* any rejection.

It must be recognized that rejection of any sort, as stated above, violates the fundamental postulate of statistical interpretation of random measurements. But, in addition to this objection, the mild warning mentioned above must be emphasized in regard to Chauvenet's or to any criterion for rejection based on the normal distribution. The elementary errors responsible for the observed variations in the n trial measurements are different for different types of measurements. As a consequence, the criterion, arbitrary at best, is generally arbitrary in a different way for different types of measurements. We should especially note that the region beyond about $|2.5\sigma|$ is just the region where, in any a priori case, we lose confidence that the normal distribution is an adequate description of the parent population.

Finally, it is important that the experimenter who rejects one or more measurements, and intends his results to be statistically significant, should report very carefully the detailed conditions of the measurements, the total number of trials, the particular measurement(s) rejected, and the criterion of rejection, all this as part of the reported final results.

4-7. Test of a Statistical Hypothesis: Example

The type of arguments made in the objective test for rejection of a "bad" measurement is also involved in the test for rejection of a statistical hypothesis. An understanding of this type of argument is essential in the statistical interpretation of the significance of almost any type of observation or theory. For practice, let us discuss now a simple example of a test of a statistical hypothesis. Also, this example will better prepare us to understand the χ^2 test of the next section.

Consider that a die has been cast 315,672 times and that either a 5 or a 6 appeared 106,602 times. The hypothesis to be tested is that the die is "true."

In this example, we wish to find out whether or not the outcomes of this experiment fit satisfactorily a binomial distribution where $n = 315,672$ and, according to the hypothesis, $p = \frac{1}{3}$. The binomial expectation value for success, i.e., for either a 5 or a 6, is $np = 315,672 \cdot \frac{1}{3} = 105,224$. This value is different from the one actually observed by a relatively small amount, viz., 1378—about $1\frac{1}{3}\%$. This difference does not seem to be very much, but the question is, Is it more than we should expect on the basis of purely random outcomes of each cast of a perfectly true die? We can answer this question with rather satisfactory reliability by the following argument.

If many experiments, an infinite number in the limit, were to be performed with a perfectly true die, each experiment consisting of 315,672 casts of the die, there would be many different numbers of successes; in fact, with an infinite number of such experiments, the frequency distribution is just the binomial distribution $B(k; n, p) = B(k; 315,672, \frac{1}{3})$, Eq. 1-20. The standard deviation in this distribution is

$$\sigma = \sqrt{npq} = \sqrt{np(1 - p)} = \sqrt{315,672 \times \tfrac{1}{3} \times \tfrac{2}{3}} = 264.9$$

Now, we may compare the deviation of the result obtained with the actual die, viz., 1378, with the standard deviation with a perfectly true die, viz., 264.9. We may express this comparison conveniently by writing the experimental standardized deviation $(1378/264.9)\sigma = 5.20\sigma$.

Our next task is to determine whether or not this observed deviation, 5.20σ, is a reasonable one owing to statistical fluctuations alone on the assumption that the die is true. We ask, What is the binomial probability, with $p = \frac{1}{3}$, of having a deviation this large or larger in a single trial set of 315,672 casts? If this probability is very small, we shall conclude that the deviation 5.20σ is "unreasonably" large and that the die is "probably" not true; but, on the other hand, if this probability is not small, the die is "probably" true. To determine this probability, we must sum over all the number of successes outside the limits $\pm 5.20\sigma$, i.e., greater than $k = 105,224$ and less than 103,846, in the binomial distribution. The arithmetic in performing this sum is simplified by noting that the normal distribution is a very good approximation to the binomial. Then we may write, with $n = 315,672$ and $p = \frac{1}{3}$,

$$B(np - 1378 < k < np + 1378;\ n, p) = \frac{2}{\sqrt{2\pi}} \int_{5.20}^{\infty} e^{-t^2/2}\, dt$$
$$= 0.000,000,2$$

using Eq. 4-15 in which the standardized variable is z/σ. Hence, the chance that a true die will give a result of 106,602 (or more) successes is about 1 in 10,000,000, and we conclude that either the die is not true or else a *most unexpected* event has occurred.*

Since, as we have just shown, it is not reasonable for p to be $\frac{1}{3}$, it is instructive to extend this example to include the question, What is the reasonable value and range of values for p as judged from the 106,602 successes? The most reasonable value for p is simply the experimental value $106,602/315,672 = 0.3377$. The proper number of significant figures with which to write this value of p is our next concern. We must decide what numerical deviations are reasonable. One commonly employed criterion, an easy one to use, is that reasonable deviations must not exceed $\pm \sigma$. The value of σ is not sensitive to the actual value of p in this example, and we may take it as 265. Hence, the limiting expectation values are $106,602 \pm 265$ and the "reasonable" limiting range of values of p is $\pm 0.000,84$ as deduced from the calculation $(106,602 \pm 265)/315,672 = 0.3377 \pm 0.000,84$.

Another commonly used criterion is that the limiting deviations are those for which the probability exceeds 0.01 (or sometimes 0.05). With

---

* This example could be rephrased to demonstrate the law of large numbers in the effective convergence of the expression for the experimental probability, Eq. 1-39.

this criterion, the limiting deviation $|z_1|$ is given implicitly by the expression

$$\frac{2}{\sqrt{2\pi}} \int_{z_{1\sigma}}^{\infty} e^{-t^2/2} \, dt > 0.01 \quad \text{(or sometimes 0.05)} \quad (4\text{-}25)$$

Using the critical value 0.01, we find $|z_1| = 2.576\sigma$ from a table of values of the error function. It follows that the limiting range of values of p is ± 0.0022 from the calculation $(106{,}602 \pm 265 \times 2.576)/315{,}672 = 0.3377 \pm 0.0022$. This is the "reasonable" limiting range if we say that on the average 99 out of 100 random observations (each observation consisting of 315,672 trials) are reasonable, and that 1 out of 100 arouses our suspicions to the extent that we declare it to be unreasonable.

The first criterion mentioned, viz., $|z_1| = \pm\sigma$, is equivalent to saying that about 68 out of 100 are reasonable and 32 out of 100 are unreasonable. This is a much more stringent requirement.

Let us quickly review what we have just done. In this binomial example, the position of the actual deviation, viz., 1378, was found to lie in the remote tails of the binomial distribution for $p = \frac{1}{3}$. For this reason, it is unreasonable to say that the deviation is due to random fluctuations alone, and so the statistical hypothesis that $p = \frac{1}{3}$ was rejected. Then, assuming that the binomial model, with the *experimental* value of p, does fit the actual observations, we found the "reasonable" range of values of p.

In this example as it is given, the statistical hypothesis as to the value of p is the only one we can test. Suppose now that, instead of having only two possible outcomes of each cast, viz., a 5 or a 6 on the one hand and a 1, 2, 3, or 4 on the other hand, there has been recorded the number of times *each* of the six different sides of the die appeared. Now we can test whether or not the multinomial distribution agrees reasonably well with the observations as well as test whether or not each of the six values of p is $\frac{1}{6}$. The test for each value of p would proceed in the same manner as above described, the problem being treated as a binomial one. But the test of the hypothesis as to the model parent distribution is more involved in just the same way that the multinomial distribution is more complex than is the binomial distribution. The test of a hypothesis that a particular model distribution fits a given experimental distribution is known as the test for "goodness of fit" and is discussed next.

4-8. Test of Goodness of Fit of a Mathematical Model

The frequency distribution of a small number n of measurements generally provides us with only sketchy information as to the parent distribution whose characteristics we seek. The experimental distribution may suggest more than one maximum, will generally show asymmetry, and it may suggest either higher or lower tails than the normal distribution. If n is increased, these nonnormal characteristics may disappear or they may not. The problem now is to decide, having only a small n, whether or not the experimental distribution can be satisfactorily assumed to be a sample from a normal parent distribution.

We shall mention two qualitative graphical tests and then two quantitative tests of the goodness of fit of the normal curve. Although the discussion here is specific for the normal model, the general methods of the tests are applicable to any model.

Graphical comparison of frequency curves. The observed frequency distribution curve of the n trial measurements is plotted with the normalized ordinate scale, i.e., with each observed frequency divided by n. Then the mean m and the standard deviation s are computed. The model value of μ is taken equal to m. The value of the model index h is obtained from σ which, in turn, is taken as given by Eq. 2-22; then,

$$h = \frac{1}{s\sqrt{2}} \left(\frac{n-1}{n} \right)^{\frac{1}{2}}$$

With μ and h known, the normal frequency curve is calculated and plotted on the same graph paper as the experimental curve. The normal curve is of course centered about the experimental mean m. A visual comparison of the experimental points relative to the normal curve affords the first test of goodness of fit.

Figure 4-7 shows a typical example of the graphical comparison of an experimental histogram and the fitted normal curve.

This comparison is sometimes extended so as to express the discrepancy as the percentage of "excess" or "deficiency" of the normal curve at each experimental value of x or at the center of each classification interval. By this extension the test becomes, in a sense, quantitative. If the percentage discrepancies are large, the fit of the model curve is obviously poor; but if the discrepancies are small, we need some further arguments to help us decide whether or not these discrepancies may be merely the fluctuations to be expected in a sample size n from a parent population of the assumed normal model distribution. The additional arguments are made later in the χ^2 test.

Graphical comparison of cumulative distribution functions: probability paper. The second qualitative test compares summations of the observed values with corresponding integrals of the normal curve. The observed deviations z with respect to the mean m are listed in the order of size, the largest negative value at the top of the list and the largest positive value at the bottom. The entire range of observed deviations is

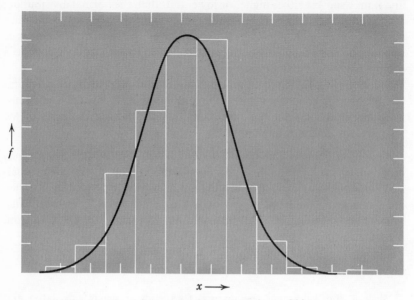

Fig. 4-7. Normal curve fitted to an experimental histogram.

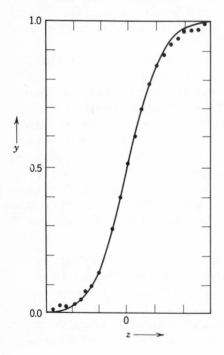

Fig. 4-8. Ogive curve for goodness of fit.

divided into M intervals, where M is about 10 or 20 or so. It is not necessary that all intervals be of the same size; in fact, it is usually best to make relatively large the intervals at the extreme ends of the range of deviations. No interval should be so small as to contain only one or two observations. These intervals are numbered consecutively 1, 2, $\cdots$, j, $\cdots$, l, $\cdots$, M. The jth interval has $(f_{obs})_j$ observed values in it, and, of course, $\sum_{j=1}^{M}(f_{obs})_j = n$, the number of measurements in the set. Now the points y_{obs} vs. z_l are plotted, where

$$y_{obs} = \sum_{j=1}^{l} (f_{obs})_j$$

and z_l is the deviation reckoned from the mean (at $z = 0$) to the center of the lth interval. (z_l is large negative for small l and is large positive for large l.) The plot consists of points such as are illustrated in Fig. 4-8. This is called the ogive curve. It is convenient to have the observed frequencies normalized, i.e., divided by n; in this case the normalized ordinate scale $(f_{obs})_j/n$ goes from 0 to 1.

Then, on the same graph paper, the corresponding quantities from the fitted normal distribution curve are plotted. These quantities are

$$y_{th} = \frac{h}{\sqrt{\pi}} \int_{-\infty}^{z} e^{-h^2 z^2} \, dz$$

where z is a continuous variable reckoned from the experimental mean m, and the parameter h is also determined from the experimental measurements as stated above. Comparison of the experimental points with the theoretical curve allows a qualitative test of the goodness of fit.

This comparison attempts to minimize the rapid fluctuations and to show trends of agreement or disagreement over extended regions of the distributions. But in the tail regions, where our concern is often most acute, the ordinate scale is too crowded, and, in consequence, this test is not satisfactorily sensitive in these regions. However, if the ordinate scale is stretched in such a nonlinear way that the y_{th} vs. z curve becomes a straight line, then the test is much better. Graph paper having such a stretched ordinate scale is called probability paper; it is symmetrical about the $y = 0.5$ line and is linear in units of z/σ in both directions from $y = 0.5$. Probability paper is illustrated in Fig. 4-9. The comparison between the observed points and the normal curve on probability paper can be made readily in the tails of the curve.

Probability paper can also be used conveniently to determine the experimental values of the mean m and the standard deviation s directly from the center and the slope, respectively, of the best-fitted straight line.

Skewness and kurtosis. Useful quantitative tests of the goodness of fit of the normal distribution can be made by comparing the numerical

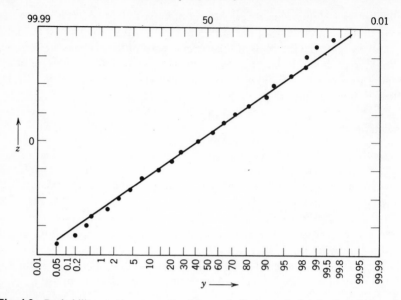

Fig. 4-9. Probability graph paper. On this graph the normal distribution plots as a straight line.

experimental values of skewness, Eq. 2-37, and of kurtosis, Eq. 2-41, with the normal values. The normal value of skewness is zero (symmetrical distribution); and a positive observed skewness means that, although more than half of the deviations are on the negative side of the mean, the majority of the large deviations are on the positive side; in other words, positive skewness means an excess of *weighted* positive deviations where the weighting is proportional to the cube of the deviation magnitude. Negative skewness means an excess of *weighted* negative deviations. The kurtosis of the normal distribution is 3; an observed kurtosis greater than 3 generally means tails higher than the normal, and lower than 3 means tails lower than the normal. By considering both the skewness and the kurtosis together, we can get a fairly good idea of the goodness of fit of the mathematical model.

Central moments higher than the fourth (kurtosis) are usually not very useful as a basis of comparison because they are so sensitive to large deviations unless the number of measurements in the set is rather large. As may be expected, however, their use increases as the number of measurements n increases.

The χ^2 test. A very useful quantitative test for the goodness of fit of a model distribution is the so-called χ^2 test ($\chi =$ chi), but it requires a minimum of about 30 measuremeuts. The χ^2 test gives a *single* numerical measure of the over-all goodness of fit for the *entire* range of deviations.

The observed deviations are ordered and classified as in the procedure for the ogive curve described above. Again, it is not required that the intervals all be of the same size, but now no interval should be so small that it contains less than about five measurements, and there should be at least about six or eight intervals. In this test, the observed frequency $(f_{obs})_j$ in the interval $(\Delta z)_j$ is compared with the theoretical model value $(f_{th})_j(\Delta z)_j$ corresponding to the center of the interval. (f_{th} is given by the product of the model probability and the number of trials n.) If the interval is so large that f_{th} cannot be assumed to be constant throughout $(\Delta z)_j$, the frequency function should be integrated over the range of the interval, but this is usually not necessary except in the first and last intervals. To maximize the statistical efficiency of the test, the square of the difference, i.e., $[(f_{th})_j - (f_{obs})_j]^2$, is taken, and this quantity is divided by $(f_{th})_j$. The quantity χ^2 is defined as the sum

$$\chi^2 \equiv \sum_{j=1}^{M} \frac{[(f_{obs})_j - (f_{th})_j]^2}{(f_{th})_j} \tag{4-26}$$

Exact fit of the model or theoretical frequency curve to the experimental measurements would correspond to $\chi^2 = 0$, an extremely fortuitous event in any real-life situation because of statistical fluctuations even if the model fits perfectly the parent distribution of which the actual set of measurements is a sample. Increasingly large values of χ^2 involve the probability arguments concerning the question of what statistical fluctuations are reasonable even if the model does fit perfectly.

If the model distribution is simply a uniform (flat) distribution, Eq. 4-26 may be written as

$$\chi^2 = \sum_{j=1}^{n} \frac{(x_j - m)^2}{m} \tag{4-27}$$

in case no attempt is made to group the n measurements into intervals.

In a general view, the χ^2 test determines the probability that a purely random sample set of measurements taken from the assumed model parent distribution would show better agreement with the model than is shown by the actual set.*

The type of arguments involved is essentially the same as was encountered in Section 3-3, in the t test and in the F test for consistency. Also, the

---

* The χ^2 test was introduced by Karl Pearson in 1900, and it is often called Pearson's χ^2 test. However, in the form of Eq. 4-27 it was first used by Lexis in 1877, and is sometimes called the Lexis divergent coefficient when written in this form.

arguments are those involved in the derivation of Eq. 3-96 by the method of maximum likelihood, and are very similar to those made in the rejection of a "bad" measurement and in the test of a statistical hypothesis. As stated before, these arguments are fundamental in almost every statistical interpretation for significance of actual data. But, although essentially the same as in the previous instances, the arguments as they are stated now are a little more complex and more difficult to follow through the first time. The reader should keep in mind, and review if necessary, the general "philosophy" of the previous examples.

In order to obtain the theoretical frequency values f_{th} devoid of random fluctuations, for each of the M intervals, we imagine an infinite number of trials or sets of measurements, all known to be sample sets from a multinomial model parent distribution. In each trial the number of possible outcomes is very large; this number is r in Eq. 1-30. r is taken as generally large but finite if the χ^2 test concerns a model having a discrete frequency distribution, or r may be infinite if the model is continuous such as the normal distribution. In any case, r is subdivided into the same M intervals used in the grouping of the experimentally observed frequencies. Then, from Eq. 1-30 with n very large, the multinomial frequency for the center of the jth interval, $(f_{th})_j$, is computed. This computation requires knowledge of the M different values of the probabilities p_j in the multinomial distribution, and this knowledge is obtained from the experimental measurements, specifically from the mean m and from the standard deviation s. By coupling the respective observed and theoretical intervals, we determine the frequency difference $(f_{obs} - f_{th})_j$ for each interval, and then the value of χ^2_{obs} from Eq. 4-26. The subscript "obs" is attached to this value of χ^2 to distinguish it from the theoretical value discussed next, which is based exclusively upon the model.

To deduce the exclusively theoretical value of χ^2, i.e., the effect of purely random fluctuations alone, we look more closely at the parent multinomial frequency distribution during its analytical formation, e.g., as the number of trial sets of hypothetical measurements builds up and becomes infinite. The multinomial probability p_j for the jth interval is the same value as was used above in determining χ^2_{obs}; this is the mean value of this probability, as may be determined with a very large number of trial sets of hypothetical measurements. But there exists a spread of values about this mean. We shall not prove it here, but this spread itself has essentially a normal frequency distribution. We make a single random theoretical trial set of measurements, then determine the difference between this random frequency value in the jth interval and the mean theoretical frequency value in this interval, and then finally determine the value of χ^2 for this random theoretical trial set of measurements. The

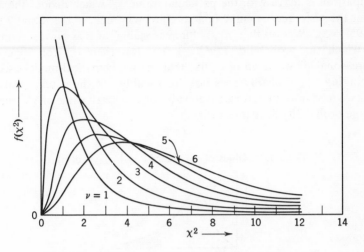

Fig. 4-10. χ^2 distribution for various degrees of freedom ν.

value of χ^2 is, of course, also one member of a frequency distribution that is spelled out and takes on its equilibrium shape as the number of random theoretical trial sets of measurements becomes infinite.

The derivation of the χ^2 frequency distribution is made from the normal variations in each of the possible outcomes, i.e., in each M interval, in the multinomial distribution. The arithmetic involved becomes tedious, and approximations are made similar to those in our derivation of the normal distribution. These approximations are reasonably good if a parameter ν (defined below) is greater than about 5, and if the number of measurements in each classification interval is greater than about 5. These conditions are imposed for similar reasons to those placed on the use of the normal approximation to the binomial distribution, viz., np and nq each greater than about 5. ν is related to M, as is mentioned presently. The expression for the χ^2 frequency distribution is*

$$f(\chi^2)\, d(\chi^2) = \frac{(\chi^2)^{\frac{1}{2}\nu - 1} e^{-\frac{1}{2}\chi^2}}{2^{\frac{1}{2}\nu}(\frac{1}{2}\nu - 1)!}\, d(\chi^2) \qquad (4\text{-}28)$$

The form of this expression was derived in Section 3-5 where $R^2\,(=2u)$ is written in place of χ^2 and n in place of ν; see Eqs. 3-95 and 3-96. The shapes of χ^2 distributions for a few values of ν are illustrated in Fig. 4-10.

As stated above, the significance of the actual value of χ^2_{obs} is found in a comparison with the theoretical value of χ^2 for the appropriate ν. This

---

* Note the close similarity of this expression to that for the Poisson distribution; and if $\chi^2 \gg 1$ and $\frac{1}{2}\nu \gg 1$, the approximation to a Gaussian is also very good.

comparison is made with the particular value $\chi_c{}^2$ which divides the area under the χ^2 frequency curve in a specified way, e.g., in the ratio 99 to 1 (or 95 to 5). We say that χ^2_{obs} is "unreasonable" if it is greater than $\chi_c{}^2$ for which the probability $P(\chi^2 > \chi_c{}^2)$ is less than 1% (or 5%). By "unreasonable" we mean of course that the mathematical model used in computing χ^2_{obs} probably does not "reasonably" fit the actual measurements. And note that, for a given value of ν, a small value of χ^2_{obs} means a large probability P as thus defined.

Table 4-8. Values of $\chi_c{}^2$ where $P = \int_{\chi_c{}^2}^{\infty} f(\chi^2) \, d(\chi^2)$

ν	$P =$ 0.80	0.50	0.30	0.20	0.10	0.05	0.02	0.01
4	1.649	3.357	4.878	5.989	7.779	9.488	11.668	13.277
6	3.070	5.348	7.231	8.558	10.645	12.592	15.033	16.812
8	4.594	7.344	9.524	11.030	13.362	15.507	18.168	20.090
10	6.179	9.342	11.781	13.442	15.987	18.307	21.161	23.209
12	7.807	11.340	14.011	15.812	18.549	21.026	24.054	26.217
14	9.467	13.339	16.222	18.151	21.064	23.685	26.873	29.141
16	11.152	15.338	18.418	20.465	23.542	26.296	29.633	32.000
18	12.857	17.338	20.601	22.760	25.989	28.869	32.346	34.805
20	14.578	19.337	22.775	25.038	28.412	31.410	35.020	37.566
25	18.940	24.337	28.172	30.675	34.382	37.652	41.566	44.314
30	23.364	29.336	33.530	36.250	40.256	43.773	47.962	50.892

Table 4-8* lists some values of $\chi_c{}^2$ for each of several values of $P(\chi^2 > \chi_c{}^2)$ and for each of several values of ν.

There remains the discussion of the quantity ν. This is simply the number of degrees of freedom. It is the number of *independent* frequency pairs being compared. If there were no constraints whatever on the calculation of χ^2, ν would be equal to M. However, one constraint is introduced by

---

* A more extensive table is found in P. G. Hoel, *Introduction to Mathematical Statistics* (John Wiley & Sons, New York, 1954), 2nd ed., p. 318, especially for values of P greater than 0.80.

the fact that the number of theoretical frequencies considered is limited to n, the number of experimental values. This constraint, viz.,

$$\sum_{j=1}^{M} f_{obs} = \sum_{j=1}^{M} f_{th} = n$$

is inherent of course in the χ^2 test. A second constraint is introduced when we locate the center of the model frequency curve. This constraint is expressed as the condition that μ in the model distribution be equal to the experimental mean value m. A third constraint is introduced when we deduce and use the universe value of the standard deviation from the experimental standard deviation. These three constraints are usually all that are made in testing the goodness of fit of a model distribution, and, if so, $\nu = M - 3$. However, if the total number of measurements is not very large, it is sometimes worthwhile to impose a fourth restraint, one in which M and the interval size are so chosen that the number of measurements in each interval is constant and nearly as large as M. This condition allows about the greatest validity of the χ^2 approximations, viz., that ν be greater than about 5 and that the number of measurements in each interval be greater than about 7. The interval sizes can be adjusted, however, without introducing a constraint if no size is influenced by any equation or approximate relation involving the experimental values.

As an example of the χ^2 test, consider 233 determinations of the velocity of light. Table 4-9 lists the frequency f_{obs} that a measurement occurs in the respective classified deviation interval. In this case the deviation is reckoned for arithmetic convenience from an arbitrary reference value of 299,000 km/sec, although the origin of the normal distribution curve is placed at the mean, 299,773.85 km/sec. The experimental standard deviation is 14.7 km/sec. The χ^2_{obs} value of 29.10 for $\nu = 13$ corresponds in Table 4-8 to a P probability of only about 0.005, and, since this is less than, say, 0.01 (or 0.05 if we prefer), the normal distribution is *not* a good fit to the actual measurements. However, if those intervals containing a small number of measurements are grouped together (as indicated by the braces in Table 4-9), reducing ν from 13 to 8, the χ^2_{obs} is 18.52 and the P probability is larger, about 0.018. This latter value is more reliable in view of the approximations made in the derivation of the $f(\chi^2)$ distribution, and the normal curve may be said to fit—at least we cannot be very *sure* it does not fit. The *formal* fit may possibly be even further improved by more appropriate grouping. This example emphasizes the arbitrariness of the criterion of fit; an unambiguous "yes" or "no" answer is not possible.

Finally, it must be pointed out that the χ^2 test can be applied in the test of the goodness of fit of *any* type of mathematical model of probability. The f_{th} of Eq. 4-26 must be calculated, of course, on the basis of the model

Table 4-9. Application of the χ^2 Test of Goodness of Fit of the Normal
Distribution to Measurements of the Velocity of Light

Deviation (km/sec)	f_{obs}	f_{th}	$(f_{obs} - f_{th})$	$\dfrac{(f_{obs} - f_{th})^2}{f_{th}}$
<741	3 ⎫	2.25 ⎫	0.75 ⎫	0.25 ⎫
741–745	7 ⎬ 14	3.04 ⎬ 11.24	3.96 ⎬ 2.76	5.15 ⎬ 0.68
746–750	4 ⎭	5.95 ⎭	−1.95 ⎭	0.64 ⎭
751–755	8	10.42	−2.42	0.56
756–760	17	16.24	0.76	0.04
761–765	23	22.60	0.40	0.01
766–770	29	28.06	0.94	0.03
771–775	45	31.09	13.91	6.23
776–780	40	30.73	9.27	2.80
781–785	17	27.11	−10.11	3.78
786–790	16	21.37	−5.37	1.35
791–795	10	14.99	−4.99	1.66
796–800	5 ⎫	9.39 ⎫	−4.39 ⎫	2.06 ⎫
801–805	2 ⎬ 14	5.27 ⎬ 19.14	−3.27 ⎬ −5.14	2.03 ⎬ 1.38
806–810	3	2.62	0.38	0.05
>810	4 ⎭	1.86 ⎭	2.14 ⎭	2.46 ⎭
	233	233		$\chi^2_{obs} = 29.10$ 18.52

in question. In testing the fit of a binomial distribution, it often happens that one or both of the two parameters p and n in $B(k; n, p)$ are specified as a part of the problem. For example, in a study of the sex distribution in families of seven children, $n (= 7)$ is known from the problem and is not obtained as a maximum likelihood estimate from the measurements; hence, $v = M - 2$. If, in this study, the objective is to test the hypothesis that $p = \frac{1}{2}$, the value of p is not obtained from the measurements; hence, in this case $v = M - 1$.* Also note that in testing the fit of a Poisson model distribution, the only parameter to be determined is μ (see Eq. 1-26) and the χ^2 test will usually involve either $M - 2$ or $M - 1$ degrees of freedom, depending upon whether μ is determined from the actual measurements or is otherwise known.

One difficulty with the χ^2 test is that, unless the number of measurements is rather large, a different value of χ^2 is obtained if the measurements are

* The remaining constraint has to do with the number N of families in the study, viz., the constraint that

$$\sum_{j=1}^{M} f_{obs} = \sum_{j=1}^{M} f_{th} = N$$

arranged into *different* groups of intervals either by their relative size or by their total number. Indeed, illustration of this fact was just given in the velocity of light example. This is partly because of the random nature of the measurements themselves and partly a consequence of the approximations that are made in the derivation of the χ^2 frequency distribution. It is largely for such reasons that we set the "rejection ratio" so low, say 1 or 5 out of 100, instead of near the ratio corresponding to the standard deviation, about 32 out of 100.

Statisticians have developed additional quantitative tests of goodness of fit, but they are seldom used by investigators in experimental science.

4-9. Conclusions

There are many direct trial measurements in experimental science that are fitted "rather well" by the normal (Gauss) distribution. These include the host of measurements that differ one from another in an essentially continuous manner as a consequence, apparently, of a large number of small elementary errors. The fit is typically less good in the tails of the distribution. This is presumably due to the fact that the idealized set of conditions on which the normal distribution (central limit theorem) is based is not quite realized in real life. However, to the extent that the fit is satisfactory, i.e, that the parent distribution is normal, the analytic form of the distribution function allows (a) very convenient predictions of the probability that any measurement, either past or future, will have a value within a specified range, (b) simple and convenient rules for the propagation of errors in a derived or computed measurement, (c) rules for assigning weights to measurements, (d) convenient equations for curve fitting, etc. Such predictions, calculations, etc., are of such great convenience in the statistical interpretation of measurements that there is a rather strong tendency for scientists to accept *uncritically* the normal distribution as the answer to their prayers.

A loud note of caution must be sounded in pointing out that the fit is typically not very good in the tails. Almost *any* set of trial measurements is generally bell shaped in the central region, and if interest in the statistics of the set is not very quantitative the normal approximation suffices. But if the interest is precise or if the tail regions are of special concern (as in rejecting a "bad" measurement"), a specific test of goodness of fit must be made and the reliability of the normal approximation judged accordingly.

In addition to its degree of quantitative fit to direct measurements and its use therein, the normal distribution is the one of most general and valid use in statistical theory in dealing with certain parameters of empirical distributions. This application of the normal distribution has been noted in the first paragraph of this chapter; to this earlier paragraph, we must now add the χ^2 test for the goodness of fit.

4-10. Problems

1. Show that the curve of the normal distribution formula has inflection points at $z = \pm\sigma$.

2. The times recorded by 37 observers of a certain phenomenon are classified to the nearest 0.1 sec as follows:

Observers Recorded	Sec
1	31.9
3	32.0
7	32.2
12	32.3
6	32.4
6	32.5
1	32.6
1	33.0

Plot the frequency distribution of these observations and then on the same graph plot a matching normal error curve. Calculate the standard deviation, probable error, mean deviation, 75% confidence limits, and 99% confidence limits, and indicate these values on both the abscissa and ordinate axes of the graph. Plot these observations on probability paper and deduce directly from this graph the values of the mean, standard deviation, and the 99% confidence limits. Discuss the reliability of these values.

3. Suppose that 5 letter grades, A, B, C, D, and F, are assigned to students in a large physics class. If the distribution is fitted by a normal curve with A representing the z interval -2.5σ to -1.5σ, B representing -1.5σ to -0.5σ, C -0.5σ to $+0.5\sigma$, D $+0.5\sigma$ to $+1.5\sigma$, and F $+1.5\sigma$ to $+2.5\sigma$,

(a) find the percentage of students who will be assigned each of the letter grades,

(b) discuss the significance of the fact that these percentages do not add up to 100%, and

(c) discuss the customary practical procedure to take care of the fact of part (b).

4. A certain time interval is measured 400 times, and the probable error of each observation is 0.3 sec. How many positive errors "should" occur between 0.2 and 0.4 sec? (ans. 57 ± 7)

5. Extend Problem 5 of Section 2-12, about the length of the iron bar, to find

(a) the probable error, and (ans. 0.0139 cm)

(b) the probability that another measurement taken under the same conditions would deviate from the mean by more than +0.006 cm. (ans. 0.773)

Discuss the validity of the assumption of a normal distribution.

6. As an example in the normal curve approximation, suppose that the probability that a marksman will hit a target is $\frac{1}{3}$ and that he takes 12 shots. Compare the binomial probability with the normal probability that he will score

(a) at best 6 hits, and   (ans. about $\frac{1}{2}\%$ discrepancy)

(b) exactly 6 hits.   (ans. about 5% discrepancy)

7. In a series of observations of an angle taken to tenths of a second of arc with $h = 0.447$ reciprocal seconds, assume a normal distribution and find

(a) the probability that the next observation will have an error between 1.0 and 1.1 sec, and

(ans. depends on interpretation of "between", e.g., 0.0204)

(b) the probability that the error will not be greater than ± 3 sec.

(ans. 0.9421)

8. If $1/h$ is 2 ft and the least count is 1 in., what is the probability that 3 randomly chosen measurements, regardless of the order of their taking, will have deviations of 8 in., 16 in., and -4 in.? What is the probability if the order is specified? Assume a normal distribution and assume that the mean is at the center of the least count interval.   [ans. $P(8) = 0.022$, $P(16) = 0.016$,

$P(-4) = 0.023$, $P_1 P_2 P_3 = 8.1 \times 10^{-6}$]

9. Show that the kurtosis of the normal distribution is equal to 3.

10. A value is quoted for the rest mass of the electron $m_0 = 9.1154 \times 10^{-28}$ (1 ± 0.00018) g, of which ± 0.00018 has the significance of a fractional probable error. Determine the probability that the value quoted

(a) is correct to within 0.0005×10^{-28} g,   (ans. 0.162)

(b) is correct to within 0.00010×10^{-28} g, and   (ans. 0.0325)

(c) is not correct to within 0.001×10^{-28} g.   (ans. 0.682)

11. In a breeding experiment, it was expected that ducks would be hatched in the ratio of 1 duck with a white bib to each 3 ducks without bibs. Of 86 ducks hatched, 17 had white bibs. Are these data compatible with expectation? Do the observations prove that the expectation was correct?

12. Should the last recorded observation in the data listed in Problem 2 be rejected according to Chauvenet's criterion?

13. (a) Compare on probability paper the binomial and normal probability distributions for $B(k; 100, 0.3)$ and $G(z; h)$ as listed in Table 4-2.

(b) Why is it not practical for a bookstore to stock probability paper for other model distributions than the normal?

14. From past experience, a certain machine properly operating turns out items of which 5% are defective. On a certain day, 400 items were turned out, 30 of which were defective.

(a) If a normal distribution is assumed in this problem, what are the coordinates of the plot of the distribution?

(b) What is the probability that the machine was operating properly on this day?

15. According to Mendelian inheritance theory, certain crosses of peas should give yellow and green peas in the ratio 3 : 1. In an experiment 176 yellow and 48 green peas were obtained.

(a) Do these conform to theory? Assume that the observation of 176 yellow peas conforms to the theory if it is within 2σ of the expected value.

(ans. conforms)

(b) Show that about 95% of the normal area is bounded by 2σ.

16. (a) Apply the χ^2 test to the fit of the normal curve to the following 500 observations of the width of a spectral band of light:

$$f_{obs} = 5 \quad 12 \quad 43 \quad 61 \quad 105 \quad 103 \quad 89 \quad 54 \quad 19 \quad 7 \quad 2 \quad \Sigma f_{obs} = 500$$
$$f_{th} = 5 \quad 14 \quad 36 \quad 71 \quad 102 \quad 109 \quad 85 \quad 50 \quad 21 \quad 7 \quad 2 \quad \Sigma f_{th} = 502$$

Here f_{th} denotes the fitted normal curve frequencies obtained by estimating the mean and the standard deviation from the actual measurements.

(b) What is the significance of the difference $(\Sigma f_{th} - \Sigma f_{obs})$?

17. How would you determine whether or not 100 given measurements (each measurement expressed, e.g., with 5 significant figures)

(a) are approximately random, and

(b) fit as members of a normal (Gauss) distribution?

Table 4-10

Hour	No. of Births	Hour	No. of Births	Hour	No. of Births
0	127	8	126	16	115
1	139	9	122	17	94
2	143	10	121	18	99
3	138	11	119	19	97
4	134	12	130	20	100
5	115	13	125	21	119
6	129	14	112	22	127
7	113	15	97	23	139

18. The hour (classification interval) at which each of 2880 births took place was recorded as in Table 4-10. Test the hypothesis that the births are uniformly distributed over the range from 0 to 24 hours.

5

"Lest men suspect your tale untrue,
Keep probability in view."

JOHN GAY

Poisson Probability Distribution

5-1. Introduction

In the preceding chapter the normal (Gauss) distribution, Eq. 4-9, was discussed as an approximation to the exact binomial distribution, Eq. 1-20. A more or less paralleling discussion is to be made for the Poisson distribution, so we shall quickly review the line of argument involved.

First, remember that the normal distribution plays a role of great fundamental importance in statistical theory in addition to its direct application to many sets of direct measurements. This is not so for the Poisson distribution, and our discussion in this chapter is concerned exclusively with applications to those sets of direct measurements that satisfy reasonably well the Poisson conditions.

The algebraic expression for the normal distribution was derived under the particular conditions that the number n of Bernoulli trials is very large and that the success probability p in each trial remains constant. The first practical advantage of the normal approximation in dealing with direct measurements is in the greatly simplified arithmetic when n is large—the factorial numbers, the fractions raised to high powers, and the tremendous algebraic summations are avoided. But the most significant advantage in dealing with direct measurements is that the Bernoulli parameters n, p, and q appear first in the product np, the location value, and then in the triple product npq. This triple product, generally considered to be the *only* parameter in the normal expression, is equal to the variance of the distribution, i.e., $npq = \sigma^2$. An estimate of the parameter σ is obtained from the standard deviation of the set of actual measurements; and the significance of the individual Bernoulli parameters is then relegated to the unidentified and little-understood elementary errors that are believed to be unavoidably present with different net effects in successive trial measurements. With σ evaluated, the simple normal formula is of inestimable aid to the investigator in designing his experiment, in allowing predictions of the probability of future measurements, and in judging the "reasonableness" of past measurements.

The Poisson distribution may also be derived as an approximation to the binomial distribution. Again, a *single* parameter is involved whose direct experimental evaluation, without regard to the values of the separate binomial parameters n, p, and q, allows very useful application in the analysis of measurements and in the design of experiments. In this case, however, we can often recognize the basic Bernoulli trials and evaluate n, p, and q from them; but often these basic trials remain hypothetical, as they are in the normal case. When the basic Bernoulli trials are recognized, their characteristics may justify immediately the application of the Poisson formulas; otherwise a test of goodness of fit, such as the χ^2 test, must be made.

Rare events. The Poisson approximation holds when the following three conditions in the binomial distribution are satisfied:

(1) n very large, infinite in the limit,

(2) p very small, zero in the limit, and

(3) the product np moderate in magnitude, i.e., that $np \ll \sqrt{n}$.*

Thus, on the average, many Bernoulli trials are required before the event called success appears. For this reason the Poisson distribution is often known as the formula for the probability of rare events.†

There are many examples of rare events for which we wish to make statistical analysis, predictions of future events, and arguments as to reasonableness. As illustrations, we may mention such classical problems as the fractional number of soldiers who die each year from the kick of a mule, the number of atoms that spontaneously decay per unit time in a radioactive sample, the chance that an average man of age 25 will die at a specified age, the incidence of an uncommon noncommunicable disease (such as polio) and its response to large-scale vaccination treatment, and the number of houses per thousand burned by fire per year. Typical rare-event problems are discussed in detail after we understand, first, the essential Poisson equations and, second, the order of magnitude of the errors involved in the approximation.

---

* A better statement of the third condition is that $k^2 + (np)^2 \ll n$, and then, if $k \sim np$, the left side need not be much less than the right side.

† The Poisson distribution is often improperly called the law of small numbers. The number of successes need not be small when n is very large. This is generally so in the case of a "spatial distribution" of events, as pointed out later.

5-2. Derivation of the Poisson Frequency Distribution Function

The derivation of the Poisson function may start with the binomial probability equation, Eq. 1-20. Noting that $p + q = 1$ and that $np = \mu$ (Eq. 2-26), we write Eq. 1-20 in the form

$$B(k; n, p) = \binom{n}{k} p^k q^{n-k} = \frac{n(n-1)(n-2)\cdots(n-k+1)}{k!}$$

$$\left(\frac{\mu}{n}\right)^k \left(1 - \frac{\mu}{n}\right)^{n-k}$$

$$= n^k \frac{1\left(1 - \frac{1}{n}\right)\left(1 - \frac{2}{n}\right)\cdots\left(1 - \frac{k-1}{n}\right)}{k!}$$

$$\left(\frac{\mu}{n}\right)^k \frac{\left(1 - \frac{\mu}{n}\right)^n}{\left(1 - \frac{\mu}{n}\right)^k}$$

$$= \frac{1\left(1 - \frac{1}{n}\right)\left(1 - \frac{2}{n}\right)\cdots\left(1 - \frac{k-1}{n}\right)}{\left(1 - \frac{\mu}{n}\right)^k}$$

$$\frac{\mu^k}{k!}\left(1 - \frac{\mu}{n}\right)^n \tag{5-1}$$

Under the Poisson conditions, viz., n very large, p very small, and the product np of moderate magnitude, the first fraction in Eq. 5-1 is essentially unity, and the last factor can be approximated as an exponential. To show this exponential approximation, write an exponential in the form of a power series,

$$e^\lambda = \frac{1}{0!} + \frac{\lambda}{1!} + \frac{\lambda^2}{2!} + \frac{\lambda^3}{3!} + \frac{\lambda^4}{4!} + \cdots \tag{5-2}$$

and write out the binomial expansion, e.g., from Eq. 1-21,

$$\left(1 - \frac{\mu}{n}\right)^n = 1 - \frac{n\left(\frac{\mu}{n}\right)}{1!} + \frac{n^2\left(1 - \frac{1}{n}\right)\left(\frac{\mu}{n}\right)^2}{2!} - \frac{n^3\left(1 - \frac{1}{n}\right)\left(1 - \frac{2}{n}\right)\left(\frac{\mu}{n}\right)^3}{3!}$$

$$+ \cdots \pm \left(\frac{\mu}{n}\right)^n$$

where the sign of the last term depends on whether n is even or odd. By comparison, it is apparent that

$$\lim_{n \to \infty} \left(1 - \frac{\mu}{n}\right)^n = 1 - \frac{\mu}{1!} + \frac{\mu^2}{2!} - \frac{\mu^3}{3!} + \frac{\mu^4}{4!} - \cdots = e^{-\mu} \tag{5-3}$$

With the first fraction of Eq. 5-1 written as unity and with the last factor as an exponential, the binomial probability becomes the Poisson probability, viz.,

$$P(k; \mu) = \frac{\mu^k e^{-\mu}}{k!} \tag{5-4}$$

Equation 5-4 is called the Poisson frequency distribution or "density" function. Note that it contains only one parameter, μ.

The Poisson cumulative distribution function is given by stopping the following sum at the desired value of k:

$$\sum_{k=0}^{n} P(k; \mu) = \sum_{k=0}^{n} \frac{\mu^k e^{-\mu}}{k!} = e^{-\mu} + \frac{\mu e^{-\mu}}{1!} + \frac{\mu^2 e^{-\mu}}{2!} + \cdots + \frac{\mu^n e^{-\mu}}{n!} \tag{5-5}$$

It is shown presently that this sum, as written, is equal to unity. The probability for observing no "success" is simply $e^{-\mu}$; for one success, $\mu e^{-\mu}$; for two successes, $(\mu^2 e^{-\mu})/2!$; etc.; for more than one success, $1 - e^{-\mu}$; for exactly k successes, Eq. 5-4; etc. Stirling's formula, Eq. 1-14, is often a help in evaluating $k!$ when k is greater than about 9.

In actual measurements, a number N of trials in an experiment may be made, each trial involving n basic Bernoulli trials. Equations 5-4 and 5-5 give the normalized probability or probabilities, as is expected of a model, and comparison of the calculations with the observed frequency or frequencies requires that either the observed values be normalized by dividing by N or that the calculated values be multiplied by N. But note the difference between the definitions of N and of n.

Shapes of Poisson frequency distributions. The shapes of the frequency distributions (or histograms) represented by Eq. 5-4 are essentially the same as the shapes of the binomial distributions for n large and p small. (Binomial distributions are illustrated in Figs. 1-2, 4-1, and 4-2, and also in Problem 6 of Section 1-9.) The shape has a positive skewness, but approaches symmetry as μ increases. When μ is rather large, the distribution is in the transition region between the Poisson and the normal distributions; in this region we may generally approximate the binomial by using either Eq. 5-4 or Eq. 4-10, whichever offers the simpler arithmetic.

The most probable value of k, viz., k_0, is generally less than the expectation value μ but never differs from it by more than unity. This was proved in a footnote in Chapter 1, p. 32. If $(n + 1)p$ is equal to an integer, k_0 is double-valued, i.e., adjacent k values at μ and at $\mu - 1$ have equal probabilities [see Problem 14 of Section 1-9].

It readily follows from Eq. 5-4 that

$$\frac{P(k+1); \mu)}{P(k; \mu)} = \frac{\mu}{k+1} \tag{5-6}$$

which indicates conveniently the rate with which $P(k; \mu)$ varies with k everywhere in the distribution.

Poisson to normal distribution. It is instructive to derive the normal density distribution from the Poisson equation, Eq. 5-4. To do this we may define the normal variable z in terms of the Poisson variable k, if $k \gg 1$ and $\mu \gg 1$, as

$$z = k - k_0 \approx k - (\mu - \tfrac{1}{2}) \tag{5-7}$$

Note that the Poisson distribution is intrinsically discrete, and by Eq. 5-7 we match in location the most probable value of k with the normal maximum. The means of the two distributions thus differ on the average by $\tfrac{1}{2}$. If $k \gg 1$ and $\mu \gg 1$, the term $\tfrac{1}{2}$ is of no practical consequence (except for k very close to μ). With Eq. 5-7 we may write

$$P((k_0 + z); \mu) = \frac{\mu^{k_0+z}e^{-\mu}}{(k_0 + z)!} = P(k_0; \mu)\frac{\mu^z}{(k_0 + 1)(k_0 + 2)\cdots(k_0 + z)}$$

$$\log_e P((k_0 + z); \mu) = \log_e P(k_0; \mu) + z \log_e\left(\frac{\mu}{k_0}\right) - \log_e\left(1 + \frac{1}{k_0}\right)$$

$$- \cdots - \log_e\left(1 + \frac{z}{k_0}\right)$$

In the normal case, k, k_0, and μ are very large compared with unity; by expanding the logarithms in a power series, Eq. 4-5, neglecting terms $[(\mu - k_0)/k_0]^2$ and higher powers, we find

$$\log_e P((k_0 + z); \mu) \approx \log_e P(k_0; \mu) + \frac{z(\mu - k_0)}{k_0} - \frac{z(z + 1)}{2k_0}$$

Then, with the definition of z in terms of μ as given by Eq. 5-7,

$$P((k_0 + z); \mu) \approx P(k_0; \mu)e^{-z^2/2k_0} = Ce^{-z^2/2k_0}$$

By the property of normalization, C may be determined as follows,

$$C \sum_{k=0}^{\infty} e^{-z^2/2k_0} = C \int_{-\infty}^{\infty} e^{-z^2/2k_0}\, dz = 1$$

and, since $q \approx 1$, and by Eqs. 1-24 and 4-8, $k_0 \approx npq = 1/2h^2$,

$$C = \frac{1}{\sqrt{2\pi k_0}} = \frac{h}{\sqrt{\pi}} \tag{5-8}$$

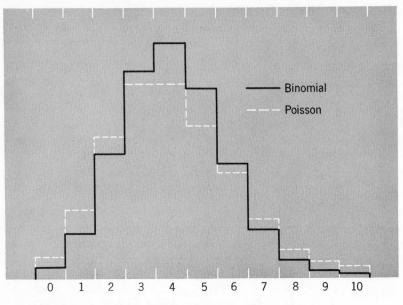

Fig. 5-1. Binomial and Poisson distributions for $n = 12$, $p = \frac{1}{3}$.

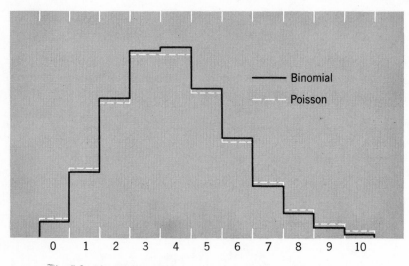

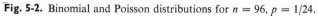

Fig. 5-2. Binomial and Poisson distributions for $n = 96$, $p = 1/24$.

We conclude that

$$P((k_0 + z); \mu) \approx P((\mu + z); \mu) \approx G(z; h) = \frac{h}{\sqrt{\pi}} e^{-h^2 z^2} \quad (5\text{-}9)$$

which is the same as Eq. 4-9 for the normal density function, or as Eq. 4-10 when $\Delta z = 1$.

Normalization. That the Poisson distribution is normalized, i.e., that the sum of all possible outcomes in the Poisson distribution is unity as $n \to \infty$, is assured by the fact that it is derived from the normalized binomial distribution, but this assurance depends upon the validity of the approximations made in the derivation. However, it is easy to show directly that this distribution is indeed exactly normalized. Write Eq. 5-5 as

$$\sum_{k=0}^{n} P(k; \mu) = e^{-\mu} \sum_{k=0}^{n} \frac{\mu^k}{k!} = e^{-\mu} \left[\frac{\mu^0}{0!} + \frac{\mu^1}{1!} + \frac{\mu^2}{2!} + \frac{\mu^3}{3!} + \cdots + \frac{\mu^n}{n!} \right]$$

As $n \to \infty$, the factor in brackets is of the same form as Eq. 5-2. Hence,

$$\lim_{n \to \infty} \sum_{k=0}^{n} P(k; \mu) = e^{-\mu} e^{\mu} = 1 \quad (5\text{-}10)$$

5-3. Errors in the Poisson Approximation

When n and p are both finite, the errors made in using the relatively simple Poisson expression, instead of the cumbersome but accurate binomial expression, are significant, of course, when the Poisson conditions are poorly approximated. For example, if $n = 12$ and $p = \frac{1}{3}$, the errors

Table 5-1. Errors in the Poisson Approximation

k	$B(k; 5, \frac{1}{5})$	$B(k; 10, \frac{1}{10})$	$B(k; 100, \frac{1}{100})$	$P(k; 1)$
0	0.328	0.3487	0.3660	0.3679
1	0.410	0.3874	0.3697	0.3679
2	0.205	0.1937	0.1849	0.1839
3	0.051	0.0573	0.0610	0.0613
4	0.006	0.0112	0.0149	0.0153
5	0.000	0.0015	0.0029	0.0031
6		0.0001	0.00046	0.00051
7		0.00001	0.00006	0.00007

are conveniently shown in graphical form as in Fig. 5–1. But the errors become rapidly smaller as either n increases or p decreases. For example, for $n = 96$ and $p = \frac{1}{24}$, the comparison is shown in Fig. 5-2. Other comparisons are illustrated in Table 5-1 for three different sets of n and p, with $np = \mu = 1$ in all three cases. It is evident from these examples that the Poisson approximation is satisfactory for most applications if n is of the order of 100 or more and if p is less than about 0.05. This is a good rule of thumb but, as noted earlier, the condition for small errors is better stated as $k^2 + (np)^2 \ll n$. It can be seen that the relative error increases as $(k - \mu)/n$ increases.

5-4. Precision Indices

To predict probability from the Poisson relations, Eqs. 5-4 and 5-5, we must first know the magnitude of the parameter μ. We have shown by the method of maximum likelihood that in the binomial distribution this parameter, the arithmetic mean, is equal to the product np. We have assumed above, with perfect validity, that in the Poisson case $\mu = np$ and is also the arithmetic mean. Just for practice let us show directly from Eq. 5-5 that μ is the mean.

Let the arithmetic mean of all k values in Eq. 5-5 be denoted by m_{th}. Then, by definition,

$$m_{\text{th}} = \sum_{k=0}^{n} kP(k; \mu) = e^{-\mu} \sum_{k=0}^{n} \frac{k\mu^k}{k!} = e^{-\mu} \sum_{k=1}^{n} \frac{k\mu^k}{k!} = e^{-\mu}\mu \sum_{k=1}^{n} \frac{\mu^{k-1}}{(k-1)!}$$

$$(5-11)$$

where the lower limit of the sum is changed from 0 to 1 because of the presence of the factor k in the numerator (the first term, for $k = 0$, is equal to zero), and where, in the last step, we divided through by k ($k > 0$) and substituted $\mu \cdot \mu^{k-1}$ for μ^k.* Then, as $n \to \infty$, the sum is equal to the exponential e^μ, as may be seen when e^μ is written as a power series, Eq. 5-2. Hence,

$$m_{\text{th}} = \lim_{n \to \infty} \sum_{k=0}^{n} kP(k; \mu) = e^{-\mu}e^\mu\mu = \mu \qquad (5-12)$$

This conclusion was also reached by the method of maximum likelihood in Section 3-1, Eq. 3-17.

Standard deviation. We know from Eq. 2-28 that, in the binomial distribution, $\sigma = \sqrt{npq}$. Hence, in the Poisson distribution, $\sigma \approx \sqrt{np}$ since $q \approx 1$, and, by Eq. 5-12 and the relation $\mu = np$,

$$\sigma = \sqrt{\mu} \qquad (5-13)$$

---

* The argument is sometimes made that, since $(-1)! = \infty$ (which can be shown by the gamma function, see discussion attending Eq. 1-16), the first term of the last sum in Eq. 5-11 is equal to zero and that, hence, the lower limit of the last sum may as well be changed from 0 to 1. But this argument would have us, for the $k = 0$ term, divide through by 0, which is not allowed.

where the = sign is used for the strict Poisson conditions. But we shall show it directly.

By definition,

$$\sigma^2 = \sum_{k=0}^{n} (k - \mu)^2 P(k; \mu) = \sum_{k=0}^{n} (k^2 - 2k\mu + \mu^2) P(k; \mu)$$

$$= \sum_{k=0}^{n} (k^2 - \mu^2) P(k; \mu) = \sum_{k=0}^{n} k^2 P(k; \mu) - \mu^2 \qquad (5\text{-}14)$$

since $\sum_{k=0}^{n} kP(k; \mu) = \mu$ by Eq. 5-12, and since $\sum_{k=0}^{n} P(k; \mu) = 0$ for $n \to \infty$ by Eq. 5-10. (Incidentally, this expression is one form of the general relation, irrespective of the type of distribution,

$$\sigma^2 = \overline{k^2} - \mu^2 \qquad (5\text{-}15)$$

where $\overline{k^2}$ is the arithmetic mean of the squares, and μ^2 is the square of arithmetic mean. This expression first appeared in this book as Eq. 2-12, and the next time as Eq. 2-19.)

Equation 5-14 can also be written with $(k(k - 1) + k)$ for k^2; then

$$\sigma^2 = \sum_{k=0}^{n} k(k - 1) \frac{\mu^k e^{-\mu}}{k!} + \mu - \mu^2 = \mu^2 \sum_{k=2}^{n} \frac{\mu^{k-2} e^{-\mu}}{(k - 2)!} + \mu - \mu^2$$

Because of the factor $k(k - 1)$ in the numerator of the first sum, the lower limit of this sum may just as well be written as $k = 2$, as is done in the second sum. Then the sum is equal to unity (for $n \to \infty$) by the property of normalization, Eq. 5-10. In conclusion,

$$\sigma^2 = \mu^2 + \mu - \mu^2 = \mu \qquad \text{and} \qquad \sigma = \sqrt{\mu} \qquad (5\text{-}16)$$

Note that the positive and negative values of σ have no simple interpretation as actual deviations because of the asymmetry of the Poisson distribution. σ is an rms deviation having an asymmetrical graphical interpretation. The rms of all positive deviations is greater than the rms of all negative deviations.

To show by the method of maximum likelihood that $\sigma = \sqrt{np} = \sqrt{\mu}$ is posed as a problem for the reader. (It is shown by this method, Problem 27 in Section 3-11, that $\sigma = \sqrt{npq}$ in the binomial distribution.)

Fractional standard deviation. The fractional standard deviation is the most commonly used precision index in those "counting" measurements for which the Poisson model is a satisfactory fit and for which μ is rather large by the design or analysis of the experiment. The fractional standard deviation in per cent is defined as

$$\text{fractional } \sigma \text{ in } \% = \frac{\sigma}{\mu} \times 100 = \frac{1}{\sqrt{\mu}} \times 100 \qquad (5\text{-}17)$$

It is the simple inverse relation with $\sqrt{\mu}$ that makes the fractional σ so popular.

When μ is moderately large, not much error is introduced by writing a single measurement k_s in place of μ. In this case, in order to have precision (fractional σ) of, say, 1%, we must observe $k_s = 10,000$ "successes."†

Standard deviation in a single measurement. Even when the single measurement is not large the question often arises, What is the precision in this single measurement? This question may be stated another way: If a highly precise value of m ($\approx \mu$) is known, as from many trial measurements, what is the probability that the single measurement k_s and μ will differ by a given amount?

To answer this question, we may consider m, instead of the single measurement k_s, to be the variable in $P(k;\ m)$. Note that m is a continuous variable although k is discrete. The likelihood function $L(m)$ for a single measurement k_s is

$$L(m) = \frac{m^{k_s}e^{-m}}{k_s!} \tag{5-18}$$

Following the procedures of the method of maximum likelihood as outlined in Chapter 3, we write

$$\log L(m) = k_s \log m - m - \log k_s! \tag{5-19}$$

$$\frac{\partial}{\partial m}\left[\log L(m)\right] = \frac{k_s}{m} - 1 \tag{5-20}$$

and

$$\frac{\partial^2}{\partial m^2}\left[\log L(m)\right] = -\frac{k_s}{m^2} \tag{5-21}$$

To find the best estimate m^* from Eq. 5-20, i.e., the most probable value from a single measurement k_s, we write

$$\frac{\partial}{\partial m}\left[\log L(m)\right]_{m=m^*} = 0 \tag{5-22}$$

$$m^* = k_s \tag{5-23}$$

This result is the one we would expect for a symmetrical distribution, but is not necessarily the expectation for an asymmetrical distribution; but remember, our only knowledge is from a *single* measurement, k_s.

To find the standard deviation in a single measurement, σ_{k_s}, we combine

† Such a large k or μ does not invalidate the Poisson condition that np be moderate; the Poisson distribution is not one of small numbers, only one of rare events.

Eqs. 5-21 and 3-25 with the reasonable assumption that the values of $L(m)$ are normally distributed about m^* ($= k_s$ from Eq. 5-23):

$$\sigma_{k_s} = \left[- \frac{1}{\dfrac{\partial^2}{\partial m^2}[\log L(m)]} \right]^{\frac{1}{2}} = \left[\frac{1}{\dfrac{k_s}{m^{*2}}} \right]^{\frac{1}{2}} = \frac{m^*}{\sqrt{k_s}} = \sqrt{k_s} \quad (5\text{-}24)$$

The consistency among Eqs. 5-16, 5-23, and 5-24 is to be expected since m^* is our best estimate of μ.†

It readily follows that the fractional standard deviation in a single measurement may be written as

$$\text{fractional } \sigma_{k_s} \text{ in } \% = \frac{\sigma_{k_s}}{\mu} \times 100 \approx \frac{1}{\sqrt{\mu}} \times 100 = \frac{1}{\sqrt{k_s}} \times 100 \quad (5\text{-}28)$$

† It is interesting to note that if the probability for each dm interval is the same as for every other dm interval, then we may write the parent mean value as

$$\mu = \int_0^\infty mL(m)\, dm$$

$$= \frac{1}{k_s!} \int_0^\infty m^{k_s+1}e^{-m}\, dm = \frac{(k_s + 1)!}{k_s!} = k_s + 1 \quad (5\text{-}25)$$

which, with Eq. 5-23, would tell us that μ differs from m^* by unity. Also, with the assumption that all dm intervals are equally likely, we may write the mean square of m as

$$\overline{m^2} = \frac{1}{k_s!} \int_0^\infty m^2 L(m)\, dm = \frac{(k_s + 2)!}{k_s!} = (k_s + 1)(k_s + 2) \quad (5\text{-}26)$$

Then, noting that Eq. 5-15 is applicable to *any* type of distribution, we may write it now for the distribution of m values and substitute in it the relations given in Eqs. 5-25 and 5-26. Thus,

$$\sigma_{k_s}^2 = \overline{m^2} - \mu^2 = (k_s + 1)(k_s + 2) - (k_s + 1)^2 = k_s + 1$$

and

$$\sigma_{k_s} = \sqrt{k_s + 1} \quad (5\text{-}27)$$

where σ_{k_s} is written here instead of σ_m so as to avoid confusion with the standard deviation in the mean obtained from many values of k.

The assumption that all dm intervals are equally likely is a desperation-in-ignorance type of guess that may or may not be valid. It is the same type of guess that Laplace made in deriving the law of succession, viz., the third guess discussed in Section 1-5 in connection with the probability that the sun will rise tomorrow. Note that it is easy to invent a dm probability function of k that would make $\mu = k_s$ or $k_s - 1$ or something else. There seems to be no compelling reason to follow Laplace's type of guess and to replace Eqs. 5-23 and 5-24 with Eqs. 5-25 and 5-27, although this is done by some authors.

Probable error. By definition, the probable error, either positive or negative, viz., $\pm pe$, is that error that marks the $+$ and $-$ limits in any distribution such that the number of measurements between the respective limit and the mean is equal to the number beyond the limit, i.e., the 50% confidence limit on either side of the mean. The median value is always enclosed within these $\pm pe$ limits, and, in most distributions of interest, the mean value m or μ also lies somewhere between $+pe$ and $-pe$. In a symmetrical distribution, the positive and negative values of pe are equal in

Table 5-2.   Numerical Coefficients pe/σ for Various
Values of μ in the Poisson Distribution

μ	pe/σ
20	0.575
60	0.613
100	0.628
200	0.640
400	0.647
1000	0.660
∞	0.6745

magnitude as reckoned from the mean, but not so for an asymmetrical distribution. For a normal (Gauss) distribution, $\pm pe = \pm 0.6745\sigma$. It is fairly widespread practice with the asymmetrical Poisson distribution to speak of the probable error as being also $\pm 0.6745\sigma$, although this is obviously not quite correct.

In a Poisson distribution, it is possible to define the probable error exactly. The definition is conveniently expressed in terms of the standard deviation which is also of unequal magnitude on either side of the mean. The numerical relationship between pe and σ depends upon the degree of asymmetry. It turns out, as shown in the next section, that the third moment about the mean, which is a good measure of asymmetry, is equal in magnitude to the mean μ in a Poisson distribution. The ratio $pe/\sigma = pe/\sqrt{\mu}$ varies with μ in this distribution, as is illustrated in Table 5-2. It must be realized that these values of pe (and of σ) are not symmetrically located with respect to the mean μ except for the case of $\mu = \infty$. The use of $pe/\sigma = 0.6745$ for *any* Poisson distribution results in a value of pe generally a little too large, but this practice is often said to be justified because it is always on the "safe" side.

The probable error in a single measurement is approximated by

$$pe_{k_s} \approx \pm 0.6745\sigma_{k_s} \approx \pm 0.6745\sqrt{k_s} \qquad (5\text{-}29)$$

if k_s is very large; otherwise a better approximation is made by choosing the appropriate numerical coefficient from Table 5-2. We can also write the fractional probable error

$$\text{fractional } pe_{k_s} \approx \frac{0.6745}{\mu} \; \sigma_{k_s} \approx \pm 0.6745 \frac{1}{\sqrt{k_s}} \tag{5-30}$$

with a similar qualification as to the magnitude of the numerical coefficient.

Skewness. The Poisson distribution is intrinsically skewed. The asymmetry or skewness decreases as the expectation value μ increases. It is interesting to see the relationship between the skewness and μ.

By definition, the third moment about the mean is

$$\sum_{k=0}^{n} (k - \mu)^3 P(k; \mu) = \Sigma(k^3 - 3k^2\mu + 3k\mu^2 - \mu^3)P(k; \mu)$$

$$= \Sigma k^3 P(k; \mu) - 3\mu\Sigma k^2 P(k; \mu) + 3\mu^3\Sigma k P(k; \mu) - \mu^3$$

By the same arguments as were used in deriving the expression for σ, Eq. 5-16, we separate the quantity $k(k - 1)(k - 2)$ out of the first term, change the first term in the sum from the $k = 0$ to the $k = 3$ term, and use the property of normalization. Then the first term becomes

$$\mu^3 + 3\Sigma k^2 P(k; \mu) - 2\Sigma k P(k; \mu).$$

We make use of the relations that $\Sigma k^2 P(k; \mu) = \sigma^2 + \mu^2$ from Eq. 5-15, that $\sigma^2 = \mu$ from Eq. 5-16, and that $\Sigma k P(k; \mu) = \mu$ from Eq. 5-12. Substituting these quantities in the expression for the third moment about the mean, we get

$$\sum_{k=0}^{n} (k - \mu)^3 P(k; \mu) = \mu \tag{5-31}$$

Finally, the skewness, by definition, is the third moment about the mean divided by σ^3,

$$\text{skewness} = \sum_{k=0}^{n} \frac{(k - \mu)^3 P(k; \mu)}{\sigma^3} = \frac{\mu}{\mu^{3/2}} = \frac{1}{\sqrt{\mu}} = \frac{1}{\sigma} \tag{5-32}$$

a very simple relation that holds for every Poisson distribution.

The derivation of the expression for kurtosis is assigned to Problem 11, Section 5-10.

5-5. Significance of the Basic Bernoulli Trials

Since $P(k; \mu)$, Eq. 5-4, contains a single parameter, μ, each of the Poisson probabilities can be calculated once μ is known. In the derivation of $P(k; \mu)$, μ is taken as equal to the product np, where n and p are the parameters in the binomial distribution and therefore are characteristics of basic Bernoulli trials. However, it is of no consequence for computational purposes whether or not n and p are separately known. (However, note that knowledge of n and p may establish immediately the applicability of the Poisson model.) It suffices to approximate μ by m from a rather large number of actual measurements by Eq. 2-2, and then to use Eq. 5-4 or 5-5 in predictions and in calculations of precision and of reasonableness.* This, however, presumes that the Poisson model satisfactorily fits the actual measurements. The question of goodness of fit is discussed later.

In practice, Poisson problems can be divided into two general classes: (a) sampling *with* replacement and (b) sampling *without* replacement. In the first class there is no known limit to the supply from which events are presumed to come; in the second class, the supply is known to be limited. In sampling with or without replacement, the experiment or measurements must be such that the basic success probability, or the Poisson probability for a given value of k, must remain constant for all samplings.

An example of the first class is in the number k of defective screws that a certain machine turns out in a given batch of known size n if the average performance of the machine is known to be μ ($\approx m$) defectives per batch of this size; p ($= \mu/n$) is the probability, assumed to be constant, that any one screw will be defective. We do not inquire into the machine factors that make a screw defective; it is presumed that the machine never changes in its performance in this regard. It is also presumed that our knowledge of n and p is such as to justify the assumption that the problem is indeed Poissonian. Another example of this class is in the number k of cosmic rays from outer space that appears in a specified solid angle in a specified time interval at noon of each day, or in the number k of X rays emitted per second from an X-ray tube under steady operation. In this example, the basic Bernoulli parameters n and p are not a priori known, but a special argument can be invoked to show that the parent distribution is satisfactorily Poissonian. This argument is the one of "spatial distribution" to be elaborated presently.

A Poisson example of sampling *without* replacement is the classical one of radioactive decay—the number k of atoms in a given radioactive specimen that decays in a specified time. To be Poissonian, this example must include the specification that the lifetime for decay must be long compared with the time interval of observation, and the number of atoms in the specimen must be rather large. In this example, the basic Bernoulli trial is whether or not a given atom decays during the interval of observation.

---

* This argument was also made in Chapter 4 regarding the normal Gauss distribution; it suffices to approximate the normal mean μ (for the position at which $z = 0$) and the parameter h from the experimental measurements. The parameters n, p, and q are not separately evaluated.

Clearly, the supply of possible events is limited, viz., is the total number of atoms in the specimen. These and other examples are discussed in detail later.

Two mechanical analogs. It was stated or implied in Sections 2-7 and 4-3 that the distinction between "success" and "failure" in a Poisson problem may be thought of as due to an unfathomable array of elementary errors. According to this view, a mechanical analog of "success" and "failure" is illustrated in Fig. 5-3. This mechanical model is a simplification of the one used for the normal distribution, Fig. 4-4, and the interpretation is quite different. In both cases, however, the deflection of the ball as it encounters a pin corresponds to an elementary error.

By the relative size and position of the "success" bin, only a small number k of the total number n of balls dropped manages to reach this bin. The Poisson probability p refers to the chance that a given ball will do so. This probability is constant if the (hypothetical) pins and their array are appropriately designed. If the n balls are gathered up and again

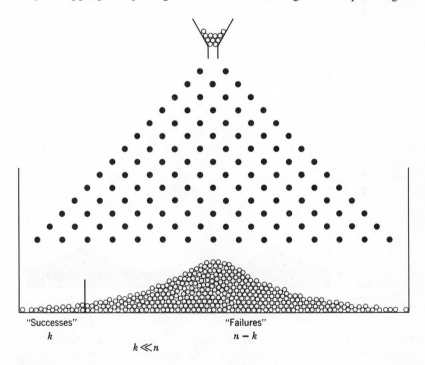

"Successes"
k

"Failures"
$n - k$

$k \ll n$

Fig. 5-3. A possible mechanical analog of "successes" and "failures" in a Poisson probability problem. A *single* trial consists in observing k balls in the "success" bin after n balls have been dropped from the nozzle at the top.

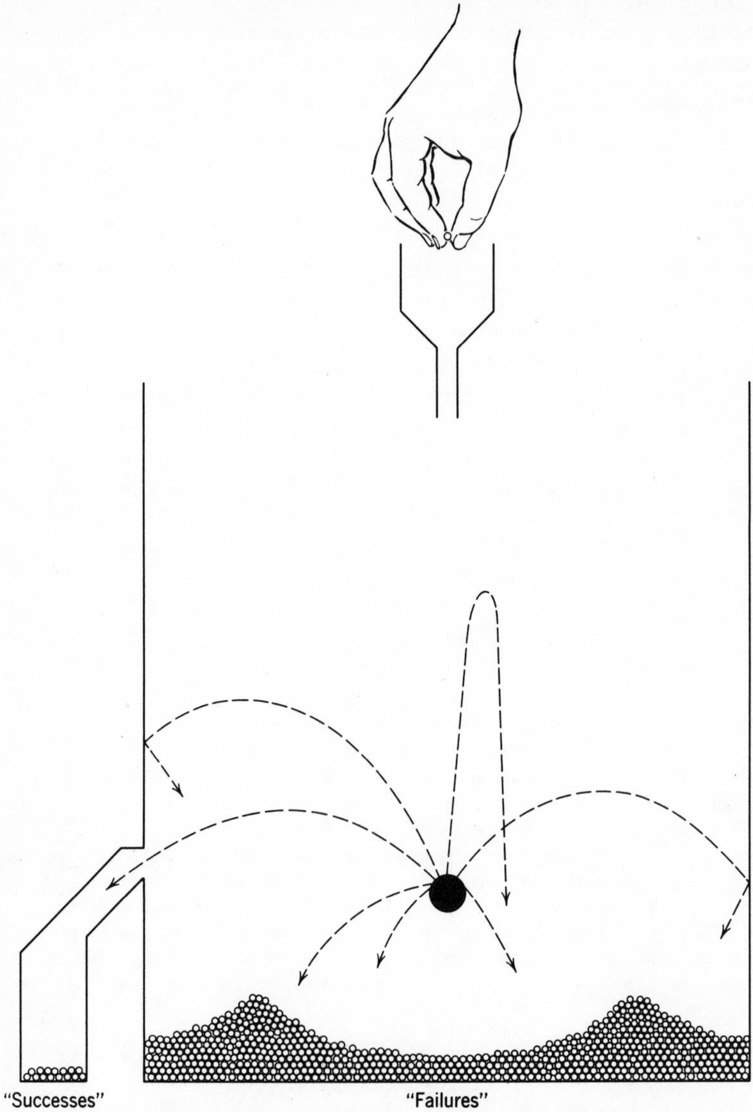

Fig. 5-4. Another possible mechanical analog of "successes" and "failures" in a Poisson problem. The angles of bounce of the dropped balls are random. A large number of ball drops gives only one Poisson measurement, viz., the number k of balls in the "success" bin.

dropped through the nozzle, as another Poisson trial, a generally different number k of successes is observed. A graph of the number of times each possible value of k is observed, from 0 to n, as the number of Poisson trials N increases indefinitely, gives the Poisson distribution. [By the geometry, $k^2 + (np)^2 \ll n$.]

In this analog, each dropped ball, not each pin, corresponds to the basic Bernoulli trial. And a single measurement is the number k, not the final position of a single ball. In the analog for the normal distribution, each elementary error (i.e., the deflection at each pin) corresponds to a basic Bernoulli trial, but not so in this Poisson analog.

It is instructive to consider another possible mechanical analog for the Poisson case. This is one in which all the elementary errors are lumped into a single deflection uncertainty. Consider the model shown in Fig. 5-4.

In this model, n identical balls are dropped irregularly one by one from the nozzle so as to strike and bounce off the rotating rough central pin. The pin is rotating and rough so as to insure that the angles of bounce are essentially random. On one side of the cylindrical box is a hole, somewhat larger than a ball, leading to the "success" bin. By having this hole small, and the radius of the cylindrical box large, the "success" probability is small.

This model, with a large number n of balls dropped, illustrates only one measurement, viz., the measurement of the relatively small number k of "successes" in a large number n of basic Bernoulli trials. If the experiment is repeated with the same number n of basic trials, the value of k will in general be different; if the experiment is repeated N times, many different k values are observed. The Poisson frequency distribution is the graph of the number of times each k value is observed vs. the k values themselves as $p \to 0$ and $N \to \infty$. [Again by the geometry, $k^2 + (np)^2 \ll n$.]

5-6. Goodness of Fit

Before the Poisson equations may be properly applied to calculate the probability of the value of the next measurement, to assess the precision, or to judge the reasonableness of past measurements, the investigator must be assured that the measurements are members of a parent distribution that is satisfactorily Poissonian.

There are two general ways of determining the goodness of fit of the Poisson distribution, viz., by a priori analysis and by test.

Analysis of the experiment usually allows the investigator to see whether or not the conditions of the basic Bernoulli trials, hence, of the Poisson approximations, are satisfactorily met. These conditions, to recapitulate, are:

(1) only two possible outcomes, viz., k and not k, in each basic trial,
(2) each outcome determined entirely by chance,
(3) the number of basic trials, n, very large,
(4) the success probability, p, constant and very small, and
(5) the product np such that $k^2 + (np)^2 \ll n$.

In experiments in which the Bernoulli parameters are directly recognizable, or are seen to be adjustable as in a spatial distribution (examples are discussed presently), the analysis for goodness of fit often indicates a priori that the parent distribution is satisfactorily Poisson, but also not infrequently indicates it to be in a transition region between binomial and Poisson or between normal and Poisson. In the transition case, or in a case in which for any reason there is a serious question of goodness of fit, it is necessary to carry out a test.

The qualitative and quantitative tests described in detail in Section 4-8 for the normal distribution are also applicable in method for the Poisson case or for any model distribution. Discussion of these tests will not be repeated here. Of them, the quantitative χ^2 test is generally the best but requires the largest number of trial measurements.

Spatial distribution. Before proceeding to examples of Poisson problems, let us elaborate the argument of spatial distribution. By this argument, many experimental problems of sampling with replacement (infinite supply of events) are recognized a priori as being satisfactorily Poissonian.

Consider a problem in which events occur randomly along a time axis, and consider a unit time interval t. (In this case, "spatial" refers to time; in other cases it may refer to space.) We may first analyze the problem in terms of Bernoulli trials, each trial being an observation during the unit time interval. In each observation, "no event" is declared to be failure and "one or more events" is declared to be success. We may repeat the observation for N successive unit intervals of time. The observed distribution of numbers of successes is represented by the binomial distribution $NB(k'; n', p')$, where p' is the success probability and k' is the number of "one or more events" observed out of n' Bernoulli trials.

In most problems, we are not satisfied with success defined as "one or more events"; we wish it to be only "one event." We may then imagine the size of the time interval reduced until the probability for observing more than one event in the reduced time interval is negligibly small. Suppose that, in doing this, we divide the unit time interval by an integer n; the time interval in the *new* Bernoulli trial is now $\Delta t = 1/n$. Since division by n is purely imaginary, we may make n as large as we please. As n becomes very large (infinite in the limit) the probability p_n that Δt contains even one event is very small (zero in the limit). We now have n imaginary Bernoulli trials that by definition in the limit satisfy *exactly* the Poisson conditions. Then, for each of the N actual observations, the probability for observing exactly k events in the unit time interval t is $B(k;\ n, p_n) = P(k;\ \mu_t)$, and the predicted frequency of observing exactly k events in N trials is $NP(k;\ \mu_t)$. The point of special significance in the spatial distribution is that the basic Bernoulli trials on which the justification for the Poisson approximation is based are hypothetical trials having no actual measuremental significance.

Instead of the unit interval t, we may start with any arbitrary time interval T, and then reduce the Bernoulli time interval by dividing by nT instead of by n. The argument to be followed is the same as before except that now, to have the same success probability p_n, we have Tn basic Bernoulli trials. The Poisson predicted frequency distribution is written with $T\mu_t$ instead of μ_t, viz., $NP(k;\ T\mu_t)$. Then we may write μ for $T\mu_t$.

It is important to realize that μ_t is a physical constant determining the density of events along the time axis independent of the value of n or of nT. μ_t is the expectation value in an actual measurement during the unit time interval. μ, the expectation value during the time interval T, is determined from the N experimental measurements, each over time T, viz., $\mu \approx m = \Sigma f_k k / N$. For convenience in practice, we adjust μ by choosing an appropriate T. This adjustment is merely a k scale factor of convenience.

5-7. Examples of Poisson Problems

Perhaps actual examples provide the best way (a) to become acquainted with the a priori analysis in determining whether or not a given problem is Poissonian, and (b) to become better acquainted with the Poisson expressions in general.

Deaths from the kick of a mule. This is a classical example mentioned in almost all textbook discussions of Poisson probabilities. Records of the number of soldiers dying per year from the kick of a mule were kept for a Prussian army unit of 200 men for a time of 20 years. It is assumed that this army unit was kept at full strength and at essentially the same routine activities throughout all of the 20 years. The records for one year are shown in Table 5-3. The mean or expectation value $m\ (\approx \mu)$ from $N\ (= 200)$ observations is given by the ratio $(\Sigma f_k k)/(\Sigma f_k) = 122/200 = 0.61$, and the Poisson probability can be readily computed. This probability, multiplied by N, is also listed in the table. Our first conclusion is that by direct comparison of the experimental and the model frequency

Table 5-3.　Deaths from the Kick of a Mule

k	f_k	$NP(k;\ 0.61)$
0	109	108.7
1	65	66.3
2	22	20.2
3	3	4.1
4	1	0.6
5	0	0.1
6	0	0.0

$$N = \Sigma f_k = 200$$

distributions we see that the Poisson is a good fit (in fact, the fit is *too* good; see Problem 36, Section 5-10).

Now let us look for the basic Bernoulli trials in this example. We shall see that it is possible to imagine several different types of trials, all of them having the same value of m ($\approx \mu$).

First, let us ask if it is reasonable to have as a basic Bernoulli trial the observation of the army unit for a period of one year. The answer is no for two reasons. First, there are several possible outcomes of such a trial— 0, 1, 2, 3, $\cdot\cdot\cdot$, deaths per year—whereas a Bernoulli trial can have only two possible outcomes. Second, although during the 20 years there are 20 such observations, we need more than 20 Bernoulli trials to give an approximation to the Poisson conditions as good as is indicated in Table 5-3. Actually, this one-year observation is one trial in a multinomial distribution, Eq. 1-30, where $p_1 = 109/200$, $p_2 = 65/200$, $\cdot\cdot\cdot$. The period of 20 years, as compared with one year, represents 20 multinomial trials, and these 20 trials allow greater precision in m ($\approx \mu$) and increased stability of the f_k values as listed in the table. But the 20 years do not represent 20 Bernoulli trials.

As a second try, we note that this problem deals with events along a time axis, and we consider the basic Bernoulli trial as an observation of the army unit for a period of, say, one week, i.e., we divide each year by $n = 52$. Now, without changing m (or μ), we have increased the number of trials from 1 to 52, decreased p by a factor of 52, and reduced the probability for more than two outcomes per trial to perhaps a negligible value. Now we have a reasonably satisfactory set of basic Bernoulli trials *if* the weekly activities of the soldiers and mules can be assumed to be the same for each successive week of the year. As we think of different seasonal activities we may well conclude that an interval of a week is already too small for the independence of successive trials and of the constancy of p_n. Another assumption of note here is that when a soldier or a mule dies he or it is replaced *immediately* by another who is equivalent insofar as soldier-mule interaction is concerned, or else the army unit is so large that one (or a few) deaths has a negligible effect in changing p_n; in order to use the argument of spatial distribution we must have sampling with replacement (or a very good approximation thereto).

Consider next as a basic Bernoulli trial the observation of one "statistically average" soldier, instead of the army as a unit, for a period of one year. In this case, the number of possible outcomes per trial is decreased effectively to only two, viz., one death or no death; the number of trials n is increased from one by a factor about equal to the number of average soldiers in the army; and p is reduced to a satisfactorily small value. p_n is kept constant in this case by the mere assumption that all soldiers, in regard to mule contacts, are equivalent. Replacement of casualties need not be immediate but if not, to approximate the Poisson conditions, it is required that the lifetime of a soldier be long, i.e., that the size of the army unit be large. This analysis is the best of the three tried.

In discussing this problem, we first considered the simplest possible basic Bernoulli trial and found it unsatisfactory. Then we explored the argument of spatial distribution and found that, along the time axis, the Bernoulli probability p_n could not be assumed to be constant. Finally, our best analysis was made in terms of the basic Bernoulli trial as the observation of a single soldier, with the assumption that all soldiers are identical. In spite of the excellent fit of the Poisson calculations to the reported measurements, Table 5-3, this problem barely qualifies as a Poisson example.

Radioactive decay. Perhaps the best known application of the Poisson distribution in physics is in "counting" experiments: counts of α-particles in radioactive decay, counts of cosmic rays, counts of X rays, counts of visible light photons, etc. And the commonest of these experiments are those for which the source intensity is safely assumed to be constant over the time of measurement.

Consider a radioactive substance emitting α-particles. This substance is placed behind a set of diaphragms which screens off all but a small solid angle of the emitted rays. The unscreened rays fall upon a sensitive counting device, such as a Geiger counter tube combined with an amplifier-scaler arrangement and a count register. The number of counts is recorded for each of $N (= 2608)$ time intervals of $T (= 7.5)$ sec each. Table 5-4 lists the frequency f_k that exactly k counts were recorded in an actual experiment. The total number of counts is $\Sigma f_k k = 10{,}094$, and the average counting rate is $10{,}094/2608 = 3.870$ per 7.5 sec. The calculated Poisson distribution, multiplied by N to make it frequency instead of probability, is also listed in the table. Direct comparison of the observed and calculated frequencies shows rather good agreement.

The fit of the Poisson model to the observed data may be judged quantitatively by application of the χ^2 test; in this example we have enough measurements to use this test to advantage. This test tells us that 17 out of 100 comparable cases would show worse agreement than appears in Table 5-4, owing to chance fluctuations alone. We conclude that the good Poisson fit establishes that the α-emission from this long-lived substance is not only governed by chance but is well represented by the Poisson model.

Table 5-4.   Radioactive Disintegrations

k	f_k	$NP(k;\ 3.870)$
0	57	54.399
1	203	210.523
2	383	407.361
3	525	525.496
4	532	508.418
5	408	393.515
6	273	253.817
7	139	140.325
8	45	67.882
9	27	29.189
≥ 10	16	17.075

$$N = \Sigma f_k = 2608$$

The numbers in this example are taken from Rutherford's famous experiment of 1910 with α's from a thin film of polonium. Much lower values of χ^2, i.e., higher probability $P(\chi^2 > \chi_c^2)$ have been obtained in recent more extensive measurements in similar experiments. In the days of 1910, "scintillations" were observed with the eye and a low-power microscope (instead of counts with a Geiger or proportional counter). The time of appearance of each scintillation was recorded on a moving tape by the observer's pressing an electric key.

It may be noted that, since α's are emitted in all directions from the polonium, the randomness observed could just as well be attributed to randomness in direction as to randomness in time. This ambiguity has since been removed by experiments with different arrangements of solid angles subtended by the detector; radioactive emission from (unpolarized*) atoms is uniform in direction as well as in time.

Now, what is the set of Bernoulli trials in this example? Actually, this

* Avoids the assumption of parity in β-decay.

example has many things in common with the one dealing with the kick of a mule, and it has two essential differences. The first difference is that, if the source intensity is satisfactorily constant during all of the measurements (i.e., long atomic lifetime and large number of atoms in the specimen), we may safely invoke the argument of spatial distribution. In this argument, the time interval T ($= 7.5$ sec for convenience in the experiment) is imagined as subdivided into n equal subintervals of time, and n may be very large indeed. The second difference is that all atoms of a given species are strictly identical, as we know from the success of the principle of indistinguishability in quantum statistical mechanics. With this knowledge we may alternatively analyze the problem in terms of the observation of each atom for 7.5 sec as the basic Bernoulli trial, the number n of such trials being equal to the number of atoms in the specimen. In terms of either set of basic Bernoulli trials, the problem is clearly Poissonian.

The analysis in terms of individual atoms, instead of the subintervals of time, is in general the more logical one in problems of radioactive decay because, often, the lifetime is too short, or the number of atoms is too small, to justify the assumption of constant source intensity and thus of constant Bernoulli probability. This type of problem was mentioned earlier as an example of sampling *without* replacement, and only if the source intensity does remain constant can the spatial distribution argument be invoked, i.e., can the problem be considered as one of sampling *with* replacement. Note also that if the lifetime is short *and* the number of atoms is small, the problem is a binomial one in which the basic Bernoulli trial is an observation of each atom.

A practical limit on the intensity of the source, or, rather on the maximum counting rate, is imposed by the measuring equipment. All detector devices have an inherent resolving time, i.e., a "dead time" immediately following a count. If one or more α-particles arrive at the detector during this dead time, it or they will not be counted. The Poisson distribution cannot "exactly" fit the measurements, of course, unless the number of "lost" counts is negligible. The dead time of the eye (as in counting scintillations) is about $\frac{1}{20}$ sec, of a typical Geiger counter about 120 μsec, of a typical proportional counter about 1 μsec, of a typical "fast" scintillation counter about 10^{-7} sec as determined now (in the year 1960) by the associated electronic circuits.

Another practical matter in regard to the source is that it must have been "conditioned"—in the early runs of data, lose molecular aggregates become detached from the emitting substance as a consequence of the atomic recoils from disintegrations within the aggregates. During the conditioning process, the value of χ^2 decreases successively as the source intensity becomes more nearly constant.

Counts per unit time: precision. The measurement of the rate of radioactive decay, if the source intensity remains satisfactorily constant, typifies many Poisson measurement problems—most of the problems in nuclear physics, cosmic rays, radioactive tracer work, carbon dating—in fact, any Poisson measurement amenable to analysis as a spatial distribution of events. A feature of especial interest in such measurement problems is precision, not yet discussed in these examples.

Consider the relative precision in counts per minute among the following three measurements:

   (a) one measurement: 100 counts in 10 min
   (b) one measurement: 1000 counts in 100 min
   (c) ten successive measurements ($N = 10$) each for 10 min, the total number of counts being 1000.

The counting rate is assumed to vary randomly on a short-time scale (e.g., minutes), but, on the average, to be constant, i.e., constant as measured on a long-time scale (e.g., days). The average counting rate is given experimentally by the mean m which is our best estimate of the desired parent mean μ; m is the same in all of the three cases.

Consider each of two dispersion indices of the parent (Poisson) distribution, viz., the standard deviation σ and the fractional standard deviation σ/μ in per cent; and consider also the standard deviation in the mean (standard error) σ_m. These indices, for the three measurement situations, are:

$$(a) \begin{cases} \text{Eq. 5-24} \quad \sigma = \sqrt{k_s} = \sqrt{100}\, c/10\ \min = \dfrac{\sqrt{100}}{10}\ \text{cpm} = 1\ \text{cpm} \\[2em] \text{Eq. 5-28} \quad \dfrac{\sigma}{\mu} = \dfrac{1}{\sqrt{k_s}} \times 100 = \dfrac{100}{\sqrt{100}} = 10\% \\[2em] \begin{array}{l}\text{2-32} \\ \text{Eqs. 3-26} \\ \text{3-45}\end{array} \quad \sigma_m = \dfrac{\sigma}{\sqrt{N}} = \dfrac{\sqrt{100}}{\sqrt{1}}\, c/10\ \min = \dfrac{\sqrt{100}}{10}\ \text{cpm} = 1\ \text{cpm} \end{cases}$$

$$(b) \begin{cases} \text{Eq. 5-24} \quad \sigma = \sqrt{k_s} = \sqrt{1000}\, c/100\ \min = \dfrac{\sqrt{1000}}{100}\ \text{cpm} \approx 0.32\ \text{cpm} \\[2em] \text{Eq. 5-28} \quad \dfrac{\sigma}{\mu} = \dfrac{1}{\sqrt{k_s}} \times 100 = \dfrac{100}{\sqrt{1000}} \approx 3.2\% \\[2em] \begin{array}{l}\text{2-32} \\ \text{Eqs. 3-26} \\ \text{3-45}\end{array} \quad \sigma_m = \dfrac{\sigma}{\sqrt{N}} = \dfrac{\sqrt{1000}}{\sqrt{1}}\, c/100\ \min = \dfrac{\sqrt{1000}}{100}\ \text{cpm} \approx 0.32\ \text{cpm} \end{cases}$$

$$(c) \begin{cases} \text{Eq. 5-16} & \sigma = \sqrt{\mu} \approx \sqrt{\dfrac{1000}{N}} = \sqrt{\dfrac{1000}{10}} = 10 \ c/10 \text{ min} = 1 \text{ cpm} \\[3mm] \text{Eq. 5-17} & \dfrac{\sigma}{\mu} = \dfrac{100}{\sqrt{\mu}} \approx \dfrac{100}{\sqrt{1000/N}} = \dfrac{100}{\sqrt{1000/10}} = 10\% \\[3mm] \begin{matrix} \text{2-32} \\ \text{Eqs. 3-26} \\ \text{3-45} \end{matrix} & \sigma_m = \dfrac{\sigma}{\sqrt{N}} = \dfrac{10}{\sqrt{10}} \approx 3.2 \ c/10 \text{ min} = 0.32 \text{ cpm} \end{cases}$$

Or, better, the standard deviation σ in case (c) may be computed from Eq. 5-24 with all 1000 counts considered as a *single* measurement over 100 min. Then, we have

$$(c') \begin{cases} \text{Eq. 5-24} & \sigma = \sqrt{k_s} = \sqrt{1000} \ c/100 \text{ min} = \dfrac{\sqrt{1000}}{10} c/10 \text{ min} \\ & \hspace{6cm} = 0.32 \text{ cpm} \\[3mm] \text{Eq. 5-28} & \dfrac{\sigma}{\mu} = \dfrac{1}{\sqrt{k_s}} \times 100 = \dfrac{100}{\sqrt{1000}} \approx 3.2\% \\[3mm] \begin{matrix} \text{2-32} \\ \text{Eqs. 3-26} \\ \text{3-45} \end{matrix} & \sigma_m = \dfrac{\sigma}{\sqrt{N}} = \dfrac{\sqrt{1000}}{10\sqrt{1}} \approx 3.2 \ c/10 \text{ min} = 0.32 \text{ cpm} \end{cases}$$

First, compare the precision of (a) with that of (b). It is a characteristic of Poisson problems that the precision in counts per unit time becomes greater as the mean m increases, but *only if* the *effective* number n of basic Bernoulli trials in each measurement also increases. In the present example, which involves hypothetical Bernoulli trials because of the spatial distribution argument, this characteristic must be stated in terms of the size of the observational interval T along the time axis instead of in terms of the number of hypothetical Bernoulli trials; the two statements are seen to be equivalent when it is realized that the gain is in the product np, not merely in n alone.* This is made clear in a penny-tossing example presently.

Second, compare (a) with (c). If the observation time per measurement remains the same, viz., $T = 10$ min, the values of σ and of σ/μ are the

---

* Note that if the counts for each of the 10 trials (each for 10 min) are known, we may use Eq. 2-23 for σ, viz., $\sigma = \left(\sum\limits_{i=1}^{10} (k_i - m)^2/9 \right)^{1/2}$, and then we may use this value of σ in Eq. 2-32 for σ_m, viz., $\sigma_m = \left(\sum\limits_{i=1}^{10} (k_i - m)^2/90 \right)^{1/2}$. These expressions apply regardless of any mathematical model. But if the Poisson model is known to fit the parent distribution, the Poisson equations lead to a greater precision with a given number of measurements.

same, respectively, in (c) as in (a). That these precision indices are unaltered by repetition of the measurements is expected from the statement in the previous paragraph relating precision to the number of basic Bernoulli trials having a given success probability. Note, however, that the additional nine trial measurements in (c) have improved the precision in the mean, the standard error σ_m. On the other hand, if (c) is considered as a single measurement of 1000 counts with the observational time interval $T = 100$ min, the precision as measured by all three indices is improved; in this view, (b) and (c') are equivalent.

Third, consider further (b) vs. (c'). This comparison has already been partially made above, but one point remains. In the expression $\sigma_m = \sigma/\sqrt{N}$ for case (c'), it is imperative that the value of σ be consistent with the value of N, i.e., the value of σ must correspond to the value deduced from the N measurements. We cannot take $\sigma = \sqrt{k_s} = \sqrt{1000} \approx 0.32$ cpm and at the same time take $N = 10$; this would yield $\sigma_m = 0.1$ cpm but is not valid.

Finally, it should be emphasized that, although we may at first be inclined to regard the subdivided data in (c) as thereby containing additional information that should somehow yield an improvement in precision, there is in fact no additional information (except in checking systematic errors as mentioned below, and in checking the applicability of the mathematical model). We have assumed that all the fluctuations in successive 10-min trials are random; and all of the information about the dispersion of the parent distribution is contained in the product np of the basic Bernoulli trials—it does not matter how this information is obtained; it may be obtained in subdivided measurements or all at once in a single measurement.

The situation is somewhat similar to that encountered in tossing pennies. If five pennies are tossed together, some one of the possible five combinations of heads and tails is observed. The five combinations form a parent binomial probability distribution $B(k; 5, \frac{1}{2})$ for which $\mu = np = \frac{5}{2}$, $\sigma = \sqrt{npq} = \sqrt{\frac{5}{4}}$, and $\sigma/\mu = (1/\sqrt{5}) \times 100\%$. If the experiment is repeated ten times, the experimental frequency distribution begins to take shape and we have additional information for the estimate m of the mean μ; i.e., σ_m is improved, but the parent distribution $10B(k; 5, \frac{1}{2})$ is unaltered (except for the normalization factor of 10); the values of μ, σ, and σ/μ are just the same. But, instead of repeating the experiment ten times, suppose that $10 \times 5 = 50$ pennies are tossed together; in this new experiment a single observation is made which is a member of the parent distribution $B(k; 50, \frac{1}{2})$, a different distribution from that with just five pennies, and one whose parameters are $\mu = np = \frac{50}{2}$, $\sigma = \sqrt{\frac{50}{4}}$, and

$\sigma/\mu = (1/\sqrt{50}) \times 100\%$. Of course, the new experiment could be performed by tossing the 50 pennies in 10 lots of 5 each, calling all 50 pennies a single observation; this is equivalent to subdividing the total number of basic Bernoulli trials. The dispersion of $B(k; 50, \frac{1}{2})$ is unaffected by any mere treatment of the data. The crucial point is in recognizing the parent distribution whose dispersion we would specify, i.e., the number of basic Bernoulli trials. It is apparent that σ in the new experiment with 50 pennies is only $\sqrt{10}$, instead of 10, times larger than σ in the old experiment with 5 pennies, and, on a "per penny" basis, the new experiment is the more precise. (The "per penny" basis is somewhat artificial here but illustrates the point. Had we started with a very large number of pennies, say 10,000, instead of 5, the "per certain large number of pennies" would make more sense.*)

A real advantage of subdivision of the data is that any significant misbehavior (change in systematic errors) of the experiment may be recognized, such as bursts of spurious background counts or a slow drift in the magnitude of the background or perhaps of the average value of the quantity being measured. If enough measurements and subdivisions are made, the χ^2 test can be used to check whether or not the systematic errors are constant, i.e., whether or not the observed fluctuations are purely random. Such a test in the radioactive decay example revealed that a changing systematic error was present until the radioactive specimen had become "conditioned."

The above conclusions as to precision, equally valid in many Poisson measurement situations, illustrate the importance of applications of probability theory and statistics in the design and performance of experiments.

More examples. The soldier-mule example and, strictly speaking, the radioactivity example discussed above illustrate Poisson sampling without replacement. But, the army was presumed to be kept up to strength at all times. And, with the condition that the source intensity remain constant, the radioactivity example was also discussed as though the supply of events were unlimited. Let us discuss some more Poisson examples.

Suppose that the volume of blood in an adult human is 6 liters, and that there are distributed in this volume C bacteria. A sample of size 0.6 mm³

---

* The situation with the pennies does not allow a convenient analog to the argument of spatial distribution, but this argument is not really involved in the present discussion. However, such an analog would require an adjustable reciprocal relation between the head probability p' and the number n' of pennies tossed for each observation with the product $n'p'$ remaining constant.

of blood is taken for examination. What is the probability that there are k bacteria in the sample? This is a Poisson problem because we may imagine, as a basic Bernoulli trial, the observation of one particular bacterium. Is this bacterium in the sample? The success probability p is the ratio of volumes, $0.6/(6 \times 10^6) = 10^{-7}$, and the number of trials n is the number of bacteria C in the total volume of blood. If the criterion $k^2 + (np)^2 \ll n$ is satisfied, the answer to the problem is $P(k; 10^{-7}C)$. If many samples are taken from the same person we have another example of sampling without replacement; it is essentially the same as the radioactivity case in which the observation is whether or not a given atom decays in a specified time interval. If each of many identical persons is used for each sample, we have sampling with replacement; but in this case the identity of different persons may be suspect. It should be noted that if the value of k we select in this problem is close to the expectation value $np = 10^{-7}C$, the standard deviation in the value k is $10^{-7/2}C^{\frac{1}{2}}$.

Also sampling with replacement: How many radio tubes in a new sample batch of 800 are reasonably expected to be defective if the manufacturing process is known to put out, on the average, 3% defectives? If the defectives appear randomly, i.e., not in bunches, the basic Bernoulli trial is obvious here—the inspection of each of the 800 radio tubes where each tube is either good or defective. The number of Bernoulli trials n is 800. The success probability p is also given as part of the problem, viz., $p = 0.03$. These Bernoulli trial characteristics are such that the parent distribution may be assumed to be Poisson. The first question is answered by the expectation value np. But this answer should be accompanied by a statement of precision, say, by the standard deviation $\pm\sqrt{np}$. Thus, a reasonably complete answer is $0.03 \times 800 \pm \sqrt{0.03 \times 800} = 24 \pm 4.9$. Another question may be asked, What is the probability that, in the batch, less than 30 tubes are defective? The answer is $800 \sum_{k=0}^{29} P(k; 24)$. Or the question may be, What is the probability that at least one tube will be defective? To this question the answer is

$$P(>1; 24) = 1 - P(0; 24) = \frac{1 - (24)^0 e^{-24}}{0!} = 1 - e^{-24} \approx 1$$

Consider another simple problem. Suppose that at a certain telephone switchboard 50,000 connections are made and that 267 of them are wrong. From a random sample of 25 connections, what is the probability that one will be wrong? Again, in this problem if the wrong connections occur randomly, the basic Bernoulli trial is the observation of each connection. The best determination of the expectation value is $25 \times 267/50,000 \approx 0.1335$. The answer to the question is $P(1; 0.1335) = 0.1335e^{-0.1335} \approx 0.117$.

As a variation of this problem, suppose that at another switchboard two wrong connections are made in 500 trials. What is the probability that one or more wrong connections will occur in the next 35 trials? This is left as an exercise for the reader.

As a final example, suppose that one night the "enemy" dropped 537 bombs in an area of 576 square blocks in the central region of Washington, D.C. We study the array of bomb hits and ask the question, Were the

Table 5-5. Bombs "Dropped" on Washington, D.C.

k	f_k	$NP(k; 0.9323)$
0	229	226.74
1	211	211.39
2	93	98.54
3	35	30.62
4	7	7.14
$\geqslant 5$	1	1.57

$$N = \Sigma f_k = 576$$

bombs aimed at the White House, or perhaps at the Capitol, each of which occupies, say, one block in area? The hit array may be as given in Table 5-5 where the number of hits is listed for each block. By looking at this hit array, especially if it is laid out on cross-section paper, most people would guess that the bombs were not randomly dropped over the entire area but rather were aimed at some one block.

Consider one basic Bernoulli trial to be whether or not a given bomb strikes a given block. The success probability in this case is constant for all bombs, $p = 1/576$, *if* the bombs were dropped at random. Viewed this way, there are $n = 537$ Bernoulli trials. These Bernoulli characteristics satisfy reasonably well the Poisson conditions. The average number of hits per block is $m = 537/576 \approx 0.9323$. The calculated Poisson frequency distribution, with $\mu \approx m$, is also listed in Table 5-5. The fit of this model is seen to be very good; by the χ^2 test the probability is 0.88 that another comparable bomb raid would show worse agreement than the bomb raid given in the table. Hence, the possibility that the White House, or any single block, was selected as a target is ruled out (or else the aim was inordinately bad). It takes well-trained judgment for a person to look at the hit array and decide, without calculations, whether or not the pattern *is* random.

$P(0; 0.9323) \approx 0.39$ is evidently the answer to the question, What is the probability that *your block* will not be hit? Now, what is the probability that *your house*, occupying 1/100 of a block, will be directly hit? The subdivision of the pertinent area into blocks was for convenience in the problem dealing with the size of the White House or the Capitol. Since your house is now the interesting unit of area, we subdivide into 57,600 units, each an equally likely target. The answer to the question posed is approximately 537/57,600. Why "approximately"?

5-8. Composite of Poisson Distributions

The observed fluctuations in any set of trial measurements are generally due to more than one source. For example, as an extreme case, the normal density function, Eq. 4-9, was derived as the composite of *numerous* elementary distributions. Now we wish to examine briefly the effect of a small number of sources of fluctuations in a typical Poisson problem.

Measuring with a background. In almost any measurement involving the counting of individual photons, α-particles, etc., the most common *second* source of fluctuations is the ubiquitous background "noise." Whether or not the primary source under study is introduced, this background is present and is producing a measurement effect.

A background is generally defined as those residual observations made when all deliberate sources are removed. Thus, a background is separately measurable.*

A typical background in a measurement with a Geiger counter or with an ionization chamber is caused by radioactive contaminations in the air or materials of the laboratory, by cosmic rays, by "spurious" counts inherent in the counter tube or ion chamber, or by the "noise" in the associated electronic circuits. The type of background we shall discuss is one that can be assumed to be constant on the average and random in detail. Since the background can be separately measured, its constancy on the average can be experimentally checked with the χ^2 test by assuming a flat distribution of measured means and by using Eq. 4-27. Generally, the background is found to be not only constant on the average but Poissonian in distribution. The randomness and distribution can be checked experimentally with the χ^2 test by assuming a Poisson distribution of individual measurements of the background.

It can be shown (and this is put as Problem 14, Section 5-10) that if both the background and the distribution of events we would measure are Poissonian, then the observed composite distribution is also Poissonian.

---

* In measuring the background in practice, the deliberate sources are preferably not physically removed—this would also remove any secondary effects (such as spurious scattering) in the background itself. It is often better to stop, by an appropriate shield, the direct source radiation from reaching the detector.

Thus,

$$\sum_{k_b=0}^{k} P(k_b; \mu_b) \cdot P(k - k_b; \mu_x) = P(k; \mu) \tag{5-33}$$

where k_b is the background count, μ_b is the mean background count, k is the observed composite count, μ_x is the mean value of the primary source activity (the quantity we are usually trying to measure), and $\mu = \mu_b + \mu_x$ is the mean composite count.

Precision. The observed composite count is

$$k = k_x + k_b' \tag{5-34}$$

and the primary source count can be written

$$k_x = k - k_b'$$

By Eq. 3-43, the standard deviation in k_x is

$$s_x^2 = s^2 + s_b^2 \tag{5-35}$$

(Note the sum, not a difference, in Eq. 5-35.) By Eq. 5-16, or Eq. 5-24 if we are dealing with a single measurement in each case, Eq. 5-35 becomes

$$s_x^2 \approx (k_x + k_b') + k_b \tag{5-36}$$

where k_b is a specific measurement of the background in the absence of k_x. k_b and k_b' are generally different because of statistical fluctuations.

The first conclusion is obvious, viz., if the signal is relatively strong, precision in determining the background is not very important. But if the signal is relatively weak, the k_b' and k_b terms in Eq. 5-36 are important, and considerable time must be spent in measuring the background.

Suppose that a time t_b is spent in measuring the background rate $b/t = B$. Then, Bt_b counts are recorded. Our best estimate of the mean background rate $\bar{B}$ and its standard deviation is

$$\bar{B} = \frac{[Bt_b \pm (Bt_b)^{1/2}]}{t_b} = B \pm \left(\frac{B}{t_b}\right)^{1/2} \tag{5-37}$$

The precision in $\bar{B}$ is inversely proportional to the square root of the time spent in determining B. Then, with the source under study introduced, suppose that a time t_x is spent in measuring the rate $(k_x + k_b')/t = X + B'$. In this case $(X + B')t_x$ counts are recorded, and our best estimate of the mean rates is

$$\bar{X} + \bar{B} = \frac{(X + B')t_x \pm [(X + B')t_x]^{1/2}}{t_x}$$

$$= X + B' \pm \left(\frac{X + B'}{t_x}\right)^{1/2} \tag{5-38}$$

By similar arguments, and using Eq. 5-35, we obtain

$$\bar{X} = X \pm \left(\frac{X + B'}{t_x} + \frac{B}{t_{b'}}\right)^{\frac{1}{2}} \tag{5-39}$$

The fractional standard deviation in per cent in X is approximately

$$\frac{s_X}{X} \approx \frac{\left(\dfrac{X + B'}{t_x} + \dfrac{B}{t_{b'}}\right)^{\frac{1}{2}}}{\dfrac{X + B'}{t_x} - \dfrac{B}{t_b}} \times 100 \tag{5-40}$$

Equations 5-39 and 5-40 could have been written directly from Eqs. 5-36 and 5-34 if the counts k and k_b had been divided by the times involved in their respective measurements. But writing X and B as rates, independent of the particular choice of observational times, is general and shows clearly, by Eqs. 5-37 and 5-38, that the precision in each case is inversely proportional to the square root of the time of measurement.

A common practical problem in precision is the following one. If the time $t_x + t_b$ is to be constant, what is the most efficient division of time? The most efficient division refers to that value of the ratio t_x/t_b such that the standard deviation s_X is a minimum. It can be shown (Problem 15, Section 5-10) that this ratio is

$$\left[\frac{t_x}{t_b}\right]_{s_X = \min} = \left(\frac{X + B'}{B}\right)^{\frac{1}{2}} \tag{5-41}$$

Another practical problem in precision occurs when the mean background counting rate $\bar{B}$ is comparable in magnitude with, or greater than, the mean primary source $\bar{X}$. In such a case, great care is required in interpreting the measurement $X + B'$. The desired signal X, obtained by subtracting B from $X + B'$, may be confused with a fluctuation peak in the background. Help in this interpretation is afforded by the tests for significance of the difference between two means, in this case between the means $\overline{X + B'}$ and $\bar{B}$. Such tests, including the useful t test, were discussed in Section 3-3.

The type of argument involved in the t test may be applied a little more simply to the difference in two means as follows. Let m and m_b be the means in question. Then our best estimate of the difference in the parent means is written, with the standard deviations, as

$$\mu - \mu_b = (m - m_b) \pm s_{(m - m_b)} \tag{5-42}$$

If we imagine a very large number of independent values of $m - m_b$ to be obtained, these values can be shown (by the central limit theorem) to be essentially normally distributed about the parent mean value $\mu - \mu_b$ with a standard deviation $s_{(m-m_b)}$. By Eq. 3-43,

$$s_{(m-m_b)} = (s_m^2 + s_{m_b}^2)^{1/2}$$

and, for the Poisson case,

$$s_{(m-m_b)} = \left(\frac{m}{n} + \frac{m_b}{n_b}\right)^{1/2} \tag{5-43}$$

by Eqs. 3-45 and 5-16, where n and n_b are the numbers of trial measurements used in determining m and m_b respectively. Again, if only a single measurement is used in either case, n or $n_b = 1$, Eq. 5-24 should be used instead of Eq. 5-16. Hence, $s_{(m-m_b)}$ can be evaluated, and with the single parameter h of the normal distribution thus known by Eq. 4-8, calculation can be made by Eq. 4-10 of the probability that $m - m_b$ will differ from $\mu - \mu_b$ by any specified value. Now, if the two parent means μ and μ_b are *assumed* for the moment to be the *same*, i.e., if there is *no* difference between $\overline{X + B'}$ and $\bar{B}$, there is a 32% chance that $m - m_b$ will be numerically greater than $s_{(m-m_b)}$. In other words, 68% of the area under the normal distribution curve, Fig. 4-6, lies within ±(standard deviation). A 32% chance is usually considered to be too large to be a satisfactory criterion that the desired signal X be declared to be clearly above the background $\bar{B}$. It is customary to take 5% as the "significance level." If the actual measurement $m - m_b$ is so far out on the tails that it is beyond the 5% limits, then the assumption that $\mu = \mu_b$ is thereby declared to be unreasonable, and consequently the desired signal is clearly above the background.

One important general conclusion of the above discussion of the high-background problem is that the *useful* sensitivity of a measuring instrument depends greatly upon the background. This dependence is *not* specified by the response of the instrument to a source of standard strength divided by the background, but the standard response must be divided by the magnitude of the *fluctuations* in the background. A very large background is perfectly acceptable if it is perfectly *constant* in magnitude.

5-9. Interval Distribution

An interesting extension can be made easily in those Poisson problems that involve a spatial distribution. This refers to the sizes of individual intervals between adjacent success events. The discussion is usually of events that occur along a time axis, and the intervals are time intervals.

As discussed so far, the Poisson distribution treats all these intervals as independent. But the so-called interval distribution answers further questions—it gives the probability for the occurrence of an interval of a specified size. This distribution is realized, of course, whenever the Poisson conditions are satisfied for events that occur randomly along some spatial axis, such as time. A spatial-distribution Poisson problem can be considered as one of measuring intervals instead of one of measuring events; the two views are obviously related. We should be acquainted with both views and choose the more convenient one in individual problems.

From Eq. 5-4, the probability that there will be no event per unit time is

$$P(0;\ \mu) = \frac{\mu^0 e^{-\mu}}{0!} = e^{-\mu} \tag{5-44}$$

where μ is the average number of events per unit time. Let the size of the time interval of interest be t; then the average number of events during this interval is μt, and

$$P(0;\ \mu t) = e^{-\mu t} \tag{5-45}$$

The probability that an event will occur in the interval dt is simply $\mu\, dt$. This is the probability for a *single* event if $\mu\, dt \ll 1$. Then, the combined probability for no event during t and for one event between t and $t + dt$ is the product $\mu e^{-\mu t}\, dt$. Designate this probability as $I(t;\ \mu)\, dt$, and write

$$I(t;\ \mu)\, dt = \mu e^{-\mu t}\, dt \tag{5-46}$$

Equation 5-46 is the probability density function for the distribution of sizes of intervals occurring between random rare events. It is immediately evident that small intervals have a higher probability than large intervals; hence, the interval distribution is asymmetrical.

A measurement of k events in time T is accompanied by K intervals, where $K = k \pm 1$ depending upon whether we start and/or end the time T with a count or with an interval. These K intervals are of many different sizes. The number n_{t_1, t_2} of intervals having sizes greater than t_1 but smaller than t_2 is given by

$$n_{t_1, t_2} = KI(t;\ \mu) = K \int_{t_1}^{t_2} \mu e^{-\mu t}\, dt \tag{5-47}$$

$$n_{t_1, t_2} = K(e^{-\mu t_1} - e^{-\mu t_2}) \tag{5-48}$$

In particular, with $t_1 = 0$, Eq. 5-47 or 5-48 is the cumulative probability distribution function.

If $t_2 > T$, the time of the actual observation for the k events, t_2, may be taken as infinite, and then

$$n_{t > t_1} = Ke^{-\mu t_1} \tag{5-49}$$

The average interval is simply $1/\mu$, so the fraction of intervals that are *larger* than the average is

$$\frac{n_{t > (1/\mu)}}{K} = e^{-1} \approx 0.37 \tag{5-50}$$

As a second interesting limiting case, suppose that $t_1 = 0$. Then, by Eq. 5-48, the fraction of intervals that are *smaller* than any specified interval t_2 is

$$\frac{n_{t<t_2}}{K} = 1 - e^{-\mu t_2} \tag{5-51}$$

Dispersion indices. In the interval distribution, the mean deviation is defined as

$$\overline{t - \tau} \equiv \frac{\displaystyle\int_0^\infty |t - \tau|\, \mu e^{-\mu t}\, dt}{\displaystyle\int_0^\infty \mu e^{-\mu t}\, dt} \tag{5-52}$$

where τ is written for the mean interval, $\tau = 1/\mu$. After performing the integration of Eq. 5-52, we have

$$\overline{t - \tau} = \frac{2\tau}{e} \approx 0.7358\tau \tag{5-53}$$

Equation 2-21 defines the variance for any continuous distribution, such as the interval distribution, and, accordingly, we write

$$\sigma^2 \equiv \frac{\displaystyle\int_0^\infty (t - \tau)^2 \mu e^{-\mu t}\, dt}{\displaystyle\int_0^\infty \mu e^{-\mu t}\, dt} \tag{5-54}$$

The standard deviation in the size of the intervals between randomly distributed events is, from Eq. 5-54,

$$\sigma = \tau = \frac{1}{\mu} \tag{5-55}$$

just equal to the average interval.

Resolving time: lost counts. It is physically impossible to measure two spatially separated events when the interval between them becomes less than the resolving ability of the measuring instrument. On a time axis, the limiting resolving ability of the instrument is called the resolving time, or the "dead time." Because short intervals are more probable than long intervals, Eq. 5-46, the finite resolving time reduces artifically the dispersion of Poisson events; it causes χ^2 to become artifically smaller (i.e., χ^2/n to become less than unity, where n is the number of Poisson measurements; see Problem 30(b), Section 5-10).

If R, the rate at which events are "received" by the instrument, is rather small, and a small fraction of the counts (or intervals) is lost, then the observed rate R_c is given by

$$R_c \approx R(1 - R_c \tau_r) \quad \text{for } R_c \tau_r \ll 1 \tag{5-56}$$

from which

$$R \approx R_c(1 + R_c \tau_r) \quad \text{for } R_c \tau_r \ll 1$$

where τ_r is the resolving time. In this case, τ_r is usually written as

$$\tau_r = \frac{R - R_c}{R R_c} \tag{5-57}$$

and, if R is known, τ_r can be measured.

If R becomes rather large, we must distinguish between two different types of counters. Equation 5-56 is satisfactory if unrecorded (lost) counts do not themselves extend the dead time; then R_c approaches the value $1/\tau_r$. But if each unrecorded count does extend the dead time, then, instead of Eq. 5-56, we must write

$$R_c = Re^{-R\tau_r} \tag{5-58}$$

In this case, when $R\tau_r = 1$, R_c reaches a maximum

$$R_{c_{\max}} = \frac{R}{e} = \frac{1}{e\tau_r} \tag{5-59}$$

and then declines. At the maximum counting rate, only $1/e = 37\%$ of the received events are counted. This type of counter, if R increases indefinitely, becomes completely paralyzed.

It is interesting to note that if, instead of the events being randomly spaced, they are *uniformly* spaced, as are "pips" from an oscillator, and if recovery were abruptly complete after the dead time interval, the second type of counter described in the preceding paragraph would follow faithfully until the rate equals $1/\tau_r$, and this is just e times $R_{c_{\max}}$ for random events. An oscillator is often used to determine the resolving time of an electronic circuit, e.g., one which is part of a counter system, but usually some allowance must be made for incomplete recovery.

Coincidence counting. There are a great many interesting problems that arise in practical applications of the Poisson statistics. We shall mention just one more.

Suppose that, in the radioactive decay of $^{28}_{13}\text{Al}$, we wish to show that the emission of the β- and γ-rays is very nearly simultaneous in the decay process, i.e., simultaneous within the resolving time of the equipment. Two counters are used and arranged so that both must respond together in order for the event to count. This is called coincidence counting.

Since each counter has a finite background, there is a certain probability that random coincidences will be counted that are unrelated to the $^{28}_{13}\text{Al}$

decay. Furthermore, in this experiment, since each counter subtends only a small fraction of the 4π solid angle of the β- and γ-emission, a β (or a γ) may be received by one counter and the related γ (or β) go in such a direction as to miss the other counter; perhaps it also enters the first counter. This situation greatly complicates the background for each counter; the *total* background includes the unrelated rays from the decaying $^{28}_{13}\mathrm{Al}$. We shall not work out the details here.

Conclusions. We have discussed in this chapter only a few selected examples of Poisson type problems—starting with the simple and proceeding to the more complex—problems that are typical in science. Other problems are legion, but let us say that they lead us beyond the scope of this book.

5-10. Problems

1. A deck of 52 cards is shuffled and placed face down on a table. Then the cards are turned up 1 at a time, each card being discarded after it is examined. The player calls each card without looking at it and promptly forgets what he calls. Show by the parameters of the basic Bernoulli trials and the Poisson conditions that the probability distribution for the number of cards he may expect to call correctly is essentially Poissonian.

2. Suppose that the weather records show that, on the average, 5 out of the 30 days in November are snowy days.

(a) What is the binomial probability that next November will have at most 4 snowy days?

(b) What is the Poisson probability for the same event?

3. Make the histogram of the following numbers of seeds germinating per unit area on damp filter paper:

$k =$	0	1	2	3	4	5	6	7	8	9	10
$f_k =$	6	20	28	12	8	6	0	0	0	0	0

Fit (a) a binomial and (b) a Poisson distribution to these measurements and plot these two frequency distributions on the same graph as the experimental histogram. (Hint: In the Poisson calculation, use Eq. 5-6.)

4. Suppose the number of telephone calls an operator receives on Tuesday mornings from 9:00 to 9:10 is fitted by a Poisson distribution with $\mu = 3$.

(a) Find the probability that the operator will receive no calls in that time interval next Tuesday.

(b) Find the probability that in the next 3 Tuesdays the operator will receive a total of 1 call in that time interval.

(c) Find the probability that the 1 call of part (b) will be in the first Tuesday.

5. A book of 600 pages contains, on the average 200 misprints. Estimate the chance that a page contains at least 3 misprints. Discuss the reliability of this estimate. [ans. p (3 or more) ≈ 0.29; $\sigma_\mu \approx 2.36 \times 10^{-2}$]

6. A life-insurance company has 1000 policies, averaging $2000, on lives of people at age 25. From a mortality table it is found that, of 89,032 alive at age 25, 88,314 are alive at age 26. Find upper and lower values for the amount which the company would reasonably be expected to pay out during the year on these policies.

7. (a) What are the binomial and the Poisson probabilities that exactly 3 people, in a random sample of 500, have birthdays on Christmas? (Assume all days of each year to be equally probable as birthdays.)

(b) What is the expectation value of the number of birthdays on February 29?

(c) What is the precision of the answer to part (b)?

(d) If a large number of random samples of 500 people per sample were investigated an experimental probability could be obtained that "exactly" 3 people out of 500 have birthdays on Christmas. Mention a few factors that would make it unlikely that this experimental probability would agree with the calculated binomial probability for this event.

8. (a) How would you determine the probability that an unspecified college girl has red hair, assuming no ambiguity in color? Discuss the reliability of your determination. Assume in the remainder of this problem that this probability is 0.05.

(b) What is the probability that in a random sample of 20 college girls 4 will have red hair?

(c) What is the probability that, of 4 girls in a physics class having a enrollment of 30, only 1 has red hair?

(d) How large must a random sample be if the probability of its containing at least 1 red head is to be 0.95 or more?

(e) List the Bernoulli and the Poisson conditions separately, and write "good," "fair," or "poor" by each condition to indicate the degree to which it is "satisfied" in part (b), in part (c), and in part (d).

9. A long-lived radioactive source emits particles at an average rate of 10/hr.

(a) What is the expectation number of particles observed in 10 min?

(ans. 1.67)

(b) What is the probability that in a 10-min run no particles are observed?

(ans. 0.188)

(c) If 20 measurements are made, each for 10 min, what can you say about a measure of fluctuations relative to the mean value?

(d) What is the precision of a single 10-min observation?

(e) If the average counting rate were 300/hr instead of 10/hr, what would the answers be for parts (a), (b), (c), and (d)?

10. If 246 cosmic-ray counts are observed in one hour, then 265 counts in the next hour, is the difference great enough to indicate a significant time variation in the cosmic-ray intensity? Treat the data three different ways, i.e., by different arguments, before finally concluding as to significance.

11. Derive the expression for kurtosis in the Poisson distribution.

12. Consider the distribution $B(k; 100, 0.05) \approx P(k; 5)$. What is the value of
(a) the mean,
(b) the most probable value,
(c) the standard deviation,
(d) the standard deviation in the mean (standard error),
(e) the skewness, and
(f) the kurtosis?

13. The probability of observing the mean value in almost any probability distribution is surprisingly small. Show that $P(\mu; \mu) = 1/(2\pi\mu)^{1/2}$, using Stirling's formula.

14. (a) Verify, for counting with a constant background, when the source rate is $k_x/t = k/t - k_b/t_b$, that

$$\sum_{k_b=0}^{k} P(k_b; \mu_b) \cdot P(k - k_b; \mu_x) = P(k; \mu_b + \mu_x) = P(k; \mu)$$

(b) Reconcile this identity with the statement (implied in Section 4-3) that a large number of component Poisson distributions gives a composite *normal* distribution.

15. If $t + t_b$ is constant, where t is the time spent in counting X rays (including the background) and t_b is the time spent in determining the background, show that the most efficient division of time between measurements of k_b/t_b and k/t is such that $t/t_b \approx (k/k_b)^{1/2}$.

16. Show, using Eq. 5-4, that the probability of observing one less than the mean value is the same as the probability of observing the mean value in a Poisson distribution.

17. As an inspector of an enormous quantity of some manufactured gadget, determine the sample size and the acceptance number so that
(a) there should be less than 1 chance in 10 that a lot with 5% defectives is accepted,
(b) there should be less than 5 chances in 100 that a lot with only 2% defectives is rejected, and
(c) that the combination (a) and (b) obtains.

18. Consider the chances of a bomber pilot surviving a series of statistically identical raids in which the chance of being shot down is always 5%.
(a) From an original group of 1000 such pilots, how many are expected to survive 1, 5, 10, 15, 20, 40, 80, and 100 raids? Plot the survival curve.
(b) What is the mean life of a pilot in number of raids?   (ans. 20 raids)
(c) In a single raid of 100 planes, what are the chances that 0, 1, 5, or 10 planes will be lost?

19. Ten cm^3 of a liquid contain 30 bacteria. Each of 10 test tubes of a nutrient material is inoculated with 1 cm^3 of this solution. What is the probability
(a) that only 1 of the test tubes shows growth, i.e., contains at least 1 bacterium,
(b) that the first test tube to be inoculated shows growth,

(c) that all 10 of the test tubes show growth, and

(d) that exactly 7 test tubes show growth?

This is a multinomial problem, but can any part or parts of it be conveniently treated as a Poisson problem?

20. How many stars must there be randomly distributed in the sky all around the earth in order that there be a 50–50 chance of having

(a) a "north" polar star, i.e., within, say, 2° of the axis,

(b) both a "north" and a "south" star,

(c) either one or both?

(d) What would the answer be to part (a) if the stars were uniformly distributed in the sky?

21. What additional information, if any, do you need in order to determine in each of the following parts whether or not it is a probability distribution, and, if it is, which of the 3 distributions emphasized in this book does it most closely approximate? Give as many a priori reasons for each answer as you can.

(a) Classification of adult men in New York State according to financial income per year.

(b) Number of defective lamp bulbs in each of many large sample batches from a factory.

(c) Repeated trial measurements of (i) very feeble and (ii) very intense light intensity.

(d) One hundred measurements of the winning time at a horse race, each measurement by a different observer using his own stop watch.

(e) Values of the height of the emperor of Japan from a poll of every tenth adult resident of Japan, the residents being randomly selected.

(f) Number vs. deflection angle of a beam of protons scattered in passing through a thin metallic foil, there being on the average (i) less than 1 scattering process per scattered proton (i.e., single scattering), and (ii) 100 scattering processes per scattered proton (i.e., multiple scattering). (Scattering is due to the proton-nucleus electrical repulsion).

22. Suppose that the average number of fatal accidents occurring in the city of Ithaca is 1.5/yr. In a particular year 4 fatal accidents occur.

(a) Is this number (4) reasonable, i.e., does it fall within the range of numbers that may be considered reasonable on the basis of chance alone?

(b) What is the critical number of fatal accidents in any one year that should prompt, say, an increase in the size of the police force if the criterion is set that the probability shall be less than 5% that this or a greater number will occur owing to chance alone?

23. It is entirely possible in a multinomial probability problem to have n large, p_i small, and np_i moderate, where p_i is the basic Bernoulli probability for k_i successes and i is any one of the r possible outcomes in Eq. 1-20. Show that for $r = 3$ the multiple Poisson distribution is normalized.

24. How would you design the experiment to distinguish between randomness in direction and randomness in time in the emission of α-particles from polonium?

Discuss your choice of classification intervals and of the total number of measurements of counting rate.

25. A proportional counter is used in the measurement of X rays of constant average intensity.

(a) A total count (source plus background) of 8000 is observed in 10 min. Then, with the X rays removed, 10 min gives a total of 2000 background counts. What is the average X-ray intensity in counts per minute, and what is the standard deviation in this value?

(b) What is the optimum fraction of time to spend measuring the background if the total time to make measurements is fixed?

26. In the measurement of γ-rays, a counter is used with a measured average background of 120 cpm. If the γ-rays enter the counter at an average rate of 240/min, what must be the duration of an observation of the γ-rays if the measurement of the number of γ's per minute is to have a probable error of 2%?

27. Show by the method of maximum likelihood that $\sigma = \sqrt{np} = \mu$ in the Poisson distribution. (See Problem 27, Section 3-11.)

28. In expressing the dispersion of a set of measurements believed to be members of a Poisson distribution, the standard deviation is used more commonly than the mean deviation.

(a) State as many reasons for this as you can.

(b) Outline in some detail a real-life measurement situation in which the mean deviation is preferable. (Assume that no common probability model "fits").

29. A college class of 80 students meets 267 times during the year. The number of class meetings f_k with k absences is listed in Table 5-6.

Table 5-6. Absenteeism in College Class Meetings

k	f_k	$267P(k;\ 8.74)$
0–2	1	2.05
3	5	4.76
4	11	10.39
5	14	18.16
6	22	26.45
7	43	33.03
8	31	36.09
9	40	35.04
10	35	30.63
11	20	24.34
12	18	17.72
13	12	11.92
14	7	7.44
15	6	4.33
>16	2	4.65

(a) Is the absenteeism random?

(b) If the day-by-day attendance records were available to you, how would you arrange the data and proceed to determine whether or not the absenteeism on days of out-of-town football games was due to random fluctuations alone?

30. (a) Make the χ^2 test of the goodness of fit of the Poisson model to the observations in Table 5-4.

(b) Show that, for a perfect fit, $\chi^2 = n$, where n is the number of trial measurements.

31. In successive 5-min intervals the background with a certain counter is $310, 290, 280, 315, 315, 275, 315$. A radioactive source of long half-life is brought up to the counter. The increased counting rate for successive 5-min intervals is $720, 760, 770, 780, 710, 780, 740, 740$.

(a) Calculate in counts per minute the average value and the probable error for (i) the background, (ii) the background plus source, and (iii) the source alone.

(b) Show quantitatively whether or not the data with the source plus background can safely be considered to be randomly distributed.

32. In counting α-particles, the average rate is 30 α's per hour. What is the fraction of the intervals between successive counts such that they are

(a) longer than 5 min,

(b) longer than 10 min,

(c) shorter than 30 sec.

33. Both α- and β-rays are emitted from a certain radioactive sample. Assume that the α- and β-emissions are independent, i.e., from different noninteracting atoms. The observed counts are A α's per minute and B β's per minute. What is the combined probability that a particular interval between two successive α's will have a duration between t and $t + dt$ and will also contain exactly x β's?

34. (a) Perform the integrations of Eqs. 5-52 and 5-54 for the mean deviation and for the standard deviation in the interval distribution.

(b) Derive the expression for the skewness of the interval distribution.

35. In a certain experiment, a counter system gives counts per minute as listed in Table 5-7. The parent distribution is expected to be Poissonian. The internal

Table 5-7. Observed Counts in a Certain Experiment

Trial	k
1	250
2	236
3	246
4	249
5	241
6	242

consistency of these measurements is suspiciously "good." What is the probability that something is wrong?   (ans. 0.99)

36. What is the probability that the data of Table 5-3 are not genuine?

37. There are more positively charged cosmic rays at sea level than negatively charged ones. In a given experiment, 2740 positive ones and 2175 negative ones were detected during the same time interval. How should the ratio of positive to negative particles be reported?

38. One g of radioactive material of atomic weight 200 is exposed to a counter which has a 5.00% efficiency for detecting disintegrations; 787 counts are registered in 30 min. What is the mean lifetime of the radioactivity? What is the most probable lifetime of single radioactive nuclei?

39. A piece of metal is exposed to neutron irradiation and therafter is placed near a counter than can detect the induced radioactivity. During the first minute after irradiation, 256 counts are recorded; during the second minute there are 49 counts. Ignore background. Assuming that only one kind of radioactivity was produced, determine the decay constant and the standard deviation in its determination. (Assume, of course, exponential decay).

40. A cosmic-ray "telescope" with a sensitive area of 100 cm² and an aperture of 0.02 steradian is pointed in a fixed direction. In 1 hr intervals at various different times the following numbers of counts are recorded:

276	295	287	280
304	320	309	298
290	265	301	327

Are these data consistent with the assumption that the particles are independent of each other and random in time? Determine the intensity of cosmic rays and its standard deviation from these data. Do these data prove that the particles are random in time?

41. The absorption coefficient of high-energy protons is measured by either (a) counting successively the number of protons reaching a distant counter in 1 min with and without an absorber 2 cm thick placed between the source and the counter, or (b) using 2 counters rather close together with the absorber placed between them, and counting simultaneously for 1 min the number of protons in counter 1 and the number of coincident counts in counters 1 and 2. Ignore the background, and assume the mean activity of the source to be constant with individual protons being emitted randomly in time. Suppose the observed numbers are, in both cases, 522 and 441. Derive for these hypothetical experiments the best value and the standard deviation of the absorption coefficient. [The absorption coefficient is defined in terms of the decrease in counting rate $R_0 - R$ and the thickness x of the absorber, viz., $(R_0 - R)/R_0 x$.]

42. A long-lived source of γ-rays is mounted in a fixed position relative to a Geiger counter. In 10 min, 3926 counts are recorded. Then a sheet of copper 1 cm thick is placed between the source and the counter. In 10 min, 1540 counts are recorded. The source is removed (i.e., the direct radiation is completely stopped by a thick shield) and in a third 10-min interval a background of 482 counts is recorded. Assume that any γ-rays that interact with the copper in any way can no longer be detected. What is the total cross section of the γ-rays in copper? What is the standard deviation in its determination?

Summary

Throughout this book we have devoted the majority of the pages to the practical mechanics of analyzing observations and measurements with an eye to the proper formulas for use in determining experimental errors and probability precision. But the discussion has been deliberately cast in the framework of the scientist rather than of the mathematician or of the statistician.

It is hoped that this book leaves the reader with a better understanding that science is a complex of observations, measurements, theoretical concepts, and predictions that are all essentially probabilistic, that all "facts" of science are probabilistic; that the "exact" or deterministic views of science of the 19th century, and indeed held by many pseudo scientists today, have given way to open-ended views. And thus can science continue to live and grow and be philosophically at home among the other intellectual endeavors of man.

Glossary

The equations listed in the five parts of this glossary are numbered as in the text; the pages in the text are also indicated.

I. CLASSICAL PROBABILITY

Definition of p; $w \equiv$ number of "wins," $n \equiv$ number of equally probable outcomes:

(1-1)
$$p \equiv \frac{w}{n}$$
p. **8**

Independent events A and B:

(1-5)
$$p(A \text{ and } B) = p(A) \cdot p(B)$$
p. **10**

$$p(B \,|\, A) = p(B) \quad \text{and} \quad p(A \,|\, B) = p(A)$$
p. **13**

Compound events; independent component events; additive theorems:

(1-3)
$$p(\text{either } A \text{ or } B) = p(A) + p(B)$$
p. **10**

(1-6)
$$p(\text{neither } A \text{ nor } B) = 1 - p(A) - p(B) + p(A) \cdot p(B)$$
p. **12**

(1-7)
$$p(\text{either } A \text{ or } B, \text{ not both}) = p(A) + p(B) - 2p(A) \cdot p(B)$$
p. **12**

(1-8)
$$p(\text{either } A \text{ or } B \text{ or both}) = p(A) + p(B) - p(A) \cdot p(B)$$
p. **12**

Partially dependent events; conditional probability:

(1-9)
$$p(A \text{ and } B) = p(A)\, p(B \,|\, A)$$
p. **13**

Permutations, total number of, n objects taken k at a time (the k objects ordered):

(1-12)
$$_nP_k = \frac{n!}{(n-k)!}$$
p. **23**

Combinations, total number of, n objects taken k at a time (the k objects unordered):

(1-17)
$$\binom{n}{k} = \frac{_nP_k}{k!} = \frac{n!}{k!(n-k)!}$$
p. **27**

Stirling's formula (for any factorial number $z!$):

(1-14)
$$z! = \sqrt{2\pi z}\left(\frac{z}{e}\right)^z \left(1 + \frac{1}{12z} + \frac{1}{228z^2} - \cdots\right)$$
p. **24**

II. MEASUREMENTS IN SCIENCE: SIMPLE STATISTICS (REGARDLESS OF "FIT" OF ANY MATHEMATICAL MODEL)

Definition (experimental) of p; $w_{obs} \equiv$ number of "win" observations, $n_{obs} \equiv$ number of identical trials:

$$\text{(1-39)} \qquad p_{obs} \equiv \lim_{n_{obs} \to \infty} \frac{w_{obs}}{n_{obs}} \qquad \text{p. 49}$$

Mean m (sample, real-life data); r different values of x, x_i observed f_i times, in n trials:

$$\text{(2-1)} \qquad m = \frac{x_1 + x_2 + \cdots x_n}{n} = \frac{\sum_{i=1}^{n} x_i}{n} \qquad \text{p. 76}$$

$$\text{(2-2)} \qquad m = \frac{f_1 x_1 + f_2 x_2 + \cdots f_r x_r}{n} = \frac{\sum_{i=1}^{r} f_i x_i}{n} \qquad \text{p. 77}$$

$$\text{(2-3)} \qquad m = \sum_{i=1}^{r} x_i p_i \qquad \text{where} \qquad p_i = \left(\frac{f_i}{n}\right)_{obs} \qquad \text{p. 77}$$

Working mean w:

$$\text{(2-4)} \qquad m = w + \Delta = w + \frac{\sum_{i=1}^{n} (x_i - w)}{n} \qquad \text{p. 78}$$

Deviation z_i:

$$\text{(2-5)} \qquad z_i = x_i - m \qquad \text{p. 79}$$

Mean deviation $\bar{z}$:

$$\text{(2-7, 2-8)} \qquad \bar{z} = \frac{\sum_{i=1}^{n} z_i}{n}; \qquad \text{fractional } \bar{z} = \frac{\bar{z}}{m} \qquad \text{pp. 80, 81}$$

Standard deviation s (sample, real-life data):

$$\text{(2-9, 2-12)} \qquad s = \left(\frac{\sum_{i=1}^{n} (x_i - m)^2}{n}\right)^{1/2} = \left(\frac{\sum_{i=1}^{n} x_i^2 - nm^2}{n}\right)^{1/2} \qquad \text{pp. 82, 84}$$

$$\text{(2-11)} \qquad \text{fractional } s = \frac{s}{m} \qquad \text{p. 83}$$

Variance s^2 (sample, real-life data) with working mean w:

$$\text{(2-13)} \qquad s^2 = \frac{\sum_{i=1}^{n} (x_i - w)^2 - n\Delta^2}{n}; \qquad \Delta = \frac{\sum_{i=1}^{n} (x_i - w)}{n} \qquad \text{p. 84}$$

Moments; kth moment about the origin θ_k^0 and about the mean θ_k^m:

$$\text{(2-15, 2-17)} \qquad \theta_k^0 = \frac{\sum_{i=1}^{n} x_i^k}{n}; \qquad \theta_k^m = \frac{\sum_{i=1}^{n} (x_i - m)^k}{n} \qquad \text{pp. 85, 86}$$

Second moment; variance s^2:

(2-19)
$$s^2 = \theta_2{}^m = \theta_2{}^0 - m^2$$
p. **86**

Universe variance σ^2, with universe mean μ, discrete universe distribution:

(2-20)
$$\sigma^2 = \lim_{n \to 0} \frac{\sum_{i=1}^{n} (x_i - \mu)^2}{n} = \lim_{n \to 0} \sum_{i=1}^{n} (x_i - \mu)^2 p_i$$
p. **86**

Same for continuous universe distribution:

(2-21)
$$\sigma^2 = \frac{\int_0^\infty (x - \mu)^2 p_x \, dx}{\int_0^\infty p_x \, dx}$$
p. **87**

Practical ("best") estimate of σ:

(2-22, 2-23)
$$\sigma \approx \left(\frac{n}{n-1}\right)^{1/2} s = \left(\frac{\sum_{i=1}^{n} (x_i - m)^2}{n - 1}\right)^{1/2}$$
p. **88**

Standard deviation in the mean s_m, real-life data and universe:

(2-31, 2-32, 2-33)
$$s_m = \frac{s}{\sqrt{n}}; \qquad \sigma_m = \frac{\sigma}{\sqrt{n}} = \left(\frac{\sum_{i=1}^{n} (x_i - m)^2}{n(n-1)}\right)^{1/2}$$
p. **93**

(2-34)
$$\text{fractional } s_m = \frac{s_m}{m} = \frac{s}{m\sqrt{n}}; \qquad \text{fractional } \sigma_m = \frac{\sigma_m}{\mu} = \frac{\sigma}{\mu\sqrt{n}}$$
p. **94**

Standard deviation in the standard deviation σ_s for approximately normal (bell-shaped) distribution:

(2-44)
$$\sigma_s \approx \sigma/\sqrt{2n}$$
p. **96**

Probable error pe, 50% confidence limits; for approximately normal (bell-shaped) distribution:

(4-21)
$$pe \approx 0.65s$$
pp. **173, 206**

Probable error in the probable error pe_{pe} for approximately normal distribution:

(2-45)
$$pe_{pe} \approx 0.65pe/\sqrt{2n} = 0.46pe/\sqrt{n}$$
p. **96**

Skewness, coefficient of:

(2-35, 2-36)
$$\text{skewness} = \frac{\sum_{i=1}^{n} (x_i - m)^3}{ns^3}\bigg|_{\text{sample}}; \qquad \lim_{n \to \infty} \frac{\sum_{i=1}^{n} (x_i - \mu)^3}{n\sigma^3}\bigg|_{\text{universe}}$$
p. **94**

Peakedness, coefficient of:

(2-41, 2-42)
$$\text{peakedness} = \frac{\sum_{i=1}^{n} (x_i - m)^4}{ns^4}\bigg|_{\text{sample}}; \qquad \lim_{n \to \infty} \frac{\sum_{i=1}^{n} (x_i - \mu)^4}{n\sigma^4}\bigg|_{\text{universe}}$$
p. **95**

III. PROPAGATION OF ERRORS

Propagation of random errors, in function $u = f(x, y)$:

$$(3\text{-}31) \qquad \delta u_i \approx \frac{\partial u}{\partial x} \delta x_i + \frac{\partial u}{\partial y} \delta y_i \qquad \text{p. 112}$$

Mean deviation $\bar{z}_u$, in $u = f(x, y)$ with $\bar{z}_x$ and $\bar{z}_y$ known:

$$(3\text{-}32) \qquad \bar{z}_u = \left[\left(\frac{\partial u}{\partial x} \right)^2 \bar{z}_x{}^2 + \left(\frac{\partial u}{\partial y} \right)^2 \bar{z}_y{}^2 \right]^{\frac{1}{2}} \qquad \text{p. 113}$$

$$(3\text{-}33) \qquad \text{fractional } \bar{z}_u = \left[\left(\frac{\partial u}{\partial x} \right)^2 \frac{\bar{z}_x{}^2}{\bar{x}^2} + \left(\frac{\partial u}{\partial y} \right)^2 \frac{\bar{z}_y{}^2}{\bar{y}^2} \right]^{\frac{1}{2}} \qquad \text{p. 113}$$

Standard deviation s_u, in $u = f(x, y)$ with s_x and s_y known:

$$(3\text{-}36,\ 3\text{-}39) \qquad s_u = \left[\left(\frac{\partial u}{\partial x} \right)^2 s_x{}^2 + \left(\frac{\partial u}{\partial y} \right)^2 s_y{}^2 \right]^{\frac{1}{2}} \qquad \text{pp. 114, 115}$$

$$\text{fractional } s_u = \frac{s_u}{\bar{u}}$$

$$(3\text{-}38,\ 3\text{-}40) \qquad \text{Same for } s_{\bar{u}} \text{ with } s_{\bar{x}} \text{ written for } s_x \text{ and } s_{\bar{y}} \text{ for } s_y \qquad \text{p. 115}$$

Probable error pe_u (or $pe_{\bar{u}}$), in $u = f(x, y)$ with pe_x and pe_y (or $pe_{\bar{x}}$ and $pe_{\bar{y}}$) known: same as for s_u (or for $s_{\bar{u}}$) with pe replacing s throughout.

IV. MORE STATISTICS

Weighted mean m^w, each x_i with weight w_i, n trials:

$$(3\text{-}57) \qquad m^w = \bar{x}^w = \frac{\displaystyle\sum_{i=1}^{n} w_i x_i}{\displaystyle\sum_{i=1}^{n} w_i} \qquad \text{p. 118}$$

Weighted grand mean $\bar{x}^w$ of N component means each weighted by inverse variance (i.e., $w_{\bar{x}_i} \propto 1/s_{\bar{x}_i}{}^2$):

$$(3\text{-}58) \qquad \bar{x}^w = \frac{\displaystyle\sum_{i=1}^{n} \bar{x}_i / s_{\bar{x}_i}{}^2}{\displaystyle\sum_{i=1}^{n} 1/s_{\bar{x}_i}{}^2} \qquad \text{p. 118}$$

Weighted standard deviation $s_x{}^w$:

$$(3\text{-}61) \qquad s_x{}^w = \left[\frac{\displaystyle\sum_{i=1}^{n} w_i (x_i - \bar{x}^w)^2}{\displaystyle\sum_{i=1}^{n} w_i} \right]^{\frac{1}{2}} \qquad \text{p. 120}$$

t in the t test for consistency of means of two sets of measurements:

$$(3\text{-}64) \qquad t = \frac{\bar{x}_1 - \bar{x}_2}{\sigma_{(x_1 + x_2)}} \left(\frac{n_1 n_2}{n_1 + n_2} \right)^{\frac{1}{2}} \qquad \text{p. 121}$$

F in the F test for consistency of standard deviations of two sets of measurements:

(3-67)
$$F = \frac{\sigma_{x_1}^2}{\sigma_{x_2}^2} = \frac{\dfrac{n_1}{n_1 - 1} s_{x_1}^2}{\dfrac{n_2}{n_2 - 1} s_{x_2}^2}$$
p. 124

χ^2 in the chi-square test for goodness of fit of a mathematical model; actual data and model subdivided into M intervals, f = frequency of measurements (actual, obs, or universe, th) in the jth interval:

(4-26)
$$\chi^2 = \sum_{j=1}^{M} \frac{[(f_{\text{obs}})_j - (f_{\text{th}})_j]^2}{(f_{\text{th}})_j}$$
p. 185

If the model distribution is uniform (flat), n total measurements:

(4-27)
$$\chi^2 = \sum_{j=1}^{n} \frac{(x_i - m)^2}{m}$$
p. 185

Curve fitting, $y = a + bx$, values of a and b:

(3-74)
$$a = \frac{\Sigma x_i^2 \Sigma y_i - \Sigma x_i \Sigma (x_i y_i)}{n \Sigma x_i^2 - (\Sigma x_i)^2}$$
p. 129

(3-75)
$$b = \frac{n \Sigma (x_i y_i) - \Sigma x_i \Sigma y_i}{n \Sigma x_i^2 - (\Sigma x_i)^2}$$
p. 129

For weighted values, see Eqs. **3-76** and **3-77**.   p. 129

For standard deviations, see Eqs. **3-78** and **3-79**.   p. 130

In case $a = 0$, see Eq. **3-83**.   p. 131

Curve fitting, $y = a + bx + cx^2$, values of a, b, c: see Eq. **3-86**.   p. 132

Correlation coefficient r for straight-line regression curve through the origin at $\bar{x}$, $\bar{y}$:

(3-107)
$$r = b \frac{s_x}{s_y} = \frac{\Sigma x_i y_i}{\Sigma x_i^2} \frac{s_x}{s_y}$$
p. 142

Covariance s_{xy} for straight-line regression curve through the origin at $\bar{x}$, $\bar{y}$ and with correlation coefficient r:

$$s_{xy} = \frac{\Sigma x_i y_i}{n} = r s_x s_y$$

V. MATHEMATICAL MODELS OF PROBABILITY

All the equations listed in Parts II, III and IV above, except Eqs. **2-44, 4-21,** and **2-45,** apply also to all the mathematical models. In some instances more powerful expressions apply specifically to the models; only the specifically more powerful expressions are listed below.

Binomial Model

Probability (distribution, discrete) for k successes, n trials, $p + q = 1$:

(1-20)
$$B(k; n, p) = \binom{n}{k} p^k q^{n-q}$$
p. 31

Cumulative probability (from $k = 0$ to $k = k'$):

(1-22) $\qquad \displaystyle\sum_{k=0}^{n'} B(k; n, p) = \sum_{k=0}^{n'} \binom{n}{k} p^k q^{n-k}; \; = 1 \Big|_{n'=n}$ $\qquad$ p. **31**

Expectation value is np. $\qquad$ p. **31**

Most probable value is k_0 in

(1-24) $\qquad\qquad\qquad |k_0 - np| \gtrless 1.$ $\qquad$ p. **32**

Mean μ:

(2-26) $\qquad\qquad\qquad \mu = np$ $\qquad$ p. **91**

Standard deviation σ; variance σ^2:

(2-28) $\qquad\qquad \sigma = \sqrt{npq}; \qquad \sigma^2 = npq$ $\qquad$ p. **92**

(2-29) $\qquad\qquad \text{fractional } \sigma = \dfrac{\sqrt{npq}}{\mu} = \left(\dfrac{1}{\mu} - \dfrac{1}{n}\right)^{\frac{1}{2}}$ $\qquad$ p. **92**

Multinomial Model

Multinomial probability (distribution) for each of more than two possible outcomes; $k_1, k_2, \cdots, k_r$ observations, n trials, $p_1 + p_2 + \cdots + p_r = 1$:

(1-30) $\quad M[(k_1; n, p_1)(k_2; n, p_2) \cdots (k_r; n, p_r)] = \dfrac{n!}{k_1! k_2! \cdots k_r!} p_1^{k_1} p_2^{k_2} \cdots p_r^{k_r}$ $\quad$ p. **37**

Normal (Gauss) Model

Probability (density or distribution, continuous), $z = $ deviation, $h = 1/\sigma\sqrt{2}$:

(4-9) $\qquad\qquad G(z; h) = \dfrac{h}{\sqrt{\pi}} e^{-h^2 z^2}$ $\qquad$ p. **160**

Cumulative probability (from $z = -\infty$ to $z = z'$):

(4-11) $\qquad\qquad \Phi(z) = \dfrac{h}{\sqrt{\pi}} \int_{-\infty}^{z'} e^{-h^2 z^2} \, dz$ $\qquad$ p. **160**

With standardized variable:

(4-14) $\qquad x = hz; \qquad \Phi(x) = \dfrac{2}{\sqrt{\pi}} \int_0^{x'} e^{-x^2} \, dx$ $\qquad$ p. **169**

(4-15) $\qquad t = \dfrac{z}{\sigma}; \qquad \text{erf } (t) = \dfrac{1}{\sqrt{2\pi}} \int_{-t}^{t} e^{-t^2/2} \, dt$ $\qquad$ p. **169**

Mean deviation $\bar{z}$ (universe):

(4-16) $\qquad\qquad \bar{z} = \dfrac{1}{h\sqrt{\pi}} = \dfrac{0.564}{h}$ $\qquad$ p. **171**

Standard deviation σ:

(4-20) $\qquad\qquad \sigma = \dfrac{1}{h\sqrt{2}} = \dfrac{0.707}{h}$ $\qquad$ p. **172**

Probable error pe (50% confidence limits):

(4-21) $\qquad\qquad pe = \dfrac{0.4769}{h} = 0.6745\sigma$ $\qquad$ p. **173**

90% confidence limits:

(4-22) $\qquad\qquad 90\% \text{ c.l.} = \dfrac{1.164}{h}$ $\qquad$ p. **173**

Poisson Model

Probability (distribution, discrete) for k successes, $n \to \infty$ trials, $p \to 0$, expectation value $np = \mu$ moderate $[k^2 + (np)^2 \ll n]$:

$$(5\text{-}4) \qquad\qquad P(k; \mu) = \frac{\mu^k e^{-\mu}}{k!} \qquad\qquad \text{p. 198}$$

Cumulative probability (from $k = 0$ to $k = k'$):

$$(5\text{-}5) \qquad\qquad \sum_{k=0}^{k'} P(k; \mu) = \sum_{k=0}^{k'} \frac{\mu^k e^{-\mu}}{k!} \qquad\qquad \text{p. 198}$$

Standard deviation σ; variance σ^2:

$$(5\text{-}13) \qquad\qquad \sigma = \sqrt{\mu} \qquad\qquad \text{p. 202}$$

$$(5\text{-}17) \qquad\qquad \text{fractional } \sigma = \frac{\sqrt{\mu}}{\mu} = \frac{1}{\sqrt{\mu}} \qquad\qquad \text{p. 203}$$

Standard deviation in a single measurement, σ_{k_s}:

$$(5\text{-}24) \qquad\qquad \sigma_{k_s} = \sqrt{k_s} \qquad\qquad \text{p. 205}$$

Probable error pe:

$$pe \approx 0.65\sigma \qquad\qquad \text{p. 206}$$

Skewness, coefficient of:

$$(5\text{-}32) \qquad\qquad \text{skewness} = \frac{1}{\sigma} \qquad\qquad \text{p. 207}$$

Optimum time ratio for counting a signal rate superposed on a background, observed combined rate $X + B$ for time t_x, observed background rate (signal removed) B for time t_b:

$$(5\text{-}41) \qquad\qquad \frac{t_x}{t_b} = \sqrt{\frac{X + B}{B}} \qquad\qquad \text{p. 226}$$

Interval Model

Probability (density or distribution, continuous) for size or duration of intervals t randomly distributed between rare events, mean number of events in interval of size t is μt, mean interval is $\tau \, (= 1/\mu)$:

$$(5\text{-}46) \qquad\qquad I(t; \mu) = \mu e^{-\mu t} \qquad\qquad \text{p. 228}$$

Cumulative probability (from $t = 0$ to $t = t'$) with K events observed in time T:

$$(5\text{-}51) \qquad\qquad \frac{n_{t < t'}}{K} = \int_0^{t'} \mu e^{-\mu t}\, dt = 1 - e^{-\mu t'} \qquad\qquad \text{p. 229}$$

Mean deviation $\overline{t - \tau}$:

$$(5\text{-}53) \qquad\qquad \overline{t - \tau} = \frac{2}{\mu e} \approx \frac{0.7358}{\mu} \qquad\qquad \text{p. 229}$$

Standard deviaton σ:

$$(5\text{-}55) \qquad\qquad \sigma = \frac{1}{\mu} \qquad\qquad \text{p. 229}$$

Index